CAUSALITY AND SCIENTIFIC EXPLANATION

Causality and
Scientific Explanation

William A. Wallace

VOLUME TWO

Classical and Contemporary Science

Ann Arbor
The University of Michigan Press

Preface

THE first volume of this work portrays the two concepts of causality and explanation as central to the development of science from its medieval precursors to its classical founders. This second and concluding volume exhibits the same concepts as the focal point of continuing debate among philosophers and methodologists of classical as well as contemporary science. The proximate inspiration behind both volumes is a difference of opinion that has begun to manifest itself between logically minded and historically minded scholars, the first of whom make stronger claims for rationality and objectivity in science than do the second, but neither of whom seem able to justify any cumulative growth of knowledge within the scientific enterprise. The work itself seeks such a justification through a historical examination and reinstatement of the dual concept of causal explanation. Its central thesis is that the search for causal explanations has provided, and continues to provide, a reliable paradigm of scientific method from its origins in the late Middle Ages down to the present day.

The first volume begins with an introductory chapter that poses the contemporary problematic and traces its source back to the *Posterior Analytics* of Aristotle. It then concentrates, in Part I, on medieval science to document the impact of the *Analytics* at the universities of Oxford, Paris, and Padua from the thirteenth to the sixteenth centuries. The three chap-

ters that make up this part constitute the major portion of the
volume. In addition to providing illustrative material for
later analysis, they attempt to evaluate the rival claims of
historians of science as to the importance of these centers
for the genesis of modern experimental method. Part II builds
on this base and is devoted to early classical science, being
concerned with its founders from William Gilbert to Isaac
Newton. It stresses elements of methodological continuity
between the medievals and early modern scientists and shows
the surprising use of causal concepts made by the latter in
their own, now classical, contributions.

This second volume is likewise divided into two parts,
the first of which may be regarded as a continuation of, and
complement to, the second part of the previous volume,
since both are concerned essentially with the classical science of the seventeenth, eighteenth, and nineteenth centuries. Whereas the treatment in the previous volume, however, concentrated on the founders of modern science — viz.,
Gilbert, Kepler, Galileo, Harvey, and Newton — the first
part of this volume is concerned with its philosophers and
methodologists. The two chapters that make up Part I are
thus devoted to philosophical and methodological discussions that reflect the changing status of causal concepts to
the latter part of the nineteenth century. Part II then turns attention to contemporary science and devotes three chapters
to this most recent period of science's history. Chapter 3
analyzes the problems that led to "the decline and fall of causality" and surveys the philosophical confusion that attended
the emergence of twentieth-century science from the ruins of
classical science, while still searching for a methodology that
would justify its results. The final chapters propose a nuanced
interpretation of causality as related to scientific explanation
that allows, on the one hand, for the possibility of cumulative
growth of knowledge within science generally and, on the
other, for the solution of special problems such as those arising within the relativity and quantum theories that led to the
demise of the classical causal concept.

In this, as in the previous volume, I have given all citations from primary sources in English, from standard translations when available, otherwise in my own translation. Gen-

erally in citing early British authors I have modernized English spelling and punctuation, and occasionally I have modified or adapted existing translations on the basis of my own reading of the text.

My debts are the same as those noted in the first volume. In a special way, however, I wish to thank Peter A. Bowman and John M. Donahue for their careful reading of both volumes, John F. Wippel for his helpful suggestions with regard to the first volume, and Edward H. Madden and Ernest Nagel for their constructive criticisms relating to the second. None of these, I am sure, would wish to assume responsibility for everything stated herein, and yet their thoughtful comments have aided me considerably in clarifying my position and eliminating errors of fact and interpretation. Finally, it would be ungracious of me not to acknowledge the continued assistance of the National Science Foundation, without whose research grants the work would never have been accomplished.

William A. Wallace

February 4, 1973
Washington, D.C.

Contents

Part One

Classical Science:
Philosophy and
Methodology

CHAPTER ONE

The Philosophers of Classical Science

It is somewhat anachronistic to propose to separate the philosophers of classical science from its founders, particularly when one considers that such science had its origin as a further articulation of natural philosophy, and thus that each scientist had as much claim to the title of philosopher as any other. With the perspective provided by the intervening centuries, however, it is possible to identify those thinkers who devoted themselves more consistently to themes now recognized as philosophical, and particularly those who reflected on the epistemological and ontological problems raised by the new science. With regard to the concept of causality, for example, the work of David Hume and Immanuel Kant was inspired by, and remained closely associated with, the scientific enterprise; at the same time it had a profound influence on the future development of philosophy. And although these two figures emerge as central in contemporary discussions of causality, their work was not done in a vacuum but was prepared for by others who attempted to supply a philosophy for the new science, and thus contributed to a developing understanding of causal explanation.

It will be the concern of the present chapter to sketch the main ideas of such philosophers of the seventeenth and eighteenth centuries. In assessing their role in this development, attention will be centered mainly on the place of causality in scientific explanation, on the attitude toward demonstrative reasoning and the certitude it engenders, on distinctive methodologies, and, in the case of those who made significant scientific contributions such as Descartes and Leibniz, on the methodology by which they achieved their results. No attempt will be made to duplicate the standard treatments of these men in histories of philosophy, since our study has a quite different aim. The dichotomous division of philosophers into rationalists and empiricists, for example, while of systematic value, frequently obscures similarities of approach when dealing with scientific problems.[1] Again, traditional interpretations stem from the reading of texts that have rightfully become classics but are no longer studied in the context for which the writer intended them. Thus Descartes's *Discourse on Method* was really published as an introduction to three other essays, themselves detailed scientific treatises, which Descartes intended as an illustration of his proposed method.[2] As a recent editor has remarked, "to study either Descartes' method or its implementation in isolation from one another is contrary to his intention," and so he urges a reconsideration of Cartesian methodology with proper emphasis on what Descartes "did in the three works to which the *Discourse* is an introduction." [3]

Here, as in the chapters of the first volume, the treatment must be selective, with figures being chosen as much for their representative character as for the influence they subsequently exerted. Descartes holds a privileged place at the outset as the codifier of the mechanical philosophy, and the inspiration, positively or negatively, behind most later work. Hobbes and Locke come next because of their close relation to Newton and to the materialism and empiricism they saw implicit in his teachings. Then are considered the reactions and clarifications of Berkeley and Hume, culminating in Hume's influential, though highly skeptical, analysis of causation. Finally, the more rationalistic strain is given representation in the work of Leibniz, whence it provoked the equally influential revolution in causal thinking that finally found expression in Kant.

1. René Descartes

In his famous eulogy of Newton, Fontenelle took occasion to draw a sharp contrast between Descartes and the man he was eulogizing, both of whom "saw the necessity of introducing geometry into physics." [4] He viewed Newton as the experimentalist who "began by taking hold of the known phenomena to climb to unknown principles," who set out from what he saw "in order to find out the cause," whereas he characterized Descartes as the a priori thinker who, "taking a bold flight, thought at once to reach the fountain of all things, and by clear and fundamental ideas to make himself master of the first principles," thus setting out from what he clearly understood "to find out the causes" of what he saw.[5] Fontenelle's contrast is illuminating, for it highlights the profound differences between these two men while stressing their common concern with causal explanation.

Thanks to his Jesuit education at La Flèche, which was both traditional and modern, Descartes was not unacquainted with scholasticism; in fact, as Gilson has shown, this exerted a deeper influence on his philosophy than has been generally acknowledged.[6] Particularly impressed with the Aristotelian demonstrative ideal of knowledge that could not be otherwise, which he saw best exemplified in mathematics, Descartes ardently desired to apply its methodology to the physical sciences. He gives indication of this in a letter to Mersenne:

> In physics I should consider that I knew nothing if I were able to explain only how things might be, without demonstrating that they could not be otherwise. For having reduced physics to mathematics, this is something possible, and I think that I can do it within the small compass of my knowledge, although I have not done it in my essays.[7]

How Aristotle himself proposed to achieve demonstrative certitude in the natural sciences, however, and how his ideas were developed by the commentators we have discussed in our first volume, seems not to have been part of Descartes's instruction.[8] Thus he had to make a new beginning for himself, to establish the rules by which others "will be able to know effects by their causes; and, to explain myself in scholastic terminology, will be able to have demonstrations a priori of everything that can be produced in this new world," i.e., the world of his own creation, which he was describing in *Le Monde*.[9]

The guarantee of certitude that Descartes hit upon, as is well known, turned out to be twofold: his clear and distinct ideas, and God as the most perfect being who would not allow intuitions of such ideas to be deceived. Armed with divine assurance, as it were, he proclaimed a dualist ontology in which substance must be either matter, viewed as pure extension and set in motion by God at the creation of the world, or mind, unextended but capable of thought. All of the physical universe could then be explained simply as matter in motion, and the laws of motion, stated by Descartes with remarkable insight and influential in Newton's later formulation, became the ultimate laws of nature.[10]

Even from this brief sketch one can see how Descartes could subscribe to the ideal of a physics demonstrated with the rigor of mathematics that would at the same time explain all of the phenomena of the universe. By his own admission, Descartes used the word *demonstrer* to cover both the proof of the truth of his system and the explanation of the facts it was designed to account for.[11] Thus, for him, scientific knowledge was not only demonstrative but also explanatory. The explanation was, of course, mechanistic, for Descartes felt he had described "the whole visible world as if it were only a machine in which there were nothing to consider but the shapes and movements of its parts."[12] Such mechanisms obviously permitted the application of mathematics and calculation to the physical universe, but, more importantly, they provided simple models in terms of which fundamental explanations could be given. Here Descartes felt that he had advanced beyond Galileo, whom he chided for his failure of nerve in not assigning any mechanism or cause to explain the free fall of bodies. To Mersenne he complained that "without having considered the first cause of nature, [Galileo] has only looked for the reasons for certain particular effects, and thus he has built without foundation."[13] For Descartes, to the contrary, causality and explanation were inseparably linked, and they would remain practically identified in the thought of many he influenced, including Spinoza and Leibniz.[14]

Descartes's ideals notwithstanding, many of the explanations he proposed for phenomena such as gravity and magnetism, to say nothing of the functioning of living organisms, were defective and proved of no lasting value.[15] With such a record of nonaccomplishment, it is difficult to explain how Descartes could have provided the inspiration for the many contributions of later scientists who subscribed to his mechanical philosophy. Part of the answer undoubtedly lies in unresolved inconsistencies within Descartes's own methodology, particularly as this relates to experimentation and to the use of hypotheses in explanatory schemata.[16] In both these areas there is an ambivalence in Descartes's writings which has led to a diversity of interpretations among Cartesian scholars.

On the subject of experimentation there are evidences, on the one hand, that Descartes regarded this as merely confirmatory and in no way capable of refuting conclusions to which he had already come by rational insight. In his *Rules for the Guidance of Our Native Powers*, for example, he states that there are two ways by which we can arrive at a knowledge of facts, viz., by experience or by deduction. He further observes "that while our experiences of things are often fallacious, deduction . . . can never be wrongly performed by an understanding that is in the least degree rational." [17] He goes on to maintain that none of the mistakes men make are due to faulty deduction, but rather to their "relying on certain imperfectly understood experiences, or . . . venturing on judgments which are hasty and groundless." [18] Regarding experiments, he writes to Mersenne that there are very few people who know how to perform them properly; "often, through doing them badly, one finds the contrary of what one should find." [19] Again, criticizing Maurolyco's measurement of the arcs subtended by the primary and secondary rainbows, Descartes emphasizes "how little faith we must have in observations which are not accompanied by true reasons." [20]

On the other hand, there is little doubt that throughout

his life Descartes was both a keen observer of natural phenomena and a careful and indefatigable experimenter. He
states explicitly in his *Discourse* that he has noticed with respect to experiments "that they become more necessary in
proportion as our knowledge advances." [21] Following this, in
a rather extended passage, he explains how, once having determined "the general principles, or first causes of all that is
or can be in the world," further explanations of detailed phenomena can only be obtained "by arriving at the [proxi-
mate] causes through their effects, and by using many particular experiments." [22] In attempting to find such causes, he
acknowledges that his "greatest difficulty is usually to discover in which of these [several different] ways the effect depends upon the principle or cause." [23] To accomplish this end
he insists "that I know no other expedient than again to
search for certain experiments which are such that their result is not the same when we explain the effect by one hypothesis, as when we explain it by another." [24]

The mention of "hypothesis" in this last citation raises
the question as to how hypothetico-deductive explanation
could be reconciled with Descartes's rationalistic ideal of certitude, and whether he was ever able to escape the charge of
circularity in the demonstrations he proposed. Like his medieval and Renaissance predecessors, Descartes saw a way out
of the latter charge by a doctrine of resolution and composition, which he referred to as analysis and synthesis, but
which he otherwise understood quite differently from the peripatetics.[25] A brief description of his analytic-synthetic methodology may thus serve to clarify the roles of hypotheses and
experimental confirmation in his overall system. Here it will
be helpful to examine not only Descartes's statements about
his methods, but the use to which he put these in the explanations he offered of detailed natural phenomena.

As Descartes conceived method, it consists of a set of
rules for assuring that the mind will be correct in its operations, which are basically only two, called by him "intuition"
and "deduction." Both operations are closely interrelated, although he maintains the classical distinction that intuition
yields the first principles of knowledge, whereas deduction
supplies conclusions that may be rigorously derived from

them.[26] Precisely how analysis and synthesis are related to these two mental operations is not completely clear in his exposition, although he seems to see these as functioning principally in the operations of deduction or proof. Thus he holds that "the method of proof is twofold, one being analytic, the other synthetic." [27] He then goes on to describe these two parts of the method of proof as follows:

> Analysis shows the true way by which a thing was methodically discovered and derived, as it were effect from cause. . . . Synthesis contrariwise employs an opposite procedure, one in which the *search* goes as it were from effect to cause (though often here the *proof* itself is from cause to effect, to a greater extent than in the former case).[28]

This text is puzzling at first sight, because in the traditional way of looking at it analysis would normally proceed from effect to cause, (not, as Descartes holds, to effect *from* cause), whereas synthesis would take the causes then discovered and recompose them to yield the desired effect, and thus would be from cause to effect (not Descartes's reversal of this process). A suggested way out of this difficulty would focus on the terms search and proof that have been italicized in the second sentence of the text just cited, and argue that the synthesis that Descartes has in mind, particularly when applying his method in detailed scientific investigations, is involved both in the *search* for truth and in its *proof* by the process of demonstration.[29] Analysis, on the other hand, seems to be concerned essentially with search, and the way in which "effect from cause" should be understood is that the analytic process discovers a proper explanation by showing that this is the effect of the operation of one particular cause rather than a variety of others that might be excogitated.[30] On this understanding, Descartes's intuition and deduction are not seen as operating exclusively in analysis and synthesis respectively. Both analysis and synthesis require intuition for their ultimate justification, and insofar as any scientific knowledge is demonstrative or synthetic, it too must involve elements of analysis and intuition.[31]

While going beyond the traditional interpretations of

Descartes, the foregoing exegesis permits a more consistent understanding of Descartes's use of hypotheses and experiments, while at the same time remaining true to the method he set as his ideal.[32] On first reading it would appear that this method consists in starting, on the basis of clear and distinct ideas, with principles that are self evident a priori, and proceeding from these primary truths as first causes to deduce all the phenomena of nature down to the last detail. Surely Descartes thought that this would be possible in principle, but in attempting to follow out the program he found that a process of a priori deduction alone could not possibly account for the particular phenomena that occurred in the world God *de facto* created. His first principles might be able to account for all the possibilities of creation, but they would have to be supplemented by additional information, gathered both hypothetically and experimentally, in order to explain particular occurrences.[33]

This, at least, provides a reasonable solution to the problem of how Descartes could, in his own mind, relate his a priori deductions to the actual world in which he performed his experiments. Both experience and experiment then become important, as they always have been regarded by Cartesian scholars, as providing the occasion whereby the mind gains an intuition of clear and distinct ideas; stated otherwise, experience provides the data for analysis whereby the mind arrives at an intuitive knowledge of the principles underlying the particulars it has experienced. More important for scientific work, however, and here is where experiment must be added to experience, is the fact that the mind can deduce, from the first causes or principles uncovered in analysis, a considerable number of possible effects. To know which of these actually occurs additional information becomes necessary, and this is obtained by observation and experiment. It is in this last step that hypotheses become important, for by studying in detail the effects that are manifest in experience, it becomes possible to search out which cause, among a number of possible ones, posited during the search as hypothetical, is actually the true cause. This is the sense in which search and synthesis function as a part of analysis, and lead to an intuition of the proper or proximate causes of particular phenomena.

For Descartes, as for Newton, the term "hypothesis"
could take on a variety of meanings. Sometimes, for example,
he offers a mechanical explanation as a mere hypothesis that
would suffice to explain a phenomenon if the hypothesis were
true, even though it is manifestly false. At other times he
speaks of hypotheses as offering possible explanations of the
phenomena in question, without seeking to justify any more
than their possibility.[34] His most interesting usage, however,
and the one most characteristic of his methodology, is that
wherein a number of possible alternative explanations, all initially regarded as hypothetical, are adjudicated on the basis
of experimental evidence, and one hypothesis finally selected
as representing the true cause. The problem posed by this
usage is that of understanding how such a hypothetico-deductive type of explanation, even though confirmed experimentally, can be regarded by Descartes as having generated absolute certitude, in terms of true causal knowledge.[35]

It is here that recourse to Descartes's *Optics* and
Meteorology, as more representative of his scientific work,
can prove helpful. At the outset of the *Meteorology,* for example, after affirming the possibility of finding "the causes of
everything that is most admirable above the earth," [36] Descartes admits that such knowledge will depend on general
principles of nature that have not yet, to his knowledge, been
accurately explained, and thus he "shall have to use certain
hypotheses at the outset." [37] He also announces his intention
"to render them so simple and easy that perhaps [the reader]
will have no difficulty in accepting them, even though they
have not been demonstrated." [38] When queried later about
this procedure, he replied in his letter to Vatier:

> As to the hypothesis that I made at the beginning of the
> *Meteorology,* I could not demonstrate it a priori without
> giving my whole physics; but the experiments that I have
> deduced from it necessarily, and which cannot be de-
> duced in the same fashion from any other principles,
> seem to me sufficiently to demonstrate it a posteriori.[39]

Again, in the *Discourse* he makes a similar reference to his
use of hypotheses:

> If some of the matters of which I have spoken in the be-
> ginning of the *Optics* and *Meteorology* should at first

sight give offense because I call them hypotheses and do not appear to care about their proof, let them [my critics] have the patience to read these in their entirety, and I hope that they will find themselves satisfied. For it appears to me that the reasonings are so mutually interwoven, that as the later ones are demonstrated by the earlier, which are their causes, the earlier are reciprocally demonstrated by the later, which are their effects.[40]

It is at this juncture that Descartes raises the question of circularity in demonstration, and he does so in much the same way as this was broached by Paul of Venice and late scholastic methodologists. Descartes denies that a vicious circle is involved, for, "since experience [or experiment] renders the greater part of these effects very certain, the causes from which I deduce them do not so much serve to prove their existence as to explain them; on the other hand, the causes are explained by the effects." [41] Elaborating further in a letter to Morin, Descartes insists that there is no circularity involved "in explaining effects by a cause and then proving a cause by them; for there is a great difference between proving and explaining." [42] In the same letter he argues that any hypothesis that explains a wide range of phenomena, extending beyond the effects initially in question, can with assurance be regarded as a true cause. He writes:

Although it is true that there are many effects to which it is easy to fit different causes, one for each, it is not always so easy to fit one and the same cause to many different effects, unless it is the true cause from which they proceed; there are even effects which are so many and diverse that it is sufficient proof of their true cause to give even one from which they can be clearly deduced; and I claim that all those of which I have spoken are of this number.[43]

Once a true cause has been so identified, moreover, it can in turn be used to prove the reality of additional effects. For, "know that each of these effects may also be proved by this cause, in case it be brought into doubt, and the cause have been proved by other effects." [44] And again there is no circle involved "in proving a cause by several effects which are known otherwise, and then reciprocally proving certain other effects from this cause." [45]

In effect, Descartes is here adumbrating Whewell's "consilience of inductions," while also defending the validity of a posteriori demonstration of causes from their effects. The way in which he differs from the peripatetics, and this consciously on his part, is that he believes he can deduce all phenomena from a single principle, such as that bodies are composed of minute particles too small to be seen, and that the true causes are revealed by mechanical explanations in terms of such particles. He thus finds it hard to believe, as he states it, "that causes from which all phenomena are clearly deduced are not true." [46] Yet, when we of the twentieth century consider in detail such "clear deductions," we have no difficulty understanding why many serious scientists, and not the least of them Newton, found his hypotheses and explanations unacceptable. Among these would be the explanation of planetary motion in terms of vortices in an imaginary ether, that of the fall of heavy bodies on earth as a settling down into places vacated by etherial particles receding from the earth's surface, that of magnetism in terms of effluvia consisting of screw-shaped particles that channel their way through the pores of magnetic materials, and that of color in terms of the rotary motion of the particles of which he believed light composed. [47]

It is not the Descartes of such hypothetical explanations, however, who exerted the profound influence on subsequent thinkers that merited for him the epithet of "father of modern philosophy." What was most significant in the eyes of his followers was that he had taken the thoroughly complex system of the scholastics, with its substantial forms, qualities of all types, elements and other principles, and in their place substituted the clear and distinct idea that bodies are composed of particles in motion, so that from this single principle he could give better explanations than those of any of his predecessors. [48] It is true that the Aristotelian ideal of strict demonstration through causes still permeated Descartes's work, but the causality he advocated was not the fourfold causality of Aristotle. Not only did he banish forms, or formal causality, from the realm of scientific explanation, but he also saw final

causality as beyond human understanding; and though he endorsed matter, and in this sense subscribed to material causality, he severely restricted its scope over the interpretations
of his predecessors.[49] Thus, in effect, there is only one type of
cause for Descartes, and this is the active or efficient cause,
which henceforth would be at the base of all scientific explanations.

Because efficient causes, in Descartes's system, were
called upon to carry the burden of all other types of causality, they were conceived by him in a quite complicated fashion and were made to perform a variety of functions. In particular, Descartes resorted to efficient causes when explaining
the being and existence of all created things, and then in a
way quite different when explaining the functioning of causes
behind the various phenomena of the physical world. In the
first way he would justify the existence of man and the universe, as he understands these in his clear and distinct ideas,
and in the second way he would go about reconstructing the
world (as in the fable of *Le Monde*, and also in the *Principles
of Philosophy*) through the mechanistic explanations mentioned above. Actually, two different concepts of efficient causality are here involved, and these merit brief consideration.[50]

The first understanding of efficient cause is applicable
only to God, who is the "efficient and total cause" (*efficiens et
totalis causa*) of everything.[51] It is in this sense that Descartes
can state that "God alone is the true cause of all that is or
can be." [52] This is true not only of every motion discovered in
the universe, but of the things of which the universe is composed, including ourselves, since "we are not the cause of
ourselves, but . . . God is." [53] The duration of things, and of
men, is attributed to the same cause. "From the fact that we
now are," writes Descartes, "it does not follow that we shall
be a moment afterwards, if some cause — the same that first
produced us — does not continue so to produce us; that is to
say, to conserve us." [54] Thus Descartes's first understanding of efficient causality is that of the link between the Creator and His creation. All of being, whether this be a thing,
its duration or its activity, or even an "eternal truth," [55] has
a necessary dependence on God as the first efficient and total
cause of all.

There is a second understanding of efficient causality in Descartes, however, and this, from the scientific point of view, has more explanatory power than the first. It is ultimately connected with Descartes's analysis of motion, which he defines in the *Principles of Philosophy* as "the transference of one part of matter or one body from the vicinity of those bodies that are in immediate contact with it, and which we regard as in repose, into the vicinity of others." [56] He insists that motion is itself nothing more than transference or transportation, and "not either the force or the action which transports," so that in his understanding "motion is always in the mobile thing, not in that which moves." [57] From this insight into the nature of motion, Descartes goes on to "treat of its cause"; in fact, he is at pains to inform us of two sorts of cause:

> first, the universal and primary cause — the general cause of all the motions in the universe; secondly the particular cause that makes any given piece of matter assume a motion that it had not before. As regards the general cause, it seems clear to me that it can be none other than God Himself. He created matter along with motion and rest in the beginning; and now, merely by His ordinary cooperation, He preserves just the quantity of motion and rest in the material world that He put there in the beginning.[58]

Hence it is clear what the first cause of motion is, namely, God the Creator. But not only did God create matter and motion in the beginning, but He also conserves, by His ordinary *concursus*, exactly the same "quantity of motion" for all time. Elaborating on this concept, Descartes thinks he is able to show an inner necessity that will govern the secondary causes of motion he is about to explain. He continues:

> Further, we conceive it as belonging to God's perfection, not only that He should be in Himself unchangeable, but also that His operation should concur in a supremely constant and unchangeable manner. . . . Consequently it is most reasonable to hold that, from the mere fact that God gave pieces of matter various movements at their first creation, and that He now preserves all this matter in being in the same way as He first created it, He must

likewise always preserve in it the same quantity of motion.[59]

Such a statement naturally arouses curiosity as to what the special causes of motion might be, granted the immutability of the general cause and the constancy of the quantity of motion proceeding from it. It comes as a surprise to learn that these secondary causes, for Descartes, are nothing more than his laws of motion. "From God's immutability we can also know certain rules or natural laws which are the secondary, particular causes of the various motions we see in different bodies." [60] And immediately following this, Descartes goes on to list his three "natural laws" of motion, as well as the seven "rules" that govern the collisions or impacts of bodies. The basic and ultimate justification for each of the laws, he then insists, "is the immutability and simplicity of the operation by which God preserves motion in matter." [61] Thus the first cause of motion, conceived as transference or transportation, is also the principle that regulates motion in all its quantitative aspects.

This second understanding of efficient causality is, of course, quite different from the traditional view. In virtue of God's immutability, laws of motion are somehow given an efficacy (*efficacitas*) [62] whereby they determine all particular effects, and so supply detailed causal, mechanical explanations. In this second understanding, Descartes can identify cause with reason (*causa sive ratio*) [63] and thus equate, in the strongest possible sense, causality with explanation. And for him, causality is efficient causality, for he is insistent "that we must not inquire into the final, but only into the efficient causes of created things." [64] The determinism of a law of nature is already built into the efficacy of mechanical motion. Ends are predetermined by God and are opaque to human understanding. But through the laws that God has predetermined, "as the efficient cause of all things," we can explain "the effects that we perceive by the senses." [65] It is this concept of deterministic causality that will impress the modern mind, and that will alternately evoke rationalism, empiricism, and finally skepticism, as valid philosophical interpretations to be put on the new science.

2. Thomas Hobbes

Much influenced by Descartes, although unwilling to admit it, and falling victim to a more rationalistic justification of mechanistic explanation on this account, was the English philosopher Thomas Hobbes.[66] Hobbes had studied at Oxford while the program there was still strongly Aristotelian, and he was a great admirer of Harvey; [67] he was also well acquainted with scholastics such as Suarez.[68] In view of his being subject to such influences, one can understand why, despite his criticisms of the peripatetics and scholastics, Hobbes has been referred to as "an Aristotelian *malgré lui*." [69] As a physicist and natural philosopher, his work was understandably inferior to that which has gained him fame as a political philosopher. Yet his ideas relating to the physical sciences remained fairly constant throughout his life; he was in personal contact with Galileo, Descartes, and Mersenne; and his writings exerted a considerable influence on his fellow Englishman, John Locke. Thus he merits at least brief consideration for his views on causality and scientific explanation.

Hobbes's *ex professo* treatment of this subject is to be found in the first section of his *Elements of Philosophy*, entitled "Concerning Body," although confirmatory references are also to be found in *Leviathan* and other writings. At the outset of the *Elements,* Hobbes defines philosophy in strict causal terms that are strongly reminiscent of Aristotle.[70] Then, in Chapter 6 of the part devoted to logic, which is concerned with method, he explains how the study of causes and effects is related to the philosophical enterprise, employing here the Aristotelian terms *hoti* and *dioti.* He writes:

> Philosophy is the knowledge we acquire, by true ratiocination, of appearances, or apparent effects from the knowledge we have of some possible production or generation of the same; and of such production, as has been or may be, from the knowledge we have of the effects. Method, therefore, in the study of philosophy, is the shortest way of finding out effects by their known causes or of causes by their known effects. We are then said to know any effect when we know that there be causes of the same, and in what subject those causes are, and in what subject they produce that effect, and in what man-

ner they work the same. And this is the science of causes
or, as they call it, of the *dioti*. All other science, which is
called the *hoti*, is either perception by sense, or the
imagination, or memory remaining after such perception.[71]

Explaining further the nature of this method, Hobbes resorts
to the procedures of resolution and composition, which he
also refers to as analytical and synthetical method. In summary:

There is therefore no method by which we find out the
causes of things, but is either compositive or resolutive,
or partly compositive and partly resolutive. And the resolutive is commonly called analytical method, as the compositive is called synthetical.[72]

Other Aristotelian overtones are sounded in Hobbes's explanation of knowledge of the *hoti* as "that any thing *is*," as
opposed to that of the *dioti*, which is knowledge "of the
causes of any thing." [73] He uses also the language of parts
and wholes, equating these with singulars and universals;
wholes are "more known to us" than the parts, but "the
causes of the parts are more known to nature than the cause
of the whole." [74]

While aware of, and utilizing, this traditional terminology, Hobbes was especially enamored of geometry, extolling
it as "the only science that it hath pleased God hitherto to be-
stow on mankind." [75] Like Descartes he wished to apply the
methods and conceptual apparatus of mathematics to develop
a new natural philosophy. He thought he could do this in
terms of three universal notions: the most fundamental is motion as the universal cause, and the others are the body that
undergoes motion and the space wherein motion occurs. No
method is required actually to discover the universal cause
that is motion, since it is known in itself. Hobbes is explicit
on this:

The causes of universal things (of those at least that have
any cause) are manifest of themselves, or (as they say
commonly) known to nature; so that they need no
method at all; for they all have but one universal cause,
which is motion.[76]

The search that is characteristic of science, on the other hand, is much more specific, "as what is the cause of light, of heat, of gravity. . ." etc.[77] For this, some method is required, and methods may be analytical or synthetical, which are further designated by Hobbes as methods "of invention" [78] ; to these he opposes the method "of teaching," which he identifies, again in the Aristotelian tradition, as that of demonstration.[79] It is in his discussion of demonstration that he admits the possibility of paralogisms, among which he enumerates supposing a "false cause." [80] This he merely illustrates by the example of one who would attempt to prove that the earth was moved in its daily rotation by the action of the wind on its surface, but otherwise he gives no directions for discerning a false cause from a true one.[81]

Hobbes's causal explanations of particular physical phenomena were not unlike Descartes's, although they were even more erroneous from the vantage point of modern science. The reason generally advanced to explain this is the complete lack of experimental verification, or indeed of any observational base, for the various explanations he proposed. Hobbes's concept of science as a rigid deductive system caused him to focus his attention mainly on deduction, and thus on the deriving of effects "from possible causes." [82] Since he was insistent that "experience concludeth nothing universally," [83] it is unlikely that he had any confidence in inductive inference, particularly not that advocated by Francis Bacon.[84] His own conviction seems to have been of a rationalistic, if not dogmatic, type, particularly with regard to his first principle that the causes of all natural phenomena are to be found in motions.[85]

Hobbes's *Elements* contains a significant chapter on cause and effect wherein he clarifies his understanding of these notions.[86] He introduces the discussion in the Aristotelian context of action and passion and their corresponding agent and patient. In this context, the cause "of all effects consists in certain accidents both in the agents and in the patients; which when they are all present, the effect is produced; but if any one of them be wanting, it is not produced. . . ." [87] The aggregate of accidents in the agent required for the production of the effect "is called the efficient cause thereof," whereas the aggregate of accidents in the patient "is usually called the material cause. . . ." [88] In Hobbes's understanding, therefore, "the efficient and material causes are both but partial causes" of what he refers to as "an entire cause." [89] What is more distinctive of Hobbes's teaching on causality enters at this point; it is the note of necessity, or necessary connection, which he sees to be associated with the operation of the entire cause. This is brought out in the following passage:

> It follows . . . from hence, that in whatsoever instant the cause is entire, in the same instant the effect is produced. For if it be not produced, something is still wanting which is requisite for the production of it; and therefore the cause was not entire, as was supposed. And seeing a necessary cause is defined to be that which being supposed, the effect cannot but follow; this also may be collected, that whatsoever effect is produced at any time, the same is produced by a necessary cause. For whatever is produced, in as much as it is produced, had an entire cause, that is, had all those things, which being supposed, it cannot be understood but that the effect follows; that is, it had a necessary cause. And in the same manner it may be shown that whatsoever effects are hereafter to be produced shall have a necessary cause; so that all the effects that have been, or shall be produced, have their necessity in things antecedent.[90]

Hobbes's idea of necessity, as can be seen from this passage, is ultimately that nothing can happen otherwise than as it does. Causality, and mechanical causality at that, is absolutely valid as a principle of explanation, and this is because everything happens necessarily. The necessity here involved, it should be noted, is that of the operation of an efficient cause, and in this Hobbes has much in common with Descartes.

Hobbes thus accounts for Aristotle's efficient and material causes, although the material cause becomes for him merely the receptor of the agent's activity. Similarly he speaks of the formal and final causes as reducible to the efficient cause:

The writers of metaphysics reckon up two other causes besides the efficient and material, namely, the essence, which some call the formal cause, and the end, or final cause, both [of] which are nevertheless efficient causes. For when it is said the essence of a thing is the cause thereof, as to be rational is the cause of man, it is not intelligible; for it is all one, as if it were said, to be a man is the cause of man; which is not well said. And yet the knowledge of the essence of anything is the cause of the knowledge of the thing itself; for, if I first know that a thing is rational, I know from thence that the same is man; but this is no other than an efficient cause. A final cause has no place but in such things as have sense and will; and this also I shall prove hereafter to be an efficient cause.[91]

Hence Hobbes is quite consistent in attempting to resolve all natural phenomena to motion as to a first cause, and in interpreting all previous terminology as simply aspects of the universal explanation he finds most rationally satisfying.

Hobbes's concept of causality, it has been maintained, "is not formed by analyzing the concept of 'experience' but by analyzing the concept of necessity."[92] And the notion of necessity that he employed, as a logician who was much enamored of geometry, could be none other than the formal necessity that generates absolute certitude.[93] In order to raise physics to the status of a science, in the strict demonstrative sense, he had to attribute a similar necessity and certitude to the cause-effect relationship and its employment in scientific explanations.

This ideal notwithstanding, however, Hobbes was not unwilling to admit the use of hypotheses in physical science.[94] This is readily discernible in his treatment of the causes of particular phenomena. He would usually be satisfied if the causal explanation was possible or *imaginabilis*, in such a way that he could deduce from it effects which would be demonstratively certain. As to the detailed fit between the explanation and the physical reality, Hobbes seemed not overly concerned. In fact, at times he would offer two quite different hypothetical explanations of the same phenomenon, being careful only to deduce this phenomenon correctly from the alternate explanations.[95]

As can be seen from even this brief sketch, there are ambiguities in Hobbes's understanding of causes and their relationship to scientific explanation. These he seems never to have resolved, and the physics he proposed passed into oblivion even more quickly than that of Descartes.[96] Yet Hobbes marks a stage in the evolution of causal thinking and, perhaps by his overstatement of the notions of necessity and certitude, provoked skeptical reactions first from Locke and then, in a more explicit and sophisticated way, from Berkeley and Hume.

3. John Locke

John Locke was well acquainted with the ideas of Descartes and Hobbes, being much taken with their corpuscularian philosophy, and attempting to apply it to a clarification of the whole of human understanding.[97] In this enterprise, and particularly in his attempts to explain how ideas are produced in man through the operation of external material objects on his senses, Locke had to employ the concepts of cause and effect, and in so doing perforce gave some indication of his own convictions regarding scientific explanation.[98] There are tensions in his thought between empiricism and rationalism, and there are many inconsistencies which he seems never to have resolved to his own satisfaction.[99] The net effect of his enquiry, however, was a gradual retrenchment with regard to man's ability to discern causal connections, and particularly those operative in the region of the very small, so that he contributed substantially to "narrowing the limits of scientific knowledge." [100]

Locke's approach to the concept of causality is made through the idea of power, whose two types he recognizes as active and passive, and where his primary concern is not how power originates in the order of nature but rather how men "come by the idea of it." [101] Like many subsequent writers, he is led from this consideration to the conclusion that man's notion of active power derives most clearly from his own experience of the operation of his mind on matter, particularly in willing the movement of his bodily parts. He writes:

> . . . if we will consider it attentively, bodies, by our senses, do not afford us so clear and distinct an idea of active power as we have from reflection on the operations of our minds. . . . A body at rest affords us no idea of any active power to move; and when it is set in motion itself, that motion is rather a passion than an action in it. . . . The idea of the beginning of motion we have only from reflection on what passes in ourselves, where we find by experience that, barely by willing it, barely by a thought of the mind, we can move the parts of our bodies which were before at rest.[102]

How this notion of power is related to cause and effect he explains in a later passage:

> Power being the source from whence all action proceeds, the substances wherein these powers are, when they exert this power into act, are called causes, and the substances which thereupon are produced, or the simple ideas which are introduced into any subject by the exerting of that power, are called effects. The efficacy whereby the new substance or idea is produced is called, in the subject exerting that power, action; but in the subject wherein any simple idea is changed or produced, it is called passion; which efficacy, however various, and the effects almost infinite, yet we can, I think, conceive it, in intellectual agents, to be nothing else but modes of thinking and willing; in corporeal agents, nothing else but modifications of motion.[103]

With this Locke sets up the most serious problem his empiricism will have to face; like Descartes, his mind produces a "clear and distinct idea" of active power, but the only source outside the mind that he can conceive as originating such an idea is mechanical motion with all its various modifications.

Unlike Descartes and Hobbes, however, Locke does not delude himself concerning man's ability to know the motion of particles and to use such motion to yield causal explanations.[104] He makes this clear when he acknowledges that man's concept of bodily extension is just as obscure as that of immaterial spirit, when both are viewed in relation to motion. "Our idea of body," he declares, "is an extended solid substance, capable of communicating motion by impulse; and our idea of soul, as an immaterial spirit, is of a substance that thinks, and has a power of exciting motion in body, by willing or thought." [105] On further reflection, however, he finds that the cohesion of solid parts in a body is "as hard to be conceived" as thinking in a soul.[106] Locke tries to account for Descartes's notion of material substance by showing "how the solid parts of bodies are united, or cohere together to make extension." [107] But after reviewing all of the mechanical explanations proposed by his contemporaries, he must finally admit defeat. The headings of the subsequent sections of the *Essay* reveal this: every attempt at explanation is either "incomprehensible" or "unintelligible." [108] Thus, when he comes finally to analyze the relationship between cause and effect, which he admits to be "the most comprehensive relation wherein all things that do, or can exist, are concerned," [109] he admits that the causal relation will have to be conceived as a simple idea or substance "beginning to exist by the operation of some other," but "without knowing the manner of that operation." [110]

As may be seen from these statements, Locke does not question the existence of causal activity; he in fact affirms a principle of causality, and even takes note of its empirical ground, namely, that it has been "constantly observed" that "like changes will for the future be made in the same things, by like agents, and by the like ways." [111] But when it is a matter of explaining the "manner" of causal operation, he becomes agnostic; apparently he is attracted to the mechanical philosophy, but he sees no way of ascribing any cogency to its detailed explanations.[112]

Locke's skepticism focuses on a topic already mentioned by Hobbes and later to be taken up by Hume, viz., that of necessary connection. Ultimately Locke is agnostic about man's ability to understand the manner of causal operation because of his inability to discern any necessary connection between the simple ideas that coexist in the same subject. We are not only ignorant "of the primary qualities of the insensible parts of bodies, on which depend all their secondary qualities," but even more seriously, "there is no discoverable connection between any secondary quality and those primary qualities which it depends on." [113] This is true for Locke even when one uses the powerful "corpuscularian hypothesis" associated with the rise of the new science:

> I have here instanced in the corpuscularian hypothesis as that which is thought to go furthest in an intelligible explication of those qualities of bodies; and I fear the weakness of human understanding is scarce able to substitute another, which will afford us a clearer and fuller discovery of the necessary connection and co-existence of the powers which are to be observed united in several sorts of them. This at least is certain, that, whichever hypothesis be clearest and truest (for of that it is not my business to determine), our knowledge concerning corporeal substances will be very little advanced by any of them, till we are made to see what qualities and powers of bodies have a *necessary* connection or repugnancy one with another; which in the present state of philosophy I think we know but to a very small degree: and I doubt whether, with those faculties we have, we shall ever be able to carry our general knowledge (I say not particular experience) in this part much further.[114]

Pursual of this line of thought leads Locke to the admission that there can be "no science of bodies within our reach." [115] In opposition to Hobbes, for whom the ideal of a demonstrative science was still regulative, Locke maintains that "certainty and demonstration are things we must not, in these matters, pretend to." [116] We know of the existence of causes and effects, and indeed observe them every day, but they cannot be productive of scientific knowledge in the traditional Aristotelian sense:

> Several effects come every day within the notice of our senses, of which we have so far sensitive knowledge: but the causes, manner, and certainty of their production, for the two foregoing reasons, we must be content to be very ignorant of. In these we can go no further than particular experience informs us of matter of fact, and by analogy to guess what effects the like bodies are, upon other trials, like to produce. But as to a *perfect science* of natural bodies, (not to mention spiritual beings,) we are, I

> think, so far from being capable of any such thing, that I
> conclude it lost labour to seek after it.[117]

Yet Locke himself has no doubts about the existence of causal
connections and, like Descartes, seeks their ultimate justification in an all-wise and all-knowing Being, God Himself:

> These and the like [ideas], though they have a constant
> and regular connection in the ordinary course of things,
> yet that connection being not discoverable in the ideas
> themselves, which appearing to have no necessary de-
> pendence one on another, we can attribute their connec-
> tion to nothing else but the arbitrary determination of
> that All-wise Agent who has made them to be, and to op-
> erate as they do, in a way wholly above our weak under-
> standings to conceive.[118]

Having conceded the opacity of the causal relationship
to the human mind, it is only logical that Locke will disavow
any universal knowledge of "real essence" or substance.[119] This
does not preclude for him, however, a certain amount of "experimental," as opposed to "universal," knowledge. The latter
is to be found in ideas alone; the former can never go beyond
particulars. Locke writes:

> Whence we may take notice that general certainty is
> never to be found but in our ideas. Whenever we go to
> seek it elsewhere, in experiment or observations without
> us, our knowledge goes not beyond particulars.[120]

While admitting this limitation in our knowledge, however,
Locke still insists on the validity of the causal principle, and
this in no uncertain terms:

> This is certain: things, however absolute and entire they
> seem in themselves, are but retainers to other parts of na-
> ture, for that which they are most taken notice of by us.
> Their observable qualities, actions, and powers are
> owing to something without them; and there is not so
> complete and perfect a part that we know of nature,
> which does not owe the being it has, and the excellencies
> of it, to its neighbours; and we must not confine our
> thoughts within the surface of any body, but look a great
> deal further, to comprehend perfectly those qualities that
> are in it.[121]

Here the thought expressed is not far from that of Newton: we may not know the cause of gravity, but this much is certain, that it has a cause, and indeed one outside the subject in which it acts, even though such a cause may escape the grasp of the human mind.

Locke's basic inclinations are toward empiricism, however, and because of this he may rightfully be regarded as one of the initial formulators of the hypothetico-deductive ideal of physical science. Seeing the impasse he has encountered in a "general knowledge" of substance, he asks: "What, then, are we to do for the improvement of our knowledge in substantial beings?" [122] His answer is predictable: we must turn to the sense knowledge of particulars, of whose existence there can be no doubt. "The want of ideas of their real essences sends us from our own thoughts to the things themselves as they exist." [123] Locke goes on:

> Experience here must teach me what reason cannot: and it is by trying alone, that I can certainly know, what other qualities co-exist with those of my complex idea, v.g., whether that yellow, heavy, fusible body I call gold, be malleable or no; which experience (which way ever it prove in that particular body I examine) makes me not certain that it is so in all, or any other yellow, heavy, fusible bodies, but that which I have tried.[124]

Yet it is this same reliance on experience, as particular if not unique and singular, that, somewhat paradoxically, renders scientific knowledge for Locke unattainable in principle:

> This way of getting and improving our knowledge in substances only by experience and history, which is all that the weakness of our faculties in this state of mediocrity which we are in in this world can attain to, makes me suspect that natural philosophy is not capable of being made a science.[125]

Such being the case, we must especially "beware of hypotheses and wrong principles," although there is a "true use of hypotheses" in the discovery of new knowledge.[126] Locke explains the true use in these words:

> Not that we may not, to explain any phenomena of nature, make use of any probable hypothesis whatsoever:

hypotheses, if they are well made, are at least great helps to the memory, and often direct us to new discoveries. But my meaning is, that we should not take up any one too hastily (which the mind, that would always penetrate into the causes of things, and have principles to rest on, is very apt to do), till we have very well examined particulars and made several experiments in that thing which we would explain by our hypothesis, and see whether it will agree to them all; whether our principles will carry us quite through, and not be as inconsistent with one phenomenon of nature, as they seem to accommodate and explain another. And at least that we take care that the name of principles deceive us not, nor impose on us, by making us receive that for an unquestionable truth, which is really at best but a very doubtful conjecture; such as are most (I had almost said all) of the hypotheses in natural philosophy.[127]

There is, of course, an ambivalence concealed in Locke's last statement, for he hastens to add, "whether natural philosophy be capable of certainty or no," that "clear and distinct ideas with settled names, and the finding of those intermediate ideas which show their agreement or disagreement, are the ways to enlarge our knowledge." [128] He thinks also that the application of the hypothetico-deductive method can lead to "the discovery of truths," as is evident in the following passage:

This sort of probability, which is the best conduct of rational experiments, and the rise of hypothesis, has also its use and influence; and a wary reasoning from analogy leads us often in the discovery of truths and useful productions which would otherwise lie concealed.[129]

But how such "truths" are discovered and lead to an enlargement "of our knowledge" is not easy to disengage from Locke's writings. "Reasoning from analogy," as he terms it, together with his employment of causal efficacy as seen in the power of particulars, probably provides the basis for such a knowledge-acquisition claim. Locke's proposals, in this connection, have turned out to be quite suggestive for recent philosophers of science, who see them as a way of avoiding Hume's complete skepticism and whose views on causal powers will be discussed in later chapters. In a similar vein, a recent study calls attention to the fact that, while Locke was dubious and skeptical about discovering necessary connections between matters of fact, he was not at all skeptical about knowing the powers and natures of particulars and about causal inferences based on such knowledge.[130] Thus he managed to keep the concepts of power and necessity distinct, and indeed seems to have linked causal efficacy to the former, not to the latter. Hume, as we shall see, conflated all three — power, cause, and necessity — and, thinking he had shown the last to be impossible, thought he could dispense with the other two also. As a consequence, he could not resort to causal reasoning, whereas Locke could, and so have a realistic ground for allowing the possibility of discovering new truths.

Despite the skeptical elements already pointed out, therefore, Locke's theory of knowledge shows a substantial commitment to realism, a "metaphysical extension," as one author puts it, of the empirical components of that theory.[131] His grasp of powers and particular natures enables him to hold that there is a "real essence" that underlies the nominal essence, that causal influences exist, and that primary qualities "do really exist in bodies themselves"; [132] he can even make appeal to God as the ultimate guarantor of the being and operation of all that is.[133] Such commitments, however, do not stand out boldly in his writing, and it would take later generations of scholars to discover them there. What did stand out for his contemporaries was the dubious and skeptical questioning to which he subjected all reasoning about the world of nature, even that of the mechanical philosophy. Wittingly or unwittingly, therefore, Locke had begun to unravel the skein of thought that had led his predecessors to unquestioned faith in the validity of causal, mechanical explanations. Thus he prepared the way for Berkeley and Hume, and ultimately for Kant, in their attempts to gain a new philosophical understanding of causality and its role in human knowledge.

4. George Berkeley

George Berkeley is usually singled out for attention as an important link between the beginnings of modern philosophy with Descartes and Locke and its culmination in Hume and Kant.[134] Berkeley did play such a mediating role, it is true, but he also contributed substantially to the development of a philosophy of science; he was particularly critical of the work of his predecessors in their attempts to interpret Newton and others, and he sought to provide an alternative that would be more open to the Christian theism to which he himself subscribed. In effect, he was not unwilling to accept the skepticism of Locke with regard to the details of the corpuscularian philosophy, but he did not wish such skepticism to be extended to the world of ordinary human experience. As Berkeley saw it, the "new science" was interpreting the universe as a purely mechanical system of extended particles that move purposelessly in the vast reaches of space and time, but in ways adequately described by mathematical laws. He would set himself to providing methodological canons that leave such laws and systems of laws intact, without drawing from them the ontological implications being accepted uncritically by Descartes and Hobbes. Berkeley therefore took over Locke's empiricism, developing it in the direction of his own *esse est percipi* doctrine, and attempted thereby to show that the world of the "new science" is merely an artifact created out of unreal abstractions, whereas the perceptible world of common sense is real and intelligible in terms of a true metaphysics.

Berkeley began to construct his philosophy while studying and then teaching at Trinity College, Dublin, where he read Newton, Locke, and Malebranche, among others, and filled a notebook with ideas that were seminal for his mature philosophy. Later he moved to London, and then traveled extensively in France and Italy; during the latter phase he wrote a brief treatise *De motu* (1720), ostensibly for the Royal Academy of Sciences at Paris, which had offered a prize for the best essay on the causes of motion. Then, toward the end of his career, he returned to this topic in his celebrated work, *Siris* (1744), a fascinating disquisition that begins by extolling the virtues of tar-water and terminates with the most profound philosophical and theological reflections on matters associated with the science of his day. It is to these two works, themselves quite consistent with his more metaphysical *Principles of Human Knowledge* (1710), that we must turn for his distinctive notions of causality and scientific explanation.

The full title of Berkeley's work on motion is *De motu sive de motus principio et natura, et de causa communicationis motuum*, and, true to its claim, it takes up respectively the principle of motion, the nature of motion, and the cause of its communication. With respect to motion's principle Berkeley makes his characteristic attack against obscure and abstract terms as these are used "by the more recent and sober thinkers of our age." [135] Among such terms are gravity and force. As used by scientists, these abstract ideas are merely occult qualities, endowed by the imagination with causal power. Berkeley is willing to concede that we perceive all of the phenomena associated with falling bodies, and that we rightfully infer "that there is some cause or principle of these phenomena . . . properly called gravity." [136] Our knowledge of gravity, however, is not sufficient for us to identify the cause of falling motions:

> But since the cause of the fall of heavy bodies is unseen and unknown, gravity in that usage cannot properly be styled a sensible quality. It is, therefore, an occult quality. But what an occult quality is, and how any quality can act or do anything, we can scarcely conceive — indeed we cannot conceive. And so men would do better to let the occult quality go, and attend only to the sensible effects. [137]

The same judgment is passed on force (*vis*) as this term is used in scientific treatises:

> Force likewise is attributed to bodies; and that word is used as if it meant a known quality, and one distinct from motion, figure, and every other sensible thing, and also from every affection of the living thing. But examine the matter more carefully and you will agree that such force is nothing but an occult quality. [138]

Neither gravity nor force, therefore, can be regarded as "the principle of motion," for, as a principle, both the one and the other is occult, and "what is itself occult explains nothing." [139] Such terms, of course, have a useful function in the physical sciences, since they serve "to abbreviate speech" and may be employed "for instructional purposes" [140] and "for reasonings and reckonings about motions and bodies in motion." [141] The same is true of such terms as attraction and action and reaction, which are utilized so extensively in Newtonian mechanics. But these are mere "mathematical hypotheses," and are not to be viewed in any way as "physical qualities." Berkeley leaves no doubt about this:

> Action and reaction are said to be in bodies, and that way of speaking suits the purposes of mechanical demonstration; but we must not on that account suppose that there is some real virtue in them which is the cause or principle of motion. For those terms are to be understood in the same way as the term *attraction;* and just as attraction is only a mathematical hypothesis, and not a physical quality, the same must be understood also about action and reaction, and for the same reason.[142]

Berkeley's search for the cause and principle of motion, having eliminated the mechanical as occult and unreal, proceeds somewhat along Cartesian lines in the sense that it would make God's action alone the real cause of motion.[143] Such a consideration, however, is of little avail to the natural philosopher, since God's causality is the proper concern of the metaphysician or the theologian. As Berkeley explains it:

> Modern thinkers consider motion and rest in bodies as two states of existence in either of which every body, without pressure from external force, would naturally remain passive; whence one might gather that the cause of the existence of bodies is also the cause of their motion and rest. For no other cause of the successive existence of the body in different parts of space should be sought, it would seem, than that cause whence is derived the successive existence of the same body in different parts of time. But to treat of the good and great God, creator and preserver of all things, and to show how all things depend on supreme and true being, although it is the most

excellent part of human knowledge, is, however, rather the province of first philosophy or metaphysics and theology, than of philosophy which today is almost entirely confined to experiments and mechanics.[144]

In view of this state of affairs, one need not reject Newtonian science because it does not lead directly to such a true cause, since this is not the proper concern of physics which should restrict itself to discovering the correct laws of motions:

> It is not, however, in fact the business of physics or mechanics to establish efficient causes, but only the rules of impulsions or attractions, and, in a word, the laws of motions, and from the established laws to assign the solution, not the efficient cause, of particular phenomena.[145]

Berkeley returns to this theme again and again, always insisting that mechanical principles and laws are the domain of the physicist, but "metaphysical principles and real efficient causes of the motion and existence of bodies or of corporeal attributes in no way belong to mechanics or experiment." [146]

Berkeley's disquisition on the nature of motion, which makes up the second division of *De motu*, is consistent with his general theory of knowledge. We perceive motion by our senses, and its nature is nothing more than the way in which we experience it *in concreto*. If we therefore wish to determine the nature of motion accurately, we must be alert to the fact that mathematical hypotheses do not reveal the true natures of things, that abstractions are not the same as reality, and that we must restrict our consideration to sensible, or at least to imaginable, motions. If we attempt to conceive motion abstractly, as have Aristotle, Descartes, and Newton, we fall into difficulties, most of which are associated with our confusing motion and its efficient cause:

> Too much abstraction, on the one hand, or the division of things truly inseparable, and on the other hand composition, or rather confusion of very different things, have perplexed the very nature of motion. For it has become usual to confuse motion with the efficient cause of motion. Whence it comes about that motion appears, as it were, in two forms, presenting one aspect to the senses and keeping the other aspect covered in dark night.

Thence obscurity, confusion, and various paradoxes of motion take their rise, while what belongs in truth to the cause alone is falsely attributed to the effect.[147]

The third division of *De motu* is concerned with the cause of the communication of motion, and here Berkeley merely sums up what he has already, in his view, established. "Most people," he asserts, "think that the force impressed on the moveable body is the cause of motion in it." [148] Yet no one has been able to assign "a known cause of motion," and even those who have spoken about force express very different opinions concerning it. So Berkeley concludes that "all forces attributed to bodies are mathematical hypotheses," and that "mathematical entities have no stable essence in the nature of things," since "they depend on the notion of the definer." [149] Despite this, it is not impossible to discover "by meditation and reasoning" what are the "truly active causes" that are operative in the physical universe.[150] This, again, is the province of metaphysics, which alone is concerned "with incorporeal things, with causes, truth, and the existence of things." [151] The physicist must be concerned with the phenomena and the laws that govern them, and when he speaks of "corporeal causes," he ought to be understood benignly, since it exceeds the power of his science to take account "of the actual seat of the forces or of the active powers or of the real cause in which they are." [152]

Berkeley's teaching in *Siris* is essentially the same as that in the *De motu,* although it is amplified somewhat, and more stress is placed on the incorporeal agent that is necessary for the understanding of all causality.[153] Thus, speaking of the nature of fire, and the force that is sometimes attributed to it, Berkeley notes that "force or power, strictly speaking, is in the Agent alone who imparts" the force attributed to this element.[154] Again, commenting on the attempts of various Newtonians to explain the gravity of bodies by the elasticity of ether, Berkeley comments that this is like explaining the unknown through the more unknown (*ignotum per ignotius*), similar to explanations of the motions and appearances of the planets by the doctrine of epicycles.[155] Anyone who is looking for explanations in a strict causal sense, moreover, would have to admit that "the mechanical philosophers never explained anything." [156] Their province is:

> only to discover the laws of nature, that is, the general rules and methods of motion, and to account for particular phenomena by reducing them under, or showing their conformity to, such general rules.[157]

And if they speak of forces and attraction, this is not to be taken in a realist sense:

> But what is said of forces residing in bodies, whether attracting or repelling, is to be regarded only as a mathematical hypothesis, and not as anything really existing in nature.[158]

As for the real exercise of causality, there is no doubt in Berkeley's mind that an incorporeal agent is necessary to account for this. He writes that "we cannot make even one single step in accounting for the phenomena without admitting the immediate presence and immediate action of an incorporeal Agent, who connects, moves, and disposes all things according to such rules, and for such purposes, as seem good to Him." [159] Even the "principle of attraction itself is not to be explained by physical or corporeal causes." [160] The reason for this is that "in strict truth, all agents are incorporeal, and as such are not properly of physical consideration." [161] Berkeley is aware, of course, that the natural philosophers of his day thought they had discovered true causes, but in this he believes they have been deceived:

> Nor, if we consider the proclivity of mankind to realize their notions, will it seem strange that mechanic philosophers and geometricians should, like other men, be misled by prejudice, and take mathematical hypotheses for real beings existing in bodies, so far as even to make it the very aim and end of their science to compute or measure those phantoms; whereas it is very certain that nothing in truth can be measured or computed beside the very effects or motions themselves.[162]

To correct these misapprehensions, Berkeley would reassert the notions of soul and mind,[163] and show how these are ultimate for anyone who would penetrate beneath the sensible

appearances to discover "the real and true causes" of phenomena.[164] When a person does this, however, as we have already indicated, he will be operating in the area of metaphysics. The essential difference between physics and
metaphysics, then, may be summarized in terms of the ontological reference of their distinctive subject matters:

> Now, although such phantoms as corporeal forces, abso-
> lute motions, and real spaces do pass in physics for
> causes and principles, yet are they in truth but hy-
> potheses, nor can they be the objects of real science.
> They pass nevertheless in physics, conversant about
> things of sense, and confined to experiments and mechan-
> ics. But when we enter the province of the *philosophia
> prima*, we discover another order of beings, mind and its
> acts, permanent being, not dependent on corporeal
> things, nor resulting, nor connected, nor contained; but
> containing, connecting, enlivening the whole frame, and
> imparting those motions, forms, qualities, and that order
> and symmetry, to all those transient phenomena which
> we term the Course of Nature.[165]

Berkeley's restriction on the physical sciences in terms of
their inability to discover causes results, of course, in a concept of scientific explanation quite different from that found
among his predecessors. Because of his emphasis on the role
of laws of motion and other rules regulating phenomena, he
has been seen as a forerunner of a reductionist view of scientific explanation, wherein the theoretical concepts used by the
physicist would themselves be simply reducible to individual
laws of phenomena. Alternatively he has been regarded as a
forerunner of the instrumentalist view with regard to theoretical entities, for he denied the conceptualizations of scientists
ontological status in the physical world, while conceding
their utility as instruments of calculation.[166] Whether Berkeley be regarded as a reductionist or as an instrumentalist,
however, what is most important in his doctrine is his insistence that there is no place for causal explanation in physical
science. The action of physical agents cannot be explained,
therefore, in terms of force, attraction, gravity, or the motion
of insensible particles. The best that the physicist can hope
for is an explanation in terms of laws, and even of these he

has not complete assurance, since they depend ultimately on the efficacy and will of the Author of Nature. Thus there is even a limitation on Berkeley's understanding of induction, as can be seen in the following passage from *The Principles of Human Knowledge:*

> By a diligent observation of the phenomena within our view, we may discover the general laws of nature, and from them deduce the other phenomena; I do not say demonstrate, for all deductions of that kind depend on a supposition that the Author of nature always operates uniformly, and in a constant observance of those rules we take for principles: which we cannot evidently know.[167]

In place of efficient causality, therefore, which we have seen raised to a supreme principle by Descartes and Hobbes, Berkeley must substitute a lawlike operation of nature, and the causal efficacy that explains this is ultimately lodged in God. In no event are forces to be said to provide us with any type of explanation in science. Yet even forces have their utilities in the context of mechanical theories, and here Berkeley seems to subscribe to a limited type of hypothetico-deductive methodology. So he can write in the *De motu:*

> Physically . . . a thing is explained not by assigning its truly active and incorporeal cause, but by showing its connection with mechanical principles, such as action and reaction are always opposite and equal.[168]

Even the "mathematical hypotheses" which we have seen questioned in terms of their ontological referents are granted a validity as principles insofar as "from them are derived both general mechanical theorems and particular explanations of the phenomena." [169]

Berkeley, therefore, is significant for inaugurating a change in direction, and for anticipating several developments of recent philosophy of science. Yet there are latent contradictions in his overall view, and particularly in his own justification of causal efficacy. For example, as we have seen, Berkeley is quite forceful in his contention that explanation in science should not involve a reference to metaphysical entities, while at the same time there is no doubt in his mind that any genuine explanation must ultimately involve metaphysical efficacy. In effect he wished to keep God out of his science, but so defined God's activity as to make science ultimately unintelligible without reference to Him.[170] These and similar inconsistencies would be taken up by Hume and Kant respectively in their attempts to justify the concept of causation, and the use man makes of it in seeking a scientific understanding of nature.

5. *David Hume*

David Hume, on cursory reading, creates the impression that he merely took Berkeley's arguments against causal explanations in science, generalized them in such a way as to dispense with such explanations, not only in natural philosophy but also in metaphysics, and thus effectively did away with causality altogether.[171] The much-cited text from Hume's *An Enquiry Concerning Human Understanding* seems to support this impression. Taking up Locke's critical examination of the notion of "necessary connection," Hume asserts categorically that "we never can, by our utmost scrutiny, discover anything but one event following another," that we are unable "to comprehend any force or power by which the cause operates, or any connection between it and its supposed effect." [172] And, in placing this restriction on the human mind, Hume apparently is not addressing scientists alone, for he has in mind all men, not excluding those who would use the causal nexus to rise to a knowledge of God.[173]

Granted, for the moment, that this is his meaning, Hume still has the problem of accounting for the fact that men speak of causal connections as if they have actually discovered them in nature. Here, where others had offered an ontological explanation, Hume would propose an alternative that is essentially psychological: the idea of necessary connection is projected into reality by man's way of associating ideas and by the expectations that naturally arise from such associations. This is how Hume explains it:

> It appears, then, that this idea of a necessary connection among events arises from a number of similar instances which occur of the constant conjunction of these events; nor can that idea ever be suggested by any one of these

instances, surveyed in all possible lights and positions. But there is nothing in a number of instances, different from every single instance, which is supposed to be exactly similar; except only, that after a repetition of similar instances, the mind is carried by habit, upon the appearance of one event, to expect its usual attendant, and to believe that it will exist. This connection, therefore, which we *feel* in the mind, this customary transition of the imagination from one object to its usual attendant, is the sentiment or impression from which we form the idea of power or necessary connection.[174]

Hume goes on to state that "nothing farther is in the case," meaning by this that there is nothing in reality that justifies the origin of the idea of necessary connection. He cites the example of a man observing motion being communicated through the impact of two billiard balls, and claims that all that the man can do is observe the balls being conjoined, since he has no basis for maintaining them to be connected. But, "after he has observed several instances of this nature, he then pronounces them to be connected." [175] What has happened in the interim that gives rise to his new idea of connection? Hume answers:

> Nothing but that he now *feels* these events to be *connected* in his imagination, and can readily foretell the existence of one from the appearance of the other. When we say, therefore, that one object is connected with another, we mean only that they have acquired a connection in our thought, and give rise to this inference, by which they become proofs of each other's existence . . .[176]

A final point, made by Hume in his *Treatise of Human Nature*, is his questioning of the apparently intuitive or demonstrable maxim generally accepted by philosophers, namely, that "whatever begins to exist, must have a cause of existence." [177] In his attack on this principle Hume attempts to show that it is neither self-evident nor capable of proof, and the technique he uses is merely one of showing that the ideas of cause and effect are distinct and readily separable in the imagination. We can easily satisfy ourselves regarding the validity of this approach, he explains, for

> as all distinct ideas are separable from each other, and as the ideas of cause and effect are evidently distinct, it will be easy for us to conceive any object to be non-existent this moment, and existent the next, without conjoining to it the distinct idea of a cause or productive principle. The separation therefore of the idea of a cause from that of a beginning of existence is plainly possible for the imagination, and consequently the actual separation of these objects is so far possible that it implies no contradiction nor absurdity . . .[178]

Thus Hume claims to have destroyed one of the strongest supports of the causal concept as it has been traditionally understood, namely, that a cause is a principle from which something else proceeds with a dependence in being or existence, and therefore that any existential beginning must be traceable to the operation of some cause. By a similar line of argument one can dispose of the principle "that every effect must have a cause," [179] and so causal argumentation in general becomes logically inefficacious.

a. The Notion of Causation

Hume's skepticism, on this analysis, bites much deeper than that of Locke, and in fact voids many of the latter's valuable insights. But Hume, like others who embrace a radical empiricism, is not completely convincing in his analysis of causality. When the entire range of his writings are taken into account, and particularly when his intentions are discerned as going beyond his actual statements, questions of interpretation arise that exercise his commentators and, not infrequently, exacerbate his critics. It is to these questions that we should now turn to gain a more balanced insight into Hume's view of causation and its relation to scientific explanation.

At the outset it should be noted that Hume, with disarming candor, admits to inconsistencies in his philosophy that he has not been able to resolve. In an important Appendix to the *Treatise* he explains that he has been working with two principles "which I cannot render consistent, nor is it in my power to renounce either of them." The principles are (1) "that all our distinct perceptions are distinct existences" and

(2) "that the mind never perceives any real connexion among distinct existences."[180] The first may be likened to a strong rationalist principle, which makes distinctions in things depend on distinctions provided by the mind, whereas the second is a radically empiricist principle, whereby the mind is concerned only with its own ideas and cannot perceive any reality outside itself. If Hume actually extrapolated Berkeley's view of force and cause in physics to all rational inquiry, he did not have the courage to accept Berkeley's spiritualistic metaphysics that would make mind the only reality, as consistent application of the first principle might have led him to conclude. Seemingly he would rather accept Locke's theory of knowledge, wherein we cannot know things without their being present to our senses, although even here he failed to inquire critically into what being present to our senses could possibly mean. Obviously the expression entails a reference to external objects, to some type of reality distinct from both sense and mind, but since impressions and ideas constitute the whole of human knowing, man is effectively cut off from any reality of this type. Hume's second principle partially enunciates the skepticism to which such an epistemology leads, seemingly without being aware that its systematic application precludes discussion of "objects," "distinct existences," and "real connections" altogether.[181]

The fact of the matter is that Hume, although deprived by his phenomenalism of the right to distinguish between objects and perceptions, nonetheless went on to speak of things whereof he should have been silent, and in so doing effectively acknowledged the validity of induction and causal reasoning as it was being used by Newton and like-minded scientists.[182] A careful comparison of Hume's "rules by which to judge of causes and effects" with Newton's *regulae philosophandi* shows the extent of this acknowledgment. And there are numerous other indications in Hume's writings which show that, whatever his disavowals of a metaphysical type of knowledge in the Berkeleyian sense, he actually subscribed to a realist epistemology when concerned with topics relating to the new "experimental" science, and this even in matters relating to causality.[183]

Hume, for example, never himself doubted the independent existence of external objects. "We may well ask," he states, "'what causes induce us to believe in the existence of body?' But it is in vain to ask 'whether there be body or not?' That is a point which we must take for granted in all our reasonings." [184] Again, of all possible relationships among objects, it is only "causation," he admits in another place, "that can be traced beyond our senses, and informs us of existence and objects, which we do not see or feel." [185] As to our knowledge of causation, Hume tried, as we have seen, to reduce this merely to the perception of constant conjunction, and yet in his famous passages on the single experiment, he makes the confident statement:

> It is certain that not only in philosophy, but even in common life, we may attain the knowledge of a particular cause merely by one experiment, provided it be made with judgment and after a careful removal of all foreign and superfluous circumstances.[186]

There is nothing in Hume's analysis of causation, which he defines merely as *de facto* constant conjunction, that permits such a statement, unless one admits that through "judgment," "understanding," and other "natural habits" of the intellect can man actually perceive the causal nexus.[187] In justifying the passage here cited, moreover, Hume has recourse to his principle of uniformity of nature, "that like objects placed in like circumstances, *will always produce* like effects," [188] although again there is nothing in his epistemology that permits him to use the future tense. Consistent with his own principles, and even countenancing his illicit use of the term "objects," the most he should have claimed would be that like objects, placed in like circumstances, *have always produced* like effects; such a statement, of course, could never justify Hume's inference on the basis of one experiment alone. Elsewhere he expresses himself favorably on the validity of inductive argument: ". . . one proposition may justly be inferred from the other; I know, in fact, that it always is inferred." [189] The validity of inductive inference was therefore not Hume's problem; it was how one might go about justifying such inference in terms of his idiosyncratic theory of knowledge.

The extent to which Hume was under the influence of

Newton's *Principia* may be seen from a number of his statements. It is the work of human reason, he asserts in the *Enquiry*, "to reduce the principles, productive of natural phenomena, to a greater simplicity, and to resolve the many particular effects into a few general causes, by means of reasonings from analogy, experience, and observation." [190] Apparently such "general causes" are discoverable by human reason, whereas the "causes of these general causes" must remain opaque to man's intellect:

> But as to the causes of these general causes, we should in vain attempt their discovery. . . . These springs and principles are totally shut up from human curiosity and enquiry. Elasticity, gravity, cohesion of parts, communication of motion; these are probably the ultimate causes and principles which we shall ever discover.[191]

Hume is here echoing Newton, but with an agnosticism that is noticeably selective; some "ultimate causes" are "probably" discoverable, but their "ultimate springs and principles" are "totally shut up" from human investigation. Again, Hume is willing to admit that much of the scientist's inquiry is concerned with discovering the secret operation of contrary causes.[192] As he expresses himself in the *Treatise*, "almost in every part of nature there is contained a vast variety of springs and principles, which are hid, by reason of their minuteness or remoteness." [193] These "concealed causes" are undoubtedly there, but, and here Locke's influence is detectable, they are insensible because of their "minuteness and remoteness," the very expression that Locke uses when speaking of "insensible corpuscles . . . the minute constitutent parts" of matter.[194] And finally, when supplying the canons for causal reasoning à la Newton to which we have already alluded, Hume is quite explicit as to his intentions. "Since, therefore, it is possible for all objects to become causes or effects to each other," he writes, "it may be proper to fix some general rules by which we may know when they really are so." [195] Hume's rules, like Newton's, are not merely ways of talking about phenomena, but rather they serve to adjudicate, by their proper application, whether or not something "really" is a cause.

How, then, is Hume's endorsement of the scientist's use of causal and inductive reasoning to be squared with his own metaphysical disavowals of causality and induction? One solution that has been suggested is to acknowledge a variety of levels in Hume's discourse, and particularly his quite different view of causality and explanation when validating scientific inquiry, as opposed to his abortive philosophical and psychological attempts to justify any such validation.[196] It is only at the first level that one can really speak of causality and scientific explanation in Hume, and at this level, if we search carefully, we find that he subscribed implicitly to the Newtonian inductive process, holding that man can actually discover causes through a variety of "general rules" and the "natural principles of the understanding." [197] And when one uncovers the "explanations" that are scientifically acceptable in Hume's analysis, these turn out to be nothing more than the lawlike uniformities that had been remarked by his predecessors.[198] Here Hume is not far different from Locke and Berkeley. Against Berkeley, it is true, he attempted to justify the autonomy of scientific reasoning, particularly its independence of metaphysics, but the scaffolding he used to support his justification proved too weak for the task it was to perform. So he ended up by carrying Locke's skepticism to its ultimate *reductio ad absurdum*. But there is no evidence that in so doing he relinquished his own faith in the "new science" and the superior knowledge he thought it provided of the world of nature.

b. Thomas Reid's Critique

Hume had a pronounced influence among his contemporaries, comparable to that still exerted in the present day, and yet he was not without his opponents. Foremost among these was Thomas Reid, founder of the Scottish school of common-sense philosophy, who took his initial inspiration from Hume but diverged from him sharply on matters relating to causality.[199] Reid's critique of Hume, moreover, has been taken up by later writers, and thus warrants consideration not only on its intrinsic merits, but also because of its impact on later thought.

Like Kant, Reid received his early training in the natural sciences and taught physics and mathematics at both Aberdeen and Glasgow, where he was a devotee of Newton's *Principia*. A student's surviving notes of his early lectures on natural philosophy, in fact, reveal his preoccupation with the *regulae philosophandi*, and these methodological canons continued to exert a dominant influence as Reid formed his own philosophy. This enthusiasm for Newton he also seems to have communicated to his contemporaries, for a recent author credits Reid with enkindling the interest in Newtonian methodology that characterized nineteenth-century British thought on epistemology and the philosophy of science.[200]

Hume, as we have seen, was also indebted to Newton and proposed to renovate moral philosophy himself along much the same lines as Newton had renovated natural philosophy. But Reid read Hume closely and found that the latter's skepticism vitiated his account of knowledge, causality, and induction, thereby bringing the empiricist program to the verge of absurdity. Relying on his own common sense, Reid countered by erecting an epistemology that "drew extensively on the insights which he had gleaned from his lengthy familiarity with the writings of Newton." [201] Indeed basic to Reid's philosophy, and here the Newtonian influence is quite apparent, was his vehement opposition to the use of hypotheses, conjectures, and even theories that are not induced directly from observation and experiment.[202] In place of a hypothetical methodology he would use a straightforward inductive method based on Newton's first rule, namely, that no more causes of natural things are to be admitted than are both true and sufficient for explaining their phenomena. The Newtonian expression, "true causes" (*verae causae*), was understood by Reid to refer to observable entities or events that can be detected through patient observation and experimentation with nature, and thus are a proper subject for inductive inference.[203] Reid felt that the inductive process was epitomized in Newton's "rules of philosophizing," and that these did not need elaborate justification, since they are nothing more than "maxims of common sense." In fact, Reid maintained that Newton's rules "are practiced every day in common life; and he who philosophizes by other rules, either concerning the material system or concerning the mind, mistakes his aim." [204]

Since Newton's rules are so dependent on causal inference, and since it was precisely the validity of causal connection that Hume questioned, a fuller account of Reid's teaching on causality would seem indicated at this point. Reid was acquainted with Aristotle's *Posterior Analytics*, having composed a quite accurate summary of this work,[205] and he knew too the uses made by various "scholastick" systematizers of Aristotle's four causes.[206] While hardly an Aristotelian himself, he was more tolerant of peripatetic teaching than many of his contemporaries, reproving Dr. James Gregory, for example, as being "too severe against Aristotle and Plato, especially the former." [207] Gregory had charged that Aristotle violated propriety in the Greek language by using *aitia* in four different senses; Reid, wryly defending Aristotle "as a man who understood Greek better than any modern," countenanced these uses while noting that the term "cause" had undergone even more changes of signification since Aristotle's time.[208] Reid stated his own preference for two different concepts of cause, one metaphysical and the other physical, in a manner somewhat reminiscent of Berkeley. According to his metaphysical concept, which Reid saw as quite opposed to Hume's notion, an efficient cause would be defined as "a being that has power and will to produce [an] effect." [209] His justification of such a definition reads as follows:

> The production of an effect requires active power, and active power, being a quality, must be in a being endowed with that power. Power without will produces no effect; but, where these are conjoined, the effect must be produced. This, I think, is the proper meaning of the word *cause* when it is used in metaphysics; and particularly when we affirm that everything that begins to exist must have a cause; and when, by reasoning, we prove that there must be an eternal First Cause of all things.[210]

Reid elaborated on this reasoning in his correspondence, explaining to Gregory "that I am not able to form a conception how power, in the strict sense, can be exerted without will;

nor can there be will without some degree of understanding,"
and going on to conclude from this that "nothing can be an
efficient cause, in the proper sense, but an intelligent
being." [211] The inspiration for Reid's analysis, as he acknowledged in another letter to Gregory, was his awareness of his
own "voluntary and deliberate actions; for I take this notion
of a cause to be derived from the power I feel in myself to
produce certain effects." [212]

Hume, in favoring his constant conjunction account, had
argued that there is no way man can obtain knowledge of
any actual influx of a cause into its effect. Reid's common-
sensical approach, as we have just seen, indicated an obvious
way around this difficulty, namely, that "we get the first conception of power, in the proper sense, from the consciousness
of our own exertions." [213] Spelling this out more explicitly, he
again wrote to Gregory:

> We get the notion of active power, as well as of cause
> and effect, as I think, from what we feel in ourselves. We
> feel in ourselves a power to move our limbs, and to pro-
> duce certain effects when we choose. Hence, we get the
> notion of power, agency, and causation, in the strict and
> philosophical sense; and this I take to be our first notion
> of these three things. [214]

Reid would concede to Hume, moreover, that if this type of
evidence were overlooked or disregarded it would be practically impossible to get beyond the notion of constant conjunction:

> I see not how mankind could ever have acquired the
> conception of a cause, or of any relation, beyond a mere
> conjunction in time and place between it and its effect, if
> they were not conscious of acts of exertions in them-
> selves, by which effects are produced. This seems to me
> to be the origin of the idea or conception of produc-
> tion. [215]

But he himself saw no reason to deny, or fail to utilize, man's
consciousness of his own causal activity, and in fact proposed
to raise this perception of causality to a "first principle," even
to what one might call a "law of human thought":

> . . . I apprehend that there is one original notion of
> *cause* grounded in human nature, and that this is the no-
> tion on which the maxim is grounded that every change
> or event must have a cause. This maxim is so universally
> held and forces itself upon the judgment so strongly that
> I think it must be a first principle, or what you call a law
> of human thought. And I think the only distinct and true
> meaning of this maxim is that there must be something
> that had power to produce the event, and did produce it.
> We are early conscious of some power in ourselves to
> produce some events; and our nature leads us to think
> that every event is produced by a power similar to that
> which we find in ourselves . . .[216]

While thus arguing against Hume on the basis of his own
metaphysical understanding of cause, Reid was quite willing
to sanction a physical usage of the term to which the Humean analysis could be correctly applied. So he concedes:

> In physics the word *cause* has another meaning which,
> though I think it an improper one, yet is distinct and
> therefore may be reasoned upon. When a phenomenon is
> produced according to a certain law of nature, we call
> the law of nature the cause of that phenomenon; and to
> the laws of nature we accordingly ascribe power, agency,
> efficiency. The whole business of physics is to discover,
> by observation and experiment, the laws of nature, and
> to apply them to the solution of the phenomena: this we
> call discovering the causes of things. But this, however
> common, is an improper sense of the word *cause*.[217]

Granted such an "improper" meaning of cause, Reid was yet
prepared to admit that "what D. Hume says of causes in general is very just when applied to physical causes, that a constant conjunction with the effect is essential to such causes,
and implied in the very conception of them." [218] But while
conceding this usage and its agreement with Hume's exposition in the *Enquiry,* Reid was in no way willing to admit that
a law of nature, even conceived in this physical sense, could
itself supply for efficient causality. Thus he cautioned:

> In natural philosophy . . . when an event is produced
> according to a known law of nature, the law of nature is
> called the cause of that event. But a law of nature is not

the efficient cause of any event. It is only the rule according to which the efficient cause acts.[219]

Elsewhere he observed that Gregory probably agreed with him in the view "that every physical cause must be the work of some agent or efficient cause." He went on:

> Thus that a body put in motion continues to move till it be stopped is an effect which, for what I know, may be owing to an inherent property in matter; if this be so, this property of matter is the physical cause of the continuance of the motion, but the ultimate efficient cause is the Being who gave this property to matter.[220]

Matter, for Reid, is totally passive or inert, and thus cannot be looked upon as an originating cause: "Matter cannot be the cause of anything; it can only be an instrument in the hands of a real cause." [221] And when it came to identifying the real cause, or the intelligent agent whose efficacy is behind all laws of nature, Reid took a position not markedly different from that of Descartes, Leibniz, Newton, and Berkeley, for he saw all motion as originating with God, the Author of Nature:

> The physical laws of nature are the rules according to which the Deity commonly acts in His natural government of the world; and whatever is done according to them is not done by man, but by God, either immediately or by instruments under His direction. These laws of nature neither restrain the power of the Author of Nature nor bring Him under any obligation to do nothing beyond their sphere. He has sometimes acted contrary to them, in the case of miracles, and perhaps often acts without regard to them in the ordinary course of His providence. Neither miraculous events, which are contrary to the physical laws of nature, nor such ordinary acts of the divine administration as are without their sphere are impossible, nor are they effects without a cause. God is the cause of them, and to Him only they are to be imputed.[222]

Having worked out in this way a conception of cause consistent with common sense and able also to serve the needs of his Christian theism, Reid could turn his attention to

Hume's notion and show its many limitations, notwithstanding its adequacy in accounting for physical laws. Reid knew "of no author before Mr. Hume," he writes, "who maintained that we have no other notion of a cause but that it is something prior to the effect, which has been found by experience to be constantly followed by the effect." [223] This is "a main pillar of his system," [224] and from this definition flow many important consequences that can be used to judge the system itself. Among these are the following:

> *First,* it follows from this definition of a cause that night is the cause of day, and day the cause of night, for no two things have more constantly followed each other since the beginning of the world.

> *Secondly,* it follows from this definition of a cause that, for what we know, anything may be the cause of anything, since nothing is essential to a cause but its being constantly followed by the effect. If this be so, what is unintelligent may be the cause of what is intelligent; folly may be the cause of wisdom, and evil of good; all reasoning from the nature of the effect to the nature of the cause, and all reasoning from final causes, must be given up as fallacious.

> *Thirdly,* from this definition of a cause it follows that we have no reason to conclude that every event must have a cause, for innumerable events happen when it cannot be shown that there were certain previous circumstances that have constantly been followed by such an event. And, though it were certain that every event we have had access to observe had a cause, it would not follow that every event must have a cause, for it is contrary to the rules of logic to conclude that, because a thing has always been, therefore it must be — to reason from what is contingent to what is necessary.

> *Fourthly,* from this definition of a cause it would follow that we have no reason to conclude that there was any cause of the creation of this world, for there were no previous circumstances that had been constantly followed by such an effect. And, for the same reason, it would follow from the definition that whatever was singular in its nature or the first thing of its kind would have no cause. [225]

All of these results were rejected by Reid, and he implied that there are few competent thinkers who would be willing to accept them, although he noted that "several of these consequences were fondly embraced by Mr. Hume, as necessarily following from his definition of a cause, and as favorable to his system of absolute skepticism." [226] Such skepticism, for Reid, was irreconcilable with the Newtonian ideal of scientific knowledge, as Kant was also to realize, and thus his own more common-sense view was to be preferred to Hume's peculiar definition of causation.

6. *Gottfried Wilhelm Leibniz*

Whatever may be the ultimate value of Hume's reflection on the efficacy of causal reasoning and induction, there can be no doubt that his efforts to assess the philosophical import of these notions exerted a profound influence on Immanuel Kant. Hume awakened Kant from his "dogmatic slumber," as is well known, but even this expression indicates another influence under which Kant labored before this awakening, namely, the dogmatism, or, to use a term less pejorative in our day, the rationalism of Gottfried Wilhelm Leibniz. A consideration of Leibniz is thus essential to understanding Kant, even though this requires us to interrupt our chronology and to backtrack somewhat, since Leibniz was the contemporary of Locke and Newton and did not live to see the force of Berkeley's criticisms and their influence on Hume.[227] Like Descartes, moreover, Leibniz was a mathematician and scientist in his own right, contributing heavily enough to the foundations of dynamics to be considered one of its founders.[228] Yet it is Leibniz's influence on Kant that assumes the greater importance for purposes of our study, and thus provides the rationale behind our mode of treatment.

Leibniz did his most creative work when Cartesianism and Newtonianism were at their height and when he himself was in contact with Europe's entire intellectual community.[229] A man of extraordinary versatility, and conciliatory by nature, Leibniz was responsive to the older Aristotelian tradition in the universities as well as to the intellectual changes wrought by recent advances in science. He wrote detailed commentaries on the works of Descartes, Spinoza, and Locke, cited practically every writer of any importance in his day, and had a long list of correspondents, ending with Samuel Clarke and the justly famous Leibniz-Clarke controversy. Leibniz's writings were encyclopedic in intent, and yet his system of thought is difficult to analyze, scattered as it is throughout a mass of brief treatises, letters, and summary accounts of a semipopular nature. Also, many of his important works were not published in full during his lifetime, and thus did not have the general impact that they probably deserved. His commentary on Locke's *Essay*, for example, although finished around 1709, did not appear until 1765, at which time, possibly by reason of its delay, it had a serious influence on Kant, second only to his reading of Hume's *Enquiry*.

The main lines of Leibniz's thought are sufficiently well known not to require extensive review.[230] Unlike other philosophers discussed in this chapter, Leibniz was a systematic thinker who aimed to reduce all of his thought to a few simple principles. Among these is the principle of continuity, according to which transitions do not take place by leaps but by gradual changes that are only matters of degree. Attributes are predicated of the individual substances, or monads, in which they are found, and these monads are themselves centers of activity and of passivity. From this ontology follow certain logical principles, such as the principle that the predicate of all true propositions inheres in the subject. This is verified in all logically necessary propositions, otherwise known as "truths of reason," which can be shown to be such by finite analysis; it is also true of logically contingent propositions, "truths of fact," but here, since the predicate is contained only virtually in the subject, an "infinite analysis" is required to show this. In the case of "truths of reason" the principle of contradiction governs the logical connection between attributes, whereas in the case of "truths of fact" the factual connection of attributes is governed by the principle of sufficient reason. The notion of force is closely associated with that of substance, and matter is dematerialized to the point of becoming a mere abstraction or, at best, an appearance. Since each substance is completely separate from every other, what appears to be an interaction between substances is really a correspondence between them, for each acts in accordance with the principle of preestablished harmony. This harmony, finally, is guaranteed by the ultimate source of all reasons, God, who directs all substances to achieve their perfection and the perfection of the whole, which is that of the best possible world.

Within this system Leibniz allowed a place for causes and for scientific explanation, and in fact subscribed to the traditional peripatetic terminology, though interpreting it in a manner that is peculiarly his own. Being concerned with the problems of motion and of the mechanical philosophy generally, it is not surprising that he worked out this terminology in terms of the causes of motion and other physical phenomena. As he progressed, there is evidence that he went from mechanical to more and more metaphysical principles, but it is also true that his general causal convictions were operative in his science, and supplied the key to the type of explanations he sought and later discovered.

One of Leibniz's early papers, written in May 1677 and applying his method of analysis and synthesis to physical and chemical problems, is entitled "On a Method of Arriving at a True Analysis of Bodies and the Causes of Natural Things." [231] In this paper he makes frequent use of the concept of an angelic mind that would acquaint man with such causes, which he conceived in quite mechanical fashion. There is no doubt that for Leibniz such cases exist and are discoverable by analysis, although they are not immediately apparent to humans. So he states:

> First of all, I take it to be certain that all things come about through certain intelligible causes, or causes which we could perceive if some angel wished to reveal them to us. And since we may perceive nothing accurately except magnitude, figure, motion, and perception itself, it follows that everything is to be explained through these four. But because we are now speaking of those things which seem to take place without perception, such as the reactions of liquids, the precipitations of salts, etc., we have no means of explaining them except through magnitude, figure, and motion, that is, through mechanism. What cannot be explained in this way will here be re-

ferred to the action of some perceiving being. Let us imagine, therefore, that some angel comes to explain the true cause of magnetic declination and the periods observed in it. He will surely not really satisfy me by saying that this is the nature of the magnet or that there is a certain sympathy or a kind of soul in the magnet by which it happens. Rather he must explain some cause to me, such that, if I understand it, I can see that the phenomena follow from it as necessarily as the cause of the hammer stroke when a given time has elapsed follows from my knowledge of a clock.[232]

Here it is clear that the only intelligible explanation will be a mechanical one, and this will supply the ultimate "true cause" of such phenomena as magnetic declination. Leibniz's hope is that through experimentation and careful observation such causes will reveal themselves, because they are, after all, quite simple. "Probably the causes of what happens in bodies . . . ," he writes, "are not very complex, and, if some angel were to unveil them and explain them to us, we should perhaps be astonished that we had not discovered them earlier ourselves." [233] Thus he embarks on a search for simple, mechanical causes, buoyed up by the hope that bodies "are not so complex that we must despair of discovering their inner structure insofar as this is necessary for our many purposes." [234]

Writing some eighteen years later, in his *Specimen Dynamicum,* Leibniz is no longer so simplistic in his view, although he remains optimistic regarding his intended goal. Aware by now that "there is no unity of opinion about the causes" of motion, he nevertheless still wishes to arrive at "the true foundations of this science," and, recognizing the defect of his paper of 1677, proposes a new solution through the concept of force.[235] In this task he has to go deeper than those who have thought of bodies "in mathematical terms only — magnitude, figure, position, and their change — " [236] to come to "something prior to extension, namely, a natural force everywhere implanted by the Author of nature." [237] Such a force can be regarded in either of two ways, as active or as passive, and so qualified it satisfies all the demands of formal and material causality as spoken of by the scholastics.

Active force, as Leibniz conceives it, is of two kinds, one
primitive and the other derived.[238] Primitive force, for him,
"is nothing but the first entelechy, [and] corresponds to the
soul or substantial form"; derivative force, on the other
hand, "is exercised in various ways through a limitation of
primitive force resulting from the conflict of bodies with each
other." [239] Similarly, passive force is of two kinds, again primitive and derived. Primitive force "constitutes the very thing
which the scholastics call *materia prima,* if rightly
interpreted" [240]; derivative force, on the other hand, "shows
itself in various ways in secondary matter," mainly by way of
resistance and inertia.[241] It is in terms of such derivative
forces that Leibniz goes on to explain his laws of action, and
these involve him in the further concepts of "living force" (*vis
viva*) and "dead force" which figure so largely in his later
controversies.[242]

In this development, it can be seen that Leibniz now
feels there are more fundamental causes operative behind
those studied in mechanics, although he admits that these are
only "general causes which cannot suffice to explain
phenomena." [243] He elaborates on this somewhat in another
paper written in 1698 entitled "On Nature Itself," and occasioned by a controversy among German thinkers over Robert
Boyle's proposal to avoid the use of the term "nature" altogether and to substitute the term "mechanism" for it. According to Boyle, observes Leibniz, "we must hold nature to be the
mechanism of bodies itself." He goes on:

> Superficially this can be approved, but, to examine the
> matter with greater care, we must distinguish principles
> from derivative matters within the same mechanism; thus
> it is not enough in explaining a clock to say that it is
> moved by a mechanical principle, without further distin-
> guishing whether it is driven by a weight or by a spring.
> I have already expressed, more than once, a view which
> I believe will be of use in preventing mechanical expla-
> nations of natural things from being carried to abuse in
> injuring piety, as if matter can stand by itself and mecha-
> nism needs no intelligence or spiritual substance — the
> view, namely, that the origin of this mechanism itself has
> come, not from a material principle and mathematical

reasons alone, but from a higher and, so to speak, a metaphysical source.[244]

Here Leibniz is referring to what he had written in the *Specimen Dynamicum,* maintaining "that all phenomena are indeed to be explained by mechanical efficient causes, but that
these mechanical laws are themselves to be derived in general from higher reasons, and that we thus use a higher efficient cause only to establish the general and remote
principles." [245] There is no doubt, moreover, that for Leibniz
the ultimate efficient cause is what causes everything to exist
and "perfectly expresses the universe, namely, God." [246] Yet
he opposes himself to the teaching of Malebranche and others
who would invoke God as the unique cause "and remove all
force of action from things themselves" [247]; his own preference
would be that God has "put into things themselves some
properties by which all their predicates can be explained." [248]
Or, as he expresses it in "On Nature Itself," while showing
how God's eternal law is carried out in the actions of creatures:

> If, on the other hand, the law set up by God does in fact
> leave some vestige of Him expressed in things, if things
> have been so informed by the command that they are
> made capable of fulfilling the will of Him who com-
> manded them, then it must be granted that there is a cer-
> tain efficacy residing in things, a form or force such as
> we usually designate by the name of nature, from which
> the series of phenomena follows according to the prescrip-
> tion of the first command.[249]

In one of his optical papers, written in 1682, Leibniz associates this type of causal explanation with that through final
causality, and is critical of Descartes, who wished, as we
have seen, to abandon the search for final causes entirely.
Final causes are quite acceptable to Leibniz, since they offer
us a chance "to discover the properties of those things whose
nature is not as yet known sufficiently clearly, so that we
could use the more proximate efficient causes for the explanation of the internal mechanism, which the Creator has used in
order to produce the effects and realize His purposes." [250]
Having adopted this "pre-established harmony of effi-

cient and final causality," as one author has put it,[251] Leibniz
was not hesitant to use both types of reasoning in his dynamical and optical researches. In a work which may be a continuation of the *Specimen Dynamicum,* entitled *Tentamen Ana-
gogicum* or "An Anagogical Essay in the Investigation of
Causes," Leibniz set himself to show how a consideration of
final causes aids in the derivation of optical and mechanical
laws. His arguments here initiate the discussion of least action and extremum principles which remain of interest down
to our own day. For such a study, Leibniz writes, "the inquiry into final causes in physics is precisely the application
of the method which I think ought to be used." [252] He is convinced that "the laws of motion cannot be explained through
purely geometric principles," since they are not "purely arbitrary," but "originate in the wisdom of their Author or in the
principle of greatest perfection, which has led to their
choice." [253] Thus mechanical explanations have to be supplemented by explanations through final causality, by which he
here means maximum and minimum principles. And this is
not merely in the metaphysical order but also in the realm of
physics itself. Leibniz is quite clear on this point:

> The most beautiful thing about this view seems to me to
> be that the principle of perfection is not limited to the
> general but descends also to the particulars of things and
> of phenomena, and that in this respect it closely resem-
> bles the method of optimal forms, that is to say, of forms
> that provide a maximum or minimum . . .[254]

"What is more," he goes on, "our thinking sometimes furnishes us with considerations revealing the value of final
causes, not merely in increasing our admiration for the supreme Author, but also in making discoveries among His
works." [255] He then details how the law of refraction can be
discovered by the application of teleological principles, and
elsewhere does the same for the laws of mechanics. Hence
Leibniz saw no conflict between explanations through efficient and final causality, but rather a complementarity between them. Or, as he puts it:

> There are, so to speak, two kingdoms even in corporeal
> nature, which interpenetrate without confusing or inter-

fering with each other — the realm of power, according to which everything can be explained mechanically by efficient causes when we have sufficiently penetrated into its interior, and the realm of wisdom, according to which everything can be explained architectonically, so to speak, or by final causes when we understand its ways sufficiently.[256]

Leibniz's physics thus fitted in well with his metaphysics, and both were consistent with his theology, particularly his understanding of the relationship between God and the material universe. It was on this last point that Leibniz disagreed with Newton, and carried out the long polemic with Dr. Samuel Clarke that terminated only with Leibniz's death. The major point of criticism was that Newton and his followers seemed to require God's perpetual intervention in the universe in order to keep it going, whereas Leibniz felt that the universe could be explained sufficiently through its own internal forces and causes, and did not need the extraordinary divine influx from without that the Newtonians seemed to require. Leibniz's criticism is pointedly made in the following excerpt from the first paper of the Leibniz-Clarke correspondence:

> Sir Isaac Newton and his followers have also a very odd opinion concerning the work of God. According to their doctrine God Almighty wants to wind up His watch from time to time: otherwise it would cease to move. He had not, it seems, sufficient foresight to make it a perpetual motion. Nay, the machine of God's making is so imperfect, according to these gentlemen, that He is obliged to clean it now and then by an extraordinary concourse, and even to mend it, as a clockmaker mends his work; who must consequently be so much the more unskillful a workman, as He is oftener obliged to mend His work and to set it right. According to my opinion, the same force and vigour remain always in the world, and only passes from one part of matter to another, agreeably to the laws of nature, and the beautiful pre-established order.[257]

The Newtonians, as Leibniz correctly discerns in this criticism, were conceiving God's intervention in the universe after the fashion of a physical force, such that, should God cut himself off from the system of the world and leave it to itself, the total motive force in the universe would gradually diminish and ultimately disappear altogether. Leibniz does not regard this as necessary, and, in fact, sees it as repugnant to his maximal principle that God has made the best possible world. So he writes in his third paper:

> If active force should diminish in the universe by the natural laws which God has established, so that there should be need for Him to give a new impression in order to restore that force, like an artist mending the imperfections of his machine, the disorder would not only be with respect to us but also with respect to God Himself. He might have prevented it, and taken better measures to avoid such an inconvenience: and therefore, indeed, He has actually done it.[258]

Leibniz is here insisting on the self-sufficiency of nature, while not denying its dependency on God in the sense that it is He who assures the constancy of force in the world by His ultimate efficacy and power. What Leibniz sets himself against is invoking any extraordinary influx from God to explain natural phenomena, whether the phenomenon be a loss of motion through impact or even gravitational attraction. Leibniz mentions this last point at the end of his third paper, concluding with the words, pointedly addressed to the Newtonians, "and therefore I maintain, that the attraction of bodies, properly so called, is a miraculous thing, since it cannot be explained by the nature of bodies." [259] In later letters Leibniz went on to characterize Newton's theory of gravitation as either "a supernatural thing" [260] and "a perpetual miracle" or else as based on an "occult quality," [261] a point, as we have seen, elaborated with telling effect by Berkeley. The debate between himself and Clarke that this occasioned has been amply analyzed by Koyré and others; [262] suffice it to say that, while both Leibniz and Clarke wished to safeguard God's causal action in the universe, their ways of understanding this were so diverse as to lead them to contradictory positions at almost every turn.

Leibniz has been hailed, understandably, as a rationalist, and there are places in his writings where he seems to equate "cause" with "reason" and to see all rational explanations with a clarity and evidence matching only that of Descartes.[263] On the other hand there are empiricist strains in Leibniz's thought, particulary in his attempts to leave all physical explanation at the level of laws of nature expressed in terms of derivative forces, rather than primitive forces functioning at a metaphysical level but lacking explanatory value in science.[264] And then there is the suspicion of occasionalism, to which Leibniz explicitly opposed himself, but which opposition is hard to reconcile with his famous statement in "First Truths" that reads as follows:

> It can be said that, speaking with metaphysical rigor, no created substance exerts a metaphysical action or influence on another. For to say nothing of the fact that it cannot be explained how anything can pass over from one thing into the substance of another, it has already been shown that all the future states of each thing follow from its own concept. What we call causes are in metaphysical rigor only concomitant requisites.[265]

This, of course, is a strange statement for one who is arguing in causal terms, for it is hard to see how a "concomitant requisite" is ontologically different from a "condition" or an "occasion," and how either could be associated with causal efficacy in its common understanding. Leibniz, therefore, like Locke, Berkeley, and Hume, was not without his inconsistencies. But what is important about his work is that he reopened all of the metaphysical questions most others had declined to consider, and in so doing prepared the way for Kant's reexamination of the causal concept in light of the conflicting claims of rationalism and empiricism.

7. Immanuel Kant

Immanuel Kant's early interests were in the field of mathematical physics, and his philosophical training was under the inspiration of Leibniz, particularly as interpreted by Christian Wolff.[266] These two early influences largely determined the development of his distinctive philosophy, which probably has as much claim to being a philosophy of science as that of any philosopher.[267] In his early writings, during what is referred to as his precritical period, Kant was fascinated with the Leibnizian concept of force, or *vis viva*, and attempted to utilize this for a metaphysical understanding of space and substance. As he persisted in these attempts, however, he more and more was attracted to the Newtonian philosophy, and particularly its insistence on an empirical methodology. Here Hume's influence, in attempting to work out a consistent empiricism, had a noticeable effect, as already noted, and this ultimately led to Kant's distinctive solution to the problem of scientific knowledge, formulated in his *Critique of Pure Reason*. In the *Critique*, however, contrary to Hume, Kant attempts to prove the principle of causality and establish its validity in a "pure science of nature," as well as justify its applicability in empirical or experimental science. The problem of the metaphysical validity of Newtonian science then continued to occupy Kant's attention after the publication of the *Critique*, with the result that, just before the appearance of the second edition of this work, he issued his *Metaphysical Foundations of Natural Science* (1786). In the latter work Kant attempted to establish that, although classical metaphysics had been shown by him to be nothing more than a "transcendental illusion," it was still possible to lay firm foundations for another type of metaphysics, i.e., that of a pure science of nature, which would be able to transcend Hume's skepticism. His procedure was to employ only one empirical concept, that of matter; using this, and the categories of the understanding already developed in the *Critique*, he would then deduce the basic principles of physical science, particularly Newton's laws of motion. It appears that even this attempt, however, did not satisfy Kant, for in his declining years he kept addressing himself to the problems of physical science, and especially how a transition might be made from his *Metaphysical Foundations* to the work of physics itself. This task was never completed, although the many notes Kant had prepared are published in his *Opus postumum*, and these show that he turned from the concept of matter to that of the "moving force" found in matter, on which ultimately to base a valid physical science.[268] Thus, as in the case of many philosophers, he returned at the end of his life to his starting point, being still essentially concerned with elaborating a metaphysics of force.

The complexity of the evolution of Kant's thought on the role of causality in physical science, and the diversity of interpretations this has given rise to among his commentators, precludes anything but a summary analysis in what follows. Here, as in previous treatments, the order will be essentially chronological, and only those points will be touched on that seem necessary to characterize Kant's distinctive understanding of the relation of causality to scientific explanation.

a. Early Writings

The Leibnizian character of Kant's early work is seen in his *Thoughts on the True Estimation of Living Forces,* which appeared in 1747 as his first published writing.[269] Although, as its full title indicates, the work is partially directed against Leibniz "and other mechanists," [270] it also has as its purpose a vindication of the Leibnizian notion of *lebendige Kraft,* the German translation of *vis viva.* Kant starts out by saying that he will "begin by defining certain metaphysical concepts bearing on force in bodies in general." [271] Philosophers prior to Leibniz, with the sole exception of the Aristotelians, regarded force "as something which is communicated to a body entirely from without, and in which the body does not participate when in a state of rest." [272] As opposed to this,

> Leibniz, to whom human reason owes so great a debt, has been the first to teach that in body there inheres a force which is essential to it, and which indeed belongs to it prior to its extension. *Est aliquid praeter extensionem, imo extensione prius:* these are his actual words.[273]

Kant goes on to explain that Leibniz referred to this as "active force," and that his successors make no advance over his teaching when they wish to name it "moving force (*vis motrix*)," since motion "is only the external phenomenon of the state of the body." [274] In fact, for Kant, it is not necessary that force be associated with motion, or that the substance wherein it resides even be related to other bodies. So he writes:

> Since all connection and relation of substances existing outside one another are derived from the reciprocal actions which the forces exercise upon one another, we

may take note of what truths may be deduced from this concept of force. Either substance is in a connection and relation with others outside itself or it is not. Since every self-sufficient being contains within itself the complete source of all its determinations, it is not necessary for its existence that it stand in relation to other things. Substances can therefore exist, and yet have no outer relation to others, nor stand in any actual connection with them.[275]

Consistent with such a line of reasoning, Kant, at this stage of his development, derives a series of propositions relating to substance, force, extension, and space. Among these is the statement that "if the substances had no force whereby they can act outside themselves, there would be no extension, and consequently no space." [276] The problem of the three-dimensionality of space also interests him, and he has no sure explanation of this, but he regards it as probable "that the three-fold dimension of space is due to the law according to which the forces in substances act upon one another," even speculating that this might be explained by the strength of the action holding "inversely as the square of the distances." [277] The latter part of the treatise he devotes to a discussion of whether the measure of this force is to be judged from the velocity, as Descartes urged, or from the square of the velocity, as Leibniz proposed. Kant feels that Descartes's account is more correct mathematically, whereas Leibniz's is more in accord with what is found in nature. Since "body as mathematically conceived is a thing quite distinct from body as it exists in nature," Kant allows that "statements can be true of the former which cannot be extended to the latter." [278] He continues:

> Mathematics does not allow in the body with which it deals any force which is not completely produced by that which is the external cause of its motion. This is to say, it does not allow any force in bodies save insofar as it is caused in it from without. This force can therefore always be found complete and in precisely the same measure in the causes whereby the body is moved. This is a fundamental law of mechanics, and being presupposed, allows no other measure of force than the Cartesian. But,

as we shall demonstrate immediately, body as it exists in nature has a quite different constitution. It has in itself a power of itself increasing the force which is awakened in it through the cause of its motion. Consequently it can have degrees of force not due to the outer cause of its motion. And since these can be greater than this cause, they cannot be measured by the Cartesian standard; they are to be estimated in a different manner.[279]

These brief excerpts show that the early Kant had a distinct metaphysical cast to his thought, and in this sense was quite disposed to agree with Leibniz's manner of philosophizing based on the findings of the new science.[280] Apart from this influence, however, Kant in his early career also became quite interested in mathematical physics in its own right, and worked out a theory of cosmogenesis that, while faulty, showed a competent grasp of mechanical principles. This was printed in 1755 with the title, *Universal Natural History and Theory of the Heavens; or an Essay on the Constitution and Mechanical Origin of the Whole Universe Treated According to Newton's Principles,* but the books were impounded because the printer went bankrupt and did not appear until some ten years later.[281] Apart from the stated thesis on cosmogony, and an anticipation in some particulars of Laplace's nebular hypothesis, the work shows that Kant had been thoroughly exposed to Newton's *Mathematical Principles* and was capable of utilizing them in a scientific treatise.[282] In fact, apart from Kant's obvious debt to Leibniz, and notwithstanding Leibniz's disputes with Newton over the priority of the invention of the calculus, there seems little doubt that Kant was by then won over to the ideal of Newtonian science, and that this henceforth exerted a profound influence on the development of his own philosophy.

b. Critical Period

The Critique of Pure Reason is rightfully hailed as Kant's major work, and already in the preface to the first edition he indicates his dissatisfaction with traditional metaphysics and "the matured judgment" of his age, "which refuses to be put off any longer with illusory knowledge." [283] In a footnote he explains that, if this reproach is warranted, it does not in the least apply to mathematics and the physical sciences:

> We often hear complaints of shallowness of thought in our age and of the consequent decline of sound science. But I do not see that the sciences which rest upon a secure foundation, such as mathematics, physics, etc., in the least deserve this reproach. On the contrary, they merit their old reputation for solidity, and, in the case of physics, even surpass it.[284]

It is on the basis of the "secure foundation" of these sciences, in fact, that Kant proposes "to institute a tribunal which will assure to reason its lawful claims." [285] The tribunal is nothing other than the critique of pure reason, and the peculiar epistemological fashion in which it will function will occupy us later. For the moment, suffice it to indicate that physics, and by this Kant means Newtonian physics, rests on an unassailable foundation. Kant is even more assured of this when he writes the preface to the second edition, when he refers in the very first sentence to "the secure path of a science," [286] and repeats this phrase or its equivalent no less than eight times in the space of its few pages. His thesis there is that metaphysics can discern its own limits, as it were, if it emulates the manner of knowing that has proved so successful in the physical sciences; it is on a basis such as this that he would constitute a type of Copernican revolution even in philosophy. This is implied in the following much-quoted statement from the preface to the second edition:

> Hitherto it has been assumed that all our knowledge must conform to objects. But all attempts to extend our knowledge of objects by establishing something in regard to them *a priori,* by means of concepts, have, on this assumption, ended in failure. We must therefore make trial whether we may not have more success in the task of metaphysics, if we suppose that objects must conform to our knowledge. This would agree better with what is desired, namely, that it should be possible to have knowledge of objects *a priori,* determining something in regard to them prior to their being given. We should then be proceeding precisely on the lines of Copernicus' primary hypothesis [mit den ersten Gedanken des Kopernikus].

Failing of satisfactory progress in explaining the movements of the heavenly bodies on the supposition that
they all revolved around the spectator, he tried whether
he might not have better success if he made the spectator
to revolve and the stars to remain at rest. A similar experiment can be tried in metaphysics, as regards the intuition of objects. If intuition must conform to the constitution of the objects, I do not see how we could know
anything of the latter *a priori;* but if the object (as object
of the senses) must conform to the constitution of our fac-
ulty of intuition, I have no difficulty in conceiving such a
possibility.[287]

The program signaled in this passage entails the entire
development of the *Critique.* In brief, Kant saw himself con-
fronted with the rationalism of Leibniz, in which he had been
educated, and the empiricism of Hume, which seemed in accord with Newtonian philosophy but which incorporated
such a large element of skepticism as to make even Newtonian science impossible of attainment. Seeking a middle
path between these extremes, Kant wished to create a synthesis that would borrow elements from both, recognizing
certain a priori elements in human knowing stressed by the
rationalists, and also the necessity of synthetic judgments
based on the experience emphasized by the empiricists. A
union between concept and experience was therefore required, so that the a priori necessity of reason could be extended into the realm of experience, and the synthetic a posteriori findings of empiricism could be given the necessity
they seemed to lack. Kant sought this synthesis in a type of
judgment that is both synthetic and a priori. In the traditional understanding that "all our knowledge must conform to
objects," such judgments turn out to be impossible. By changing one's viewpoint, however, and here Kant invokes his analogy with Copernicus, one may employ the opposite supposition, namely, "that objects must conform to our knowledge,"
and in this way we are able "to have knowledge of objects *a
priori,* determining something in regard to them prior to their
being given." [288] As a consequence of this supposition, however, "we can know *a priori* of things only what we ourselves
put into them," [289] and the further implication of this is that

synthetic a priori knowing "has to do only with appearances, and must leave the thing in itself as indeed real *per se*, but as not known by us." [290]

Kant's adoption of this critical posture involved almost a complete reversal of the philosophy he had expressed in *Thoughts on the True Estimation of Living Forces*. There, as we have seen, he was concerned with the problem as to how one substance could act on any other, basically that of cause and effect, and how space and extension can be constituted only by the interaction of substances. Again, in his earlier period, Kant mistrusted the power of mathematics to provide a valid understanding of the structure of bodies as they exist in nature. Now, however, instead of substance being his basic explanatory principle, the a priori forms of sensibility and of understanding fill this function. Space becomes the form of the external sense faculties, i.e., "the subjective condition of sensibility, under which alone outer intuition is possible for us." [291] Time fulfills the same role for the inner sense, and to both space and time are assigned an "empirical reality," [292] as the conditions that alone render man's perception of objects a possibility. Similarly, there are twelve "pure concepts of the understanding which apply *a priori* to objects of intuition in general." [293] Referred to as "the categories," these can be shown to be the "conditions of the possibility of experience and are therefore valid *a priori* for all objects of experience." [294] Such "objects of experience," however, must be understood not as things in themselves, but merely as "appearances in space and time." [295] It is in this way that Kant restricts the domain of a priori knowledge to "objects of possible experience." [296]

Similarly limited are the principles that teach reason how "to apply to appearances the concepts of understanding." [297] The principle of causality is one such principle, namely, "the principle of succession in time in accordance with the law of the connection of cause and effect." [298] Principles such as these serve to explain the synthetic a priori judgments of science, with regard to their possibility. But to attempt to utilize such principles to come to a knowledge of substance as it is in itself, or to transcend the domain of sensible intuition, as had been the concern of classical metaphysics, is to fall victim to "transcendental illusion." [299] If reason stays within its proper bounds, therefore, it can generate the infallible truth of mathematics and natural science, whereas if it attempts to transcend these bounds it can only fall into metaphysical error.

Kant was convinced, of course, of the validity of the principle of causality as he had now formulated it, and he offered a detailed proof in Book Two of the Transcendental Analytic, which is the Analytic of Principles. The proof has been much discussed by commentators and its adequacy has been frequently contested.[300] In brief, Kant focusses attention on the difference between the order in which one apprehends the appearance of a house when viewing it from top to bottom or from left to right, and the order in which one perceives the positions of a ship as it moves downstream.[301] There is a difference in the two cases in the sense that there is no determined order in the series of perceptions of the house, whereas there is such an order in the perceptions of the movement of the ship. In the latter case, therefore, "we must derive the *subjective succession of apprehension* from the *objective succession* of appearances." [302] This can be done, however, only if there is some type of rule determining our perceptions in such a way that the objectively later event should succeed the objectively earlier, and it is this type of rule that obviously entails some type of causal necessity. Only if such a rule exists can one say that there is truly a sequence in phenomena, as opposed to one's apprehension of such a sequence, which is "only another way of saying that I cannot arrange the apprehension otherwise than in this very succession." [303] The principle of causality, therefore, is the necessary ground of the possibility of such experience, and actually precedes it a priori in the understanding. The argument by which Kant justifies this conclusion is not too lengthy and so may be given here in its entirety:

> All empirical knowledge involves the synthesis of the manifold by the imagination. This synthesis is always successive, that is, the representations in it are always sequent upon one another. In the imagination this sequence is not in any way determined in its order, as to what must precede and what must follow, and the series

of sequent representations can indifferently be taken either in backward or in forward order. But if this synthesis is a synthesis of apprehension of the manifold of a given appearance, the order is determined in the object, or, to speak more correctly, in an order of successive synthesis that determines an object. In accordance with this order something must necessarily precede, and when this antecedent is posited, something else must necessarily follow. If, then, my perception is to contain knowledge of an event, of something as actually happening, it must be an empirical judgment in which we think the sequence as determined; that is, it presupposes another appearance in time, upon which it follows necessarily, according to a rule. Were it not so, were I to posit the antecedent and the event were not to follow necessarily thereupon, I should have to regard the succession as a merely subjective play of my fancy; and if I still represented it to myself as something objective, I should have to call it a mere dream. Thus the relation of appearances (as possible perceptions) according to which the consequent event, that which happens, is, as to its existence, necessarily determined in time by something preceding in conformity with a rule — in other words, the relation of cause to effect — is the condition of the objective validity of our empirical judgments, in respect of the series of perceptions, and so of their empirical truth; that is to say, it is the condition of experience. The principle of the causal relation in the sequence of appearances is therefore also valid of all objects of experience ([insofar as they are] under the conditions of succession), as being itself the ground of the possibility of such experience.[304]

It is difficult to know what to make of this proof. Ewing, for example, has maintained "that the essential part of Kant's message on the subject of causality is not that our mind arranges (synthesises) nature according to the category of causality, but that we can prove the universal validity of the causal principle by showing that without it knowledge would be impossible." [305] Given the text of Kant's development of his proof, one would have to concede that this is a correct estimate of his intentions with regard to the knowledge he viewed as scientific, that, namely, of Newtonian physics. And yet there is a deep-lying subjectivism in Kant's entire treat-

ment of causality, for it seems that the a priori limitation he
has put on human knowing, that man can know only what his
understanding has itself produced, effectively reduces any
claim for causal knowledge to the somewhat gratuitous operation of mind-structuring reality according to a causal principle it has itself fabricated. This, perhaps unfortunately, has
become the more common interpretation of the results of the
famous critique.

Paradoxically for such an interpretation, Kant himself
saw no problem with causality, since it guaranteed the truth
of natural science, which he assumed as the starting point for
the critique. The peculiar tribunal he had constructed, as already noted, was one wherein reason, as innocent and capable of arriving at absolute truth in the sciences, could accuse
spurious reason, which had given rise to metaphysics as a
transcendental illusion, as guilty of error. For Kant, the starting point of the trial is the fact that scientific truth exists;
thus it is quite proper for him to inquire into the conditions
of the possibility of such truth. Kant takes it as equally obvious that metaphysical truth does not yet exist, although
man has a "natural disposition" to seek after this type of
knowledge. The investigation of the tribunal therefore attempts to lay bare the structure of the thinking subject as
such, and in terms of this to arrive at a verdict whereby reason can explain the paradoxical character of both its true and
false claims, showing why scientific truth is possible, why metaphysical error is also possible, and why metaphysics in the
classical sense is actually a delusion.[306]

c. Metaphysical Foundations

The cornerstone of Kant's case, obviously, is the infallible character of Newtonian science. Although he would restrict the classical extension of metaphysics, he must provide
enough of a "metaphysics" to justify the truth-claims of a
"pure science of nature." Kant attempted to do this in the
Critique of Pure Reason, and he turned to the problem again
in his Metaphysical Foundations of Natural Science (1786).[307]
In the preface to this work he makes clear that any true natural science must presuppose a metaphysics. Thus he writes:

What may be called natural science proper presupposes metaphysics of nature; for laws, i.e., principles of the necessity of that which belongs to the *existence* of a thing, are occupied with a conception which does not admit of construction, because its existence cannot be presented in any *a priori* intuitions; natural science proper, therefore, presupposes metaphysics.[308]

Kant would provide such a metaphysics, as we have already noted, through an analysis of the conception of matter in terms of the table of the categories, and in particular of the four classes of pure concepts of understanding, namely, quantity, quality, relation, and modality.[309] The outline of his projected work thus reduces to the following schema:

The *metaphysical* foundations of natural sciences may thus be brought under *four* main divisions, of which the *first* — motion considered as pure *quantum* according to its composition, without any *quality* of the moveable, may be termed phoronomy; the *second*, which regards it as belonging to the *quality* of the matter, under the name of an original moving force, may be called dynamics; and the *third*, where matter with this quality is conceived as by its own reciprocal motion in *relation*, appears under the name of mechanics; and the *fourth*, where its motion or rest [is conceived] merely in reference to the mode of presentation or *modality*, in other words as determined as phenomenon of the external sense, is called phenomenology.[310]

Of these four divisions, the second and third have most relevance for the topic of interest in this study, and thus may profitably be the subject of brief comment.

Kant summarizes his "metaphysical foundations of dynamics"[311] in a series of propositions, of which the following are representative:

[Propositions:]
1. Matter fills a space, not by its mere *existence,* but by a *special moving force.*[312]
2. Matter fills its spaces by the repulsive forces of all its parts, i.e., by its own force of extension, which has a definite degree, beyond which smaller or larger [degrees] can be conceived to infinity. . . .[313]

4. Matter is *divisible to infinity* into parts, of which each
is again matter.[314]

5. The possibility of matter requires a *force of attraction*
as its second essential fundamental force. . . .[315]

6. By mere attraction, without repulsion, no matter is
possible. . . .[316]

As can be seen from these and the remaining propositions of
this division, Kant reduces all of dynamics to a force principle, and this itself is the basic reality in terms of which all of
material nature is to be understood. Kant is definite on this:

> The universal principle of the dynamics of material na-
> ture, that all [that is] real in the objects of our external
> sense, that, namely, which is not mere determination of
> space (place, extension, and figure), must be regarded as
> moving force; by which, therefore, the so-called solid, or
> absolute impenetrability, is banished from natural sci-
> ence as an empty conception, and in its stead a repulsive
> force is posited; while the true and immediate attraction
> is defended against all the sophistries of a metaphysics
> that misunderstands itself, and is explained as a funda-
> mental force necessary even to the possibility of the con-
> ception of matter.[317]

In terms of this fundamental force, Kant attempts to give detailed explanations of the concepts of density, cohesion,
friction, elasticity, and other forces that are involved in mechanics and chemistry. From this, and from his animadver-
sions on "the mechanical mode of explanation," [318] one sees
that Kant reduces all causal explanation to that of efficient
causes, conceived as fundamental forces. So he states:

> All natural philosophy consists rather in the reduction of
> given forces in appearance diverse to a small number of
> forces and powers, adequate to the explanation of the ef-
> fects of the former, but which reduction only extends to
> fundamental forces, beyond which our reason cannot
> proceed. And thus metaphysical research behind what
> lies at the foundation of the empirical conception of mat-
> ter is only useful for the purpose of leading natural phi-
> losophy, so far as is possible, to the investigation of dy-
> namical grounds of explanation, as these alone admit the
> hope of definite laws and consequently of a true rational
> coherence of explanations.[319]

He goes on to insist that "this is all that metaphysics can ever accomplish to the construction of the conception of matter," i.e., to see its properties as essentially dynamical, and in this way to transcend what "a mere mathematical treatment would postulate." [320]

It is in his "metaphysical foundations of mechanics" that Kant takes up Newton's laws of motion and attempts to provide their metaphysical justification. The first law of mechanics, as Kant conceives it, is nothing more than a principle of the conservation of the quantity of matter throughout "all changes of corporeal nature," [321] and thus has little direct causal interest. The "third mechanical law" likewise, which Kant formulates as "in all communication of motion, action and reaction are always equal to one another," [322] presupposes causal action more than it explains it, and thus is not too helpful for refining Kant's views of physical causality. His statement of the second law, however, does throw light on this concept, and thus is repeated here, with its demonstration, in its entirety:

> *Second law of mechanics.* — All change of matter has an external cause. (Every body remains in its state of rest or motion in the same direction and with the same velocity, if not compelled by an external cause to forsake this state).
>
> ### Demonstration
>
> (From universal metaphysics the proposition that all change has a cause is laid at the foundation; here it only remains to be proved of matter, that its change must always have an *external cause*). Matter, as mere object of the external sense, has no determinations but those of external relation in space, and hence is subject to no change except through motion. In respect of this a change of one motion with another, or of the same with rest, and conversely, a cause of the same through this, must be traceable (according to principles of metaphysics). But this cause cannot be internal, for matter has no absolutely internal determinations and grounds of determination. Hence all change of a matter is based upon external causes (i.e., a body continues &c.).[323]

In his explanation of this demonstration, Kant rules out all internal principles of change, holding that there can be no de-

sire, thought, feeling, or will in matter itself, because as such
it is lifeless. Therefore any change must result from without,
from an external efficient cause.

Kant believed that he had thus been able to reduce the
"three laws of universal mechanics" to the categories he had
constructed in the *Critique*, with the result that "the entire
propositions of the present science exactly answer to the categories of *substance, causality,* and *community,* insofar as
these conceptions are applied to matter . . ."[324] When one reflects on the "metaphysics" he has elaborated in the process,
however, it can be seen that this is not far different from that
of his precritical period. Much the same conclusion results
from an examination of the manuscripts on which he was
working just before his death, one of which was for a work to
be entitled *On the Transition from the 'Metaphysical First
Principles of Natural Science' to Physics.*[325] In this, and in the
related treatise *On the Elementary System of Motor Forces,*
the force concept is again given the prominence it had in
Leibniz's system.[326] One wonders how Kant could have reconciled these changes of position, and how they stand up before the tribunal he has instituted in the *Critique.* Even in the
Critique, of course, there is an ambiguity in his presentation
of the doctrine of causation, for, although he insists on the
transcendental deduction of causality at a general level, he
also insists that "we must resort to experience" for any detailed knowledge of its empirical laws.[327] The inconsistencies
that we have seen plaguing Hume and Leibniz are thus also
inherited by Kant. Attempts to save him may be made by focusing on different levels of causality implicit in his treatment, such as transcendental causality, empirical causality,
and metaphysical causality, and by discerning a "looseness of
fit" between the various levels that would bring him more in
line with recent philosophies of science.[328] But the fact remains that Kant, like most of the philosophers of classical science discussed in this chapter, presumes more than his explicit statements seem to allow, particularly when dealing
with the problem of causality. Scientific explanations, for him,
are causal explanations, and these are made ultimately
through forces that are real, that provide a "secure foundation" for Newtonian physics. So secure is this foundation, in

fact, that such physics can become the model for all infallible truth concerning the physical universe, and in so doing even provide the touchstone for discerning error and "metaphysical illusion." Whether Kant himself ultimately fell victim to the same illusion is a question over which philosophers will argue endlessly. Whatever their verdict, it seems certain that Kant saw causal knowledge as the only way of guaranteeing the possibility of science, and of science's existence and certitude he never permitted himself the slightest doubt.

CHAPTER TWO

The Methodologists of Classical Science

FROM the preceding chapter and the whole of the first volume it may be seen that methodology was a concern of all investigators of the world of nature from Aristotle to Kant. Yet, with few exceptions, those studied thus far are not known primarily as methodologists. For the most part they achieved fame as scientists, whose primary intent was to discover new knowledge and whose concern with method was mainly one of justifying their discoveries, or as philosophers, who studied the implications of the new science and its methods for renovating the whole of human knowledge or for erecting new systematic views of the cosmos. As classical science developed, however, it was inevitable that some investigators would begin to reflect on the process and methods by which this development was achieved, and would consciously address themselves to problems of scientific methodology.[1] The period during which such a movement became clearly discernible was the nineteenth century, a time when the expression "philosophy of science" began to appear and thus heralded the expansion of this discipline in the present century.[2]

The methodologists who most typify this movement and who will be the chief objects of study in this chapter are John F. W. Herschel, William Whewell, John Stuart Mill, and

Claude Bernard.[3] In additon, two thinkers who are somewhat atypical are also given consideration, if only for the fact that their teachings were the object of concern, not to say criticism, on the part of these methodologists. The first is Francis Bacon, who is atypical only in the sense that he belongs two centuries earlier, for his primary interests were programmatic for the new science, and this even before its startling discoveries were fully enunciated by its celebrated founders. The other is Auguste Comte, who, while belonging to the nineteenth century, is atypical in the sense that his methodological views were somewhat too advanced for that century, and thus were criticized by the classical methodologists, although he foreshadowed in many ways the teachings that characterize twentieth-century philosophy of science.

1. *Francis Bacon*

Francis Bacon was a contemporary of Gilbert, Galileo, Kepler, and Harvey, but he was not intimately associated with any of them and was not particularly appreciative of their scientific contributions.[4] A lawyer and statesman by profession, he became interested in the new science mainly through classical sources, with the result that his own contributions to the growth of science remained predominantly literary in character. Apart from his interest in natural philosophy and the philosophy of scientific method, to which he turned after reverses in his political career, Bacon is important for his projects for the practical organization of the scientific community. He also wrote extensively on law, politics, and moral philosophy, and maintained an active interest in religion, although these matters do not concern us here.[5]

Bacon's guiding motivation was a reform of all of human learning through a new type of philosophy that would break with the Aristotelian tradition and yet preserve much of the latter's terminology. The projected reform was a mammoth undertaking, and many of the writings Bacon planned never reached a form sufficiently complete for publication. Enough of his work is available, however, to discern the main elements of his reformation.[6] In brief, he was dissatisfied with Aristotle's distinctions between the various sciences and wished to reunite physics, or the science of nature, with the practical arts, even if this meant denying an independent status to mathematics. His interest in the Bible stimulated him to transfer some of Aristotle's ethical and metaphysical studies to the province of revealed theology. The foundation of his own scheme for science, or philosophy, was to be natural history, which would serve as the base of a pyramid, above which would be physics; this in turn would culminate in metaphysics at the apex, itself assuming the form of a universal physics. Both physics and metaphysics would supply causal explanations of the world of nature, differing from each other only in the generality of their principles or axioms. The latter would be arrived at by a new logic essentially inductive in character. This begins with particulars that are sorted out within natural history and lead to the discovery of forms or causes at the level of science. Since whatever is truly known in science as cause will also function in nature as operation, both physical and metaphysical knowledge can yield inventions that will be of value in serving man's needs, and it is this that confers a pragmatic value — as opposed to Aristotle's purely contemplative ideal — on the pursuit of speculative knowledge.

Bacon's insistence on the use of induction, together with the role he assigned to experiment in the discovery of causes, has led him to be hailed as the father of inductive or experimental philosophy. Such a title, however, should not be understood in a strong empiricist sense, as though there were no rationalist elements in Bacon's system. The ideal of science he had formulated, in fact, was even more Aristotelian than Aristotle's, in that he was searching for certain and infallible knowledge through causes, which he believed existed in the physical world, thereby evidencing a strong realist commitment, and which he was also convinced could be known by men, and this rather quickly once they got on to the proper method.[7] Such a method Bacon called the "interpretation of nature," to distinguish it from the currently accepted peripatetic method, "a thing rash and premature," which he referred to as the "anticipation of nature." [8] In the latter, "almost all the work is spent about the syllogism," which for the most part is "improperly and over-hastily abstracted from facts,

vague, not sufficiently definite, faulty in short in many ways
. . ." [9] Bacon therefore rejected this defective instrument and
in its place proposed a new "form of demonstration," which
he called "induction." As he explains it:

> Although therefore I leave to the syllogism and these fa-
> mous and boasted modes of demonstration their jurisdic-
> tion over popular arts and such as are matter of opinion
> (in which department I leave all as it is), yet in dealing
> with the nature of things I use induction throughout, and
> that in the minor propositions as well as the major. For I
> consider induction to be that form of demonstration
> which upholds the sense, and closes with nature, and
> comes to the very brink of operation, if it does not ac-
> tually deal with it.[10]

The reason for making this change is to relinquish once and
for all the probable opinions of the scholastics and put in
their place a type of certainty that will satisfy the human
mind.[11] As Bacon reasons, "hitherto the proceeding has been
to fly at once from the sense and particulars up to the most
general propositions . . . a short way, no doubt, but precipitate. . . ." [12] As opposed to this "easy and ready way to dis-
putation,"

> my plan is to proceed regularly and gradually from one
> axiom to another, so that the most general are not
> reached till the last: but then when you do come to them
> you find them to be not empty notions, but well defined,
> and such as nature would really recognize as her first
> principles, and such as lie at the heart and marrow of
> things. But the greatest change I introduce is in the form
> itself of induction and the judgment made thereby. For
> the induction of which the [peripatetic] logicians speak,
> which proceeds by simple enumeration, is a puerile
> thing, concludes at hazard [*precario concludit*], is al-
> ways liable to be upset by a contradictory instance,
> takes into account only what is known and ordinary, and
> leads to no result. Now what the sciences stand in need
> of is a form of induction which shall analyze experience
> and take it to pieces, and by a due process of exclusion
> and rejection lead to an inevitable conclusion [*necessa-
> rio concludat*].[13]

The certainty of the new inductive knowledge that
Bacon would provide, according to the foregoing passage, derives from two sources: it must have a solid basis in experience, and there must be some sure method of exclusion that
would avoid the pitfalls of Aristotelian induction by so-called
"simple enumeration." It is with regard to the first point that
Bacon argues for a broadening of experience through experimental knowledge. He acknowledges that experiments have
been performed in the past, and even continue in the present,
"but the manner of making experiments which men now use
is blind and stupid." [14] They are not methodical in their
search, and they "make their trials carelessly, and as it were
in play; slightly varying experiments already known, and, if
the thing does not answer, growing weary and abandoning
the attempt." [15] As distinct from this malpractice, Bacon urges
that men "educe some science or theory from their
experiments," [16] and suggests the following procedure:

> In the true course of experience, and in carrying it on to
> the effecting of new works, the divine wisdom and order
> must be our pattern. Now God on the first day of cre-
> ation created light only, giving to that work an entire
> day in which no material substance was created. So must
> we likewise from experience of every kind first endeavor
> to discover true causes and axioms and seek for experi-
> ments of light, not for experiments of fruit. For axioms
> rightly discovered and established supply practice with
> its instruments, not one by one, but in clusters, and draw
> after them trains and troops of works.[17]

Later on in the *Novum organum* Bacon gives a further indication as to what he means by "experiments of light." He
writes:

> Then only will there be good ground of hope for the fur-
> ther advance of knowledge, when there shall be received
> and gathered together into natural history a variety of
> experiments, which are of no use in themselves, but sim-
> ply serve to discover causes and axioms; which I call "ex-
> perimenta lucifera," experiments of light, to distinguish
> them from those which I call "fructifera," experiments of
> fruit. Now experiments of this kind have one admirable
> property and condition; they never miss or fail. For since

they are applied not for the purpose of producing any particular effect but only of discovering the natural cause of some effect, they answer the end equally well whichever way they turn out, for they settle the question.[18]

So Bacon goes on to urge "a greater abundance of experiments," while insisting that these be made in regular and orderly fashion, so that they can supply the solid base in experience from which new causal knowledge may be derived.[19]

The experimental history of phenomena that Bacon would thus provide is a necessary, but only a preparatory, stage for the inductive process itself. From experience and experiment one has to go about classifying this new knowledge by means of tables of presence, tables of absence, and tables of comparison. Baconian induction takes place when the mind considers these tables and through their use puts into effect the method of exclusion which will supersede that of simple enumeration. In the second book of the *Novum organum,* Bacon provides a detailed example of the use of such tables in arriving at the true nature of heat.[20] In this instance the table of presence surveys all the entities and situations in which heat is found, whereas the table of absence gives a similar list of cases where heat might be expected but is not found. The table of comparison shows how other natures, or forms, increase or decrease when the form of heat is subjected to corresponding variations. The work of exclusion comes about when, with the aid of these tables, all forms are rejected except the one form that is exclusively associated with the presence of heat in a subject. This form, for Bacon, is motion, and so he concludes his inductive process with the simple statement that "heat itself, its essence and quiddity, is motion and nothing else." [21]

To complete this summary account, mention must be made of other helps that Bacon has devised for the mind in assuring the adequacy of the inductive process. Such helps include the twenty-seven prerogative instances whose discussion occupies a major part of the second book.[22] Chief among these are the *instantiae crucis,* which enable one to make a decisive judgment whenever "the understanding is so balanced as to be uncertain to which of two or more natures the cause of the nature in question should be assigned." [23] In such a case, the *instantiae crucis* have the role of showing "the union of one of the natures with the nature in question to be sure and indissoluble, of the other to be varied and separable. . . ." [24] Thus "the question is decided, and the former nature is admitted as the cause, while the latter is dismissed and rejected." [25] The examples that Bacon gives are interesting for the commentary they provide on much of the scientific knowledge acquired by his predecessors, for example, the cause of the ebb and flow of the tides, the rotation of the heavenly bodies, the nature of weight and heaviness, the polarity of magnets, and the cause of projectile motion.[26] In none of these cases does Bacon, as has been noted, make a significant contribution to the science of his day.

Through the continued use of this method of exclusion and the *instantiae crucis*, however, Bacon was hopeful that a complete enumeration of all the "particulars" of nature would eventually be achieved, and that this would not take an inordinate time. Thus he writes:

> Let no man be alarmed at the multitude of particulars, but let this rather encourage him to hope. For the particular phenomena of art and nature are but a handful to the inventions of the wit, when disjoined and separated from the evidence of things. Moreover this road has an issue in the open ground and not far off; the other has no issue at all, but endless entanglement. For men hitherto have made but short stay with experience, but passing her lightly by, have wasted an infinity of time on meditations and glosses of the wit. But if someone were by that could answer our questions and tell us in each case what the fact in nature is, the discovery of all causes and sciences would be but the work of a few years.[27]

And this "discovery of all causes and sciences" to be accomplished in "a few years" should result from the new *forma demonstrationis* that Bacon would substitute for Aristotle's syllogistic reasoning. This is to achieve the same result that Aristotelian demonstration purported to provide, namely, certain knowledge through causes, but its method is more foolproof, in the sense that it "leads from certain premises derived from experience to certain conclusions necessarily entailed by them." [28] As Bacon presents his method, no hypotheses are involved in attaining the new knowledge; there is no room for a hypothetico-deductive type of explanation, for this is precisely the pitfall into which the scholastics had fallen.[29] Bacon's method, as he details it, is purely inductive, and if this method is properly applied it will lead to certain and infallible truth, to the knowledge of true causes. Bacon's goal is ultimately to build "in the human understanding a true model of the world, such as it is in fact, not such as a man's own reason would have it to be." [30] The latter idols and fancies "are nothing more than arbitrary abstractions," whereas what Bacon is searching after "are the Creator's own stamp upon creation, impressed and defined in matter by true and exquisite lines." [31]

Bacon's concern, therefore, is with causal explanations, and these alone will he regard as truly scientific. Yet he was not completely satisfied with the doctrine of causes as this had come down to him, though he was willing to accept the Aristotelian ideal and even its fourfold division. So he concedes:

> It is a correct position that "true knowledge is knowledge by causes." And causes again are not improperly distributed into four kinds; the material, the formal, the efficient, and the final. But of these the final cause rather corrupts than advances the sciences, except such as have to do with human action. The discovery of the formal is despaired of. The efficient and the material (as they are investigated and received, that is, as remote causes, without reference to the latent process leading to the form) are but slight and superficial, and contribute little, if anything, to true and active science.[32]

It is in this spirit that he defines both physics and metaphysics in terms of the types of causes they consider, while making the necessary qualifications as to precisely the types of knowledge entailed in this division.[33] Thus he writes that,

> . . . avoiding all height of language, I will state the matter perspicuously and familiarly. I divided natural philosophy into the inquiry of causes and the production of effects. The inquiry of causes I referred to the theoretical

part of philosophy. This I subdivide into physics and
metaphysics. It follows that the true difference between
them must be drawn from the nature of the causes that
they inquire into. And therefore to speak plain and go no
further about, physics inquires and handles the material
and efficient causes, metaphysics the formal and final.[34]

Fuller details are provided in Bacon's other writings. So
in the second book of the *Novum organum* he ties in this
knowledge of causes with the discovery of natures or forms.
Here he explains:

> Of a given nature to discover the form, or true specific
> difference, or nature-engendering nature, or source of
> emanation (for these are the terms which come nearest to
> a description of the thing), is the work and aim of human
> knowledge. Subordinate to these primary works are two
> others that are secondary and of inferior mark; to the
> former, the transformation of concrete bodies, so far as
> this is possible; to the latter, the discovery, in every case
> of generation and motion, of the latent process carried on
> from the manifest efficient and the manifest material to
> the form which is engendered; and in like manner the
> discovery of the latent configuration of bodies at rest and
> not in motion.[35]

In light of this general situation, Bacon would then "let the
investigation of forms, which are (in the eye of reason at
least, and in their essential law) eternal and immutable, constitute metaphysics; and let the investigation of the efficient
cause, and of matter, and of the latent process, and the latent
configuration (all of which have reference to the common and
ordinary course of nature, not to her eternal and fundamental
laws) constitute physics." [36]

The principal meaning that Bacon has in mind when he
uses the term "cause" seems to be that of formal causality,
which he takes as equivalent to law. His use of the term
"form" is not in the sense of any "abstract forms and ideas." [37]
Rather,

> when I speak of forms, I mean nothing more than those
> laws and determinations of absolute actuality, which
> govern and constitute any simple nature, as heat, light,

weight, in every kind of matter and subject that is susceptible of them. Thus the form of heat or the form of light is the same thing as the law of heat or the law of light.[38]

This is not a scholastic usage, but it does mirror to some degree the terminology of the founders and philosophers of classical science, as recounted in the preceding chapter and in the last chapter of the first volume. Bacon was less sympathetic in his treatment of final causes, particularly as in his oft-quoted remark that "the inquisition of final causes is barren, and like a virgin consecrated to God produces nothing." [39] This statement, taken out of context, creates the impression that Bacon was opposed to the search for such causes, whereas this is not the case, since he regarded the doctrine on final causality as a legitimate part of metaphysics, while admitting that this part of metaphysical teaching, of its very nature, had no practical application.[40] Consistent with his announced intention, however, his terminological usage of causal language turns out to be quite different from that of the scholastics, and one should be careful in interpreting statements that seem to show any pronounced similarity to Aristotelian thought.[41]

Whatever the difficulties of understanding Bacon, there can be no doubt that he exerted a profound influence on the development of scientific methodology. His writings in this area are not so important for the fact that they immediately produced positive results by way of new discoveries in the sciences; in fact, it is generally admitted that Baconian induction, as outlined in the *Novum organum,* is singularly sterile when conceived as a logic of scientific discovery.[42] At the same time, Bacon's work laid a foundation that would serve as a corrective to the rationalism of Cartesian physics, and that would be taken over by most English thinkers in their attempts to put the new science on a strong empirical base. This was particularly true of the members of the Royal Society, who frequently lauded Bacon for the methodological assistance he provided to their endeavors.[43] Thus Thomas Sprat, the official historian of the Royal Society, could write in 1667 in his *History of the Royal Society:*

> I shall only mention one great man, who had the true
> imagination of the whole extent of this enterprise [i.e.,
> that of the Royal Society] as it is now set on foot, and
> that is the Lord Bacon. In whose books there are every-
> where scattered the best arguments that can be produced
> for the defense of experimental philosophy and the best
> directions that are needful to promote it.[44]

Some scientists, such as Newton, seemingly were much impressed by Bacon's strictures against hypotheses, and attempted to utilize the method of Baconian induction to establish their conclusions with the new demonstrative certitude.
Others, while paying lip service to such induction, used this
together with a hypothetico-deductive type of methodology,
and thus inaugurated a new direction that would lead to the
methods practiced in contemporary science. Among the latter
group were French thinkers as well as English, for Baconian
views were instrumental in the encyclopedist movement of
the French Enlightenment.[45] Bacon's works were known also
to Auguste Comte, whose quite different concept of scientific
method will next occupy us. But they bore most immediate
fruit among English philosophers, such as Locke and Hume,
and finally with Herschel, Whewell, and Mill, Bacon's ultimate successors as logicians of scientific method.

2. *Auguste Comte*

A considerable time-lapse is involved in the leap from Bacon
to Auguste Comte, whose ideas on scientific methodology did
not take form until two centuries after Bacon's death.[46] Yet
there are similarities between the thought of the two men, at
least to the extent that both regarded the new science as the
prototype for all human knowledge and both were intent on
providing a positive or empirical ground for the scientific enterprise. Comte cites Bacon frequently in his masterwork, the
Cours de la philosophie positive, ranking him with Galileo,
Kepler, and Newton as heralds of the new positive stage, the
highest attainable level of human knowledge.[47]

Comte was eccentric — "crazy" is the term preferred by
George Sarton [48] — a circumstance that deprived him of the
hearing his more serious writings otherwise might have

gained him among his contemporaries. In his youth he repudiated his parent's Catholicism, but in his later years, under
the stress of a series of emotional crises, he turned again to
religion, developing his own godless "cult of humanity,"
which was patterned after many of the accidental features of
Catholicism but differed from it in every essential.[49] The
"positivist calendar" that Comte constructed, analogous to the
calendar of saints within the Catholic Church, is revealing,
however, for the knowledge he there manifests of the history
of science and the importance he attaches to scientists, particularly those of the seventeenth and eighteenth centuries, in
advancing the cause of humanity.[50]

Comte's main interest was in the fields of methodology
and epistemology, and his philosophy, to which he gave the
name "positivism," is principally concerned with them.[51] He
adopted a historical approach, attempting to outline the progressive development of knowledge through the various
stages of human growth, both collectively and individually.
The search for causes, which we have seen to be characteristic of Bacon's method, Comte relegated to the earlier phases
of this development, and insisted that it could not be part of
the positive method. The latter, in place of causes, seeks only
correlations between facts which can be expressed as general
laws, and which otherwise mark the culmination of scientific
inquiry. As ancillary to the formulation of laws, Comte also
endorsed the methods of prediction, hypothetical reasoning,
and verification, and on this account can rightfully be regarded as a precursor of contemporary scientific methodology.

The details of Comte's teaching are best approached
through the famous "law of the three stages," which supplies
the key to his methodology:

> The law is this: that each of our leading conceptions —
> each branch of our knowledge — passes successively
> through three different theoretical stages: the theological,
> or fictitious; the metaphysical, or abstract; and the scien-
> tific, or positive. In other words, the human mind, by its
> nature, employs in its progress three methods of philoso-
> phizing whose characteristics are essentially different
> and even radically opposed: first the theological method,

> then the metaphysical, and finally the positive. . . . The
> first is the necessary point of departure of the human un-
> derstanding and the third is its fixed and definitive state;
> the second is merely a state of transition.[52]

When at the theological stage the human mind, supposing
that all phenomena are produced by the immediate action of
supernatural beings, seeks "the essential nature of beings, the
first and final causes of all effects." [53] At the metaphysical
stage the mind replaces supernatural agents with "abstract
forces" and other entities that are "personified abstractions,"
regarding these as capable of producing all phenomena. It is
only at the last, or positive, stage, that the mind gives over
"the vain search after absolute notions, the origins and desti-
nation of the universe, and the deeper causes of phenomena,
and applies itself . . . to the study of their laws — that is,
their invariable relations of succession and resemblance." [54]
The knowledge of such laws is attained by observation and
reasoning, and they provide true scientific explanations. As
Comte expresses it:

> The explanation of facts, reduced to its real terms, will
> henceforth be only the relationships established between
> different particular phenomena and some general facts,
> the number of which tend to decrease more and more
> with the progress of science.[55]

By the expression "general facts" Comte probably means
what later methodologists would refer to as lawlike statements,[56] and even individual facts or "particular phenomena"
are related, in his view, to some theory or rational scheme.
Thus he writes:

> If it is true that every positive theory must be based upon
> observed facts, it is equally true that facts cannot be ob-
> served without the guidance of some theory. Without
> such guidance, it would be impossible to gather together
> isolated facts and they would remain barren; we could
> not retain them: for the most part we could not even per-
> ceive them.[57]

Whereas Bacon had tended to identify causal and lawlike explanations, in Comte's mind there is a sharp dichotomy
between these, although in setting up the dichotomy Comte

tends to understand "cause" uniquely in the sense of something ultimate, whether this be first or final. This becomes clear when he goes about describing the proper nature of the positive philosophy:

> The basic characteristic of the positive philosophy is that it regards all phenomena as subjected to invariable natural laws. Our business is — seeing how vain and senseless is any search into what are called causes, whether first or final — to pursue an accurate discovery of these laws, with a view to reducing them to the smallest possible number. . . . We have no intention of exposing the generating causes of phenomena . . . Our real business is merely to analyze accurately the circumstances of their production, and to connect them by the normal relations of succession and resemblance.[58]

Comte goes on to exemplify this with what, in his mind, is the ideal scientific explanation, that provided by the law of universal gravitation. This serves to explain the general phenomena of the universe in terms of a general fact that "itself is a simple extension of a phenomenon that is perfectly familiar to us, and which we therefore say we understand — the weight of bodies on the surface of the earth." [59] As to the nature of weight or of attraction, however, Comte maintains that "these are questions we regard as completely insoluble," although theologians and metaphysicians may endlessly dispute over them.[60]

Apart from the role of law in scientific explanation, Comte accorded law an equally important status in the work of prediction, which he regarded as essential to scientific activity, if not constituting its main goal. Prediction, in fact, assumes an even more important role for him than explanation, because it is through prediction that scientific laws become testable or verifiable, thus leading to another of Comte's important themes, namely, that of verification. Prediction also is closely associated with the Baconian ideal of using scientific knowledge for the control of nature. Comte, after acknowledging his debt to Bacon, explains his own conception of this utilitarian aspect of the scientific enterprise:

> Doubtless, when one looks collectively at all the works of the human species, one may conceive the study of nature

as destined to furnish a sure rational basis for man's action on nature, since the knowledge of the laws of phenomena that enables us continually to predict can itself evidently lead us, in our activities, to modify one work by the other to our own advantage. Our direct and natural means of acting on the bodies that surround us are extremely feeble and completely disproportionate to our needs. Whenever we come to exercise a significant action, this is only because our knowledge of natural laws permits us to introduce some elementary modifiers among the determinate circumstances under whose influence various phenomena are effected, and these, feeble as they may be in themselves, are sufficient in certain cases to produce from the multitude of external causes definitive results that work to our satisfaction. In sum, science yields prediction, prediction yields action: such is the quite simple formula that expresses, in a precise manner, the general relation between science and art, taking these two terms in their full meaning.[61]

It should be noted in this text that Comte acknowledges the existence of "action," "modifiers," "influence," and even "external causes," while also admitting that scientific knowledge is conducive to the production of effects. Yet he is somewhat perverse in concealing such admissions, and obviously it is not under these causal aspects that he is interested in explanatory laws; rather it is the ability to predict what will happen through operations performed in conformity with such laws. And so, when treating astronomy, where man's efforts (in Comte's day) had been totally ineffective in changing the course of supraterrestrial bodies, Comte could yet insist on the value of the predictive character of its laws. He writes:

No part of natural philosophy can thus make more evident the truth of this fundamental axiom: all science has prediction as its goal. This serves to distinguish real science from simple erudition, which is limited merely to recounting past events with no view of the future.[62]

Again, writing of physics, Comte insists that even the perfection of this science consists in its ability to predict. He states:

. . . every science worthy of the name must clearly have the possibility of establishing a corresponding order of prediction. It is then necessary to add, to give such a definition its real completion, that the final goal of physical theories is to predict, as accurately as possible, all of the appearances that a body will present when placed in any given types of circumstances, excluding only those that could alter its nature. That this end be rarely attained in a complete and precise manner is not at all being questioned, but this results merely from the fact that the science is imperfect.[63]

Finally, coming to chemistry, he is aware that this hardly qualifies to be called a science because it is unable, for the most part, to supply accurate predictions:

. . . it is clear that, in the greater part of its researches, present-day chemistry hardly deserves to be called a true science, because it practically never leads to real and certain prediction. When one introduces into chemical operations, already well investigated, certain determinate modifications — even those incidental and few in number — it is rarely possible to predict with certitude the changes they will produce, and nonetheless without this indispensable condition, as I have so frequently established in this treatise, there is no science at all properly speaking; there is only erudition, no matter how important and how numerous the facts collected. To think otherwise is to mistake the quarry for the building.[64]

Despite his insistence on a "positive philosophy," Comte should not be identified with a strict empiricist tradition, nor with one that advocates inductive procedures alone. He holds that there are two general scientific procedures and that these are induction and deduction. He seems to view induction as of primary importance for establishing the fundamental laws of a science; deduction, on the other hand, has value for establishing particular conclusions relating to special topics of research.[65] Deduction, again, is essential for the work of prediction, since predictions are normally deduced from laws that have already been established. It is in this sense that Comte could maintain that we only make inductions so as to be in a position later to make deductions.[66] By thus insisting on this twofold process of induction and deduction in scientific method, Comte hoped also to steer a middle course between the empiricists and the rationalists (whom he referred to as "empiricists and mystics" [67]), the former pretending to derive laws from facts alone and the latter from a priori intuitions of the mind. As we have already seen, Comte felt that even a scientific fact, or an experiment, would be impossible without some theory behind it. He was obviously opposed also to pure metaphysical speculation, made without reference to the facts of experience. Thus he countenanced both the use of theories and hypotheses in science, and indeed regarded them as important elements leading ultimately to a method of verification.

With regard to hypotheses, contrary to Bacon's strictures on them, Comte maintains the importance, indeed the inevitability, of their use in scientific research. He insists, consistent with what we have already seen, that there are only two ways of discovering "the real law of any phenomena," [68] viz., either by inducing it from observed facts or by deducing it from a known law of greater generality. He goes on:

> But, either way would certainly be insufficient, even with respect to the most simple phenomena, in the eyes of anyone who has well understood the essential difficulties involved in a profound study of nature, if one does not begin by some anticipation of the results, by making a provisional supposition, at first essentially conjectural, with respect to some of the very notions that constitute the final object of the research. Hence the introduction, in a way that is strictly indispensable, of hypotheses into natural philosophy.[69]

Without the use of such hypotheses, "the effective discovery of natural laws would be clearly impossible, and this in cases of any complication, while in all other cases real progress would be, at the least, greatly slowed down." [70]

Yet, somewhat as in the writings of Descartes and Newton, the word "hypothesis" had several meanings for Comte, and some types of hypotheses he clearly would not allow in his method. So he goes on, after having stated that hypotheses are practically indispensable, to add "a fundamental condition" [71] that must attend their use and that is directly associated with the process of verification:

This condition, hitherto imperfectly analyzed, consists in employing only those hypotheses that are susceptible, by their very nature, of a positive verification, more or less involved but always clearly attainable, and whose degree of precision is in exact accord with what one can attain in the study of corresponding phenomena. In other words, truly philosophical [i.e., scientific] hypotheses should always have the character of simple anticipations of what experience [experiment] and reasoning could make immediately apparent, if the circumstances of the problem were more favorable.[72]

On the other hand, other types of hypotheses would be excluded from scientific investigation, for example, those that would be concerned with first causes or ultimate causes, and thus would violate the "fundamental condition." Thus Comte goes on:

If one presumes to reach by hypothesis what is itself radically inaccessible to observation and reasoning, the fundamental condition will be disregarded and the hypothesis, passing out of the truly scientific domain, necessarily would become injurious.[73]

As can be seen from the foregoing, much of what Comte wrote about scientific method, and particularly the use of hypothetico-deductive reasoning and verification, finds echo in twentieth-century writing on philosophy of science. He himself, however, was not completely consistent in applying his own criteria, particularly when it came to selecting from among hypotheses relating to atoms and to elastic fluids, for he accepted the former while rejecting the latter as unverifiable and inconceivable, although he had no direct evidence of either.[74]

Of special interest in the light of our remarks in the first volume on Newton and gravity is Comte's evaluation of the "law of gravitation," which is given at length in Lesson 24 of the second volume of his *Cours.* Here he attempts a positivist reading of the implications of Newton's discovery, although the interpretation he provides is again not free of inconsistency. Comte accepts Newton's arguments that would estab-

lish "the identity between the tendency of the moon towards
the earth and weight properly speaking," [75] and argues from
this, as we have already seen in the excerpts from his first
volume, that the concept of weight is so familiar to us that
the identity enables us to understand, and even actually explain, the moon's motion.[76] He then goes on to expound in
some detail why he favors the use of the term "gravitation,"
while being quite definitely opposed to another term that is
frequently used in its place, namely, "attraction." With regard
to gravitation Comte has this to say:

> It is in order to express succinctly this fundamental simi-
> larity between weight and the accelerative force of the
> stars that the felicitous expression "gravitation," under-
> stood as exactly synonymous with universal weight, has
> been coined to designate the action of the sun on the
> planets and of the latter on their satellites. The use of
> this term has the great philosophical advantage of giving
> precise indication of a simple general fact, mathemati-
> cally established, without any vain search for the essen-
> tial nature and the first cause of the celestial action or of
> terrestrial gravity. It tends to put into proper perspective
> the true characteristic of all of our positive explanations,
> which actually consist in establishing relationships and
> making comparisons to whatever degree possible. Evi-
> dently we cannot know whatever there is at the base of
> this mutual action of the stars and this weight of ter-
> restrial bodies: any effort whatsoever in this direction
> would be, of necessity, quite delusive as well as com-
> pletely useless; only minds that are alien to scientific
> studies can so occupy themselves in this day. But we
> know, with complete certitude, the existence of the law
> of these two orders of phenomena; and we know, more-
> over, that they are identical. It is this that makes possible
> their true mutual explanation, by an accurate comparison
> of the less known with the more known. For the geome-
> ter, whom a long and habitual meditation has deeply
> familiarized with the true mechanism of the celestial
> movements, terrestrial weight is explained when he sees
> it as a particular case of general gravitation. On the
> other hand it is weight that makes celestial gravitation
> comprehensible to the physicist properly speaking, as
> well as to the common man, to whom the former notion

alone is sufficiently familiar. We can never really go beyond relationships of this kind.[77]

As opposed to this endorsement of the term "gravitation,"
Comte does "not know how to criticize more strongly the irrational usage, still so common, of the term 'attraction' in the
study of celestial mechanics." [78] His objection to this word is
that it puts one back into a prescientific mentality by pretending to explain how the sun acts on the planets and the
earth on weights.[79] Moreover, and this Comte sees as typical
of the French reaction to Newtonian conceptions, it harkens
back to the metaphysical stage by reintroducing the "occult
qualities that our great Descartes had, with such great effort,
justly banished" from philosophy.[80] Yet, despite the unfortunate connotations of Newton's term, Comte does not wish to
take anything away from him, particularly in regard to his superiority over Descartes. Up to Newton's time, Comte explains, "the human mind could not raise itself, in the person
of our great Descartes, to a mechanical conception of general
phenomena, except by creating an enormous hypothesis relating to their mode of production that was without any positive
base." [81] Descartes thus kept men's mind in servitude to metaphysical ways of thinking, whereas Newton shook them free
and set them off in the positive, scientific direction. So Comte
concludes:

> The philosophical effect of Newton's discovery has been
> to start movement in the true positive direction that is
> open to real and unlimited progress. It has carefully con-
> served from Descartes the fundamental idea of a mecha-
> nism; but [it has done this] by definitively by-passing, as
> radically inaccessible to our powers, every search for its
> source and its mode of production. It has shown, by an
> admirable example, how, without penetrating to the es-
> sence of phenomena, we can come to relate them and
> compare them precisely, in such a way as to attain, with
> exactness as well as certitude, the true definitive aim of
> our real studies, an exact prediction of events, and it is
> this that a priori conceptions are by their nature incapa-
> ble of providing.[82]

The study of these passages shows that Comte was wrestling with the same basic problems as Newton, and seemingly

came to similar solutions while stating these in ways that were quite opposed to Newton's. Both men were agnostic regarding the ultimate cause of gravity, and neither wished to formulate any hypotheses as to what such an ultimate cause might be. Both Newton and Comte likewise agreed on the reality of gravity and the existence of actions, tendencies, and accelerating forces. Comte also spoke favorably of a mechanism, and otherwise used terms with normal causal connotations. Yet, apparently he had set his mind irrevocably against the express use of causal terminology and against the explicit acknowledgment of any causes, even the most proximate. This attitude, easily explained in terms of his positive philosophy, was also consistent with the French tradition of analytic physics, with its emphasis on quantitative correlations of phenomena, as evidenced in the work of Laplace, Lagrange, Fourier, and Ampère.[83] On the other hand, the Comtean interpretation of gravity and other forces was quite opposed to the mainstream of mechanical thought, particularly as seen in Newton's own writings and in those of his followers, the Newtonians.[84] Thus it is not surprising that such an interpretation would generally be rejected by English methodologists, particularly by Herschel and Whewell, to whose teachings we now turn.

3. John F. W. Herschel

Unlike Bacon and Comte, John Herschel was a practicing scientist who concerned himself with problems of methodology, and this at a time when his efforts could be hailed as "the first attempt by an eminent man of science to make the methods of science explicit."[85] The only son of William Herschel, pioneer of sidereal astronomy and justly famous in his own right,[86] John studied at Cambridge with George Peacock and Charles Babbage, there becoming quite proficient in mathematics. After a brief flirtation with law as a career, he decided to follow in his father's footsteps and quickly attained a reputation as a scientist second to none in early Victorian England.[87] Apart from his contributions to astronomy and physical optics, Herschel was interested in making science better understood among his educated contemporaries, and wrote numerous encyclopedia articles with this goal in mind. In a similar vein, he contributed two extraordinary volumes to the Reverend Dionysius Lardner's Cabinet Cyclopaedia, the first entitled *A Preliminary Discourse on the Study of Natural Philosophy* (1830) [88] and the second *A Treatise on Astronomy* (1833).[89] The latter was subsequently enlarged as *Outlines of Astronomy*,[90] went through twelve English editions, and was widely translated. It is thus not surprising that Herschel's name became a household word in England and that the chemist Charles Daubeny, addressing the British Association in 1838, could effectively encourage his fellow members to achieve perfection as scientists by emulating physical astronomers, i.e., by becoming as much like John Herschel as possible.[91]

Herschel was not trained as a philosopher, but he did bring a considerable breadth of knowledge to his expositions, and he adorned these with so many examples of actual scientific practice that they could be studied with profit by later philosophers of science, John Stuart Mill included. While quite disparaging of Greek beginnings and according practically no credit to the Middle Ages for scientific origins in the West,[92] Herschel in effect took over the search for causal explanations that characterized both these periods, illustrating this search in ways that would have delighted Aquinas, Nifo, and Zabarella. His own method of analyzing phenomena, it has been observed, "has much in common with the method of resolution and composition of the medieval period — the 'regressus' of the school of Padua and of Galileo." [93] Herschel's acknowledged masters, on the other hand, are Francis Bacon and Isaac Newton, on both of whom he lavishes fulsome praise. His methodology is thus partial to British empiricism, and on first examination it would even seem that Hume exerted a considerable influence on its elaboration, just as Kant might be seen as influencing Whewell's more a priori account.[94] Closer study reveals, however, that Herschel subscribed to a stronger notion of causality than is to be found in Hume, being more partial to analyses such as Reid's. He was implicitly opposed to Comte and the positivists,[95] and in fact thought that causal argumentation could give support to natural theology. "The testimony of natural reason . . . ," he confidently asserts, "places the existence and principal attri-

butes of a Deity on such grounds as to render doubt absurd
and atheism ridiculous. . . ." [96] His may not have been the
express apologetic of the Bridgewater Treatises, to which his
friend the Reverend William Whewell contributed so admira-
bly, but there is every reason to believe that he was quite sin-
cere in seeing science as providing rational support for his
beliefs as a Christian.[97]

a. General Methodology

The general lines of Herschel's thought on scientific
method may be gathered from the *Preliminary Discourse*, the
first two parts of which are concerned with the nature of science and the principles and rules "by which a systematic explanation of nature should be conducted." [98] Herschel divides
science into two broad categories, the first being abstract science, which is purely rational and is concerned with the
subject matter of logic and mathematics, and the second
being natural science, which is concerned with knowledge "of
causes and their effects and of the laws of nature." [99] The
truths of abstract science are necessary and can be known
without causal analysis.[100] This is so in the sense that "no one
causes or *makes* all the diameters of an ellipse to be bisected
in its center," for this is the way in which ellipse is defined
and to assert the contrary would be "to deny our own
words." [101] "But in natural science," Herschel goes on,

> *cause* and *effect* are the ultimate relations we contem-
> plate and *laws,* whether imposed or maintained, which
> for aught we can perceive might have been other than
> they are. This distinction is very important. A clever
> man, shut up alone and allowed unlimited time, might
> reason out for himself all the truths of mathematics by
> proceeding from those simple notions of space and num-
> ber of which he cannot divest himself without ceasing to
> think. But he could never tell, by any effort of reasoning,
> what would become of a lump of sugar if immersed in
> water or what impression would be produced in his eye
> by mixing the colours yellow and blue.[102]

It is for this reason that Herschel sees natural history as the
source from which "all sciences arise," as providing "an as-
semblage of phenomena to be explained, of effects to be de-

duced from causes, and of materials to be prepared to our hands for the application of our principles to useful purposes." [103] Abstract science is also necessary, however, for anyone who would make progress in physics.[104] It gives the user facility in reasoning, since its objects and notions are so definite and distinct as to permit deductions to be made with certitude.[105] Therefore:

> . . . some acquaintance with abstract science may be regarded as highly desirable in general education, if not indispensably necessary, to impress on us the distinction between strict and vague reasoning, to show us what demonstration really *is*, and to give us thereby a full and intimate sense of the nature and strength of the evidence on which our knowledge of the actual systems of nature, and the laws of natural phenomena, rests.[106]

In Herschel's view, the world of experience is made up of phenomena, or facts, and the task of natural science is to analyze these and thereby come to their understanding. As examples of phenomena, following the practice of his time, he would instance such observables as heat, light, sound, motion, and processes that were problematic for his contemporaries, such as chemical combination, oxidation, conduction, and the polarization of light. All of these Herschel regarded as complex and thus as resolvable to simpler phenomena that could be viewed as their causes. As he explains it:

> The first thing that a philosophic mind considers when any new phenomenon presents itself is its *explanation*, or reference to an immediate producing cause. If that cannot be ascertained the next is to *generalize* the phenomenon, and include it with others analogous to it in the expression of some law, in the hope that its consideration in a more advanced state of knowledge may lead to the discovery of an adequate proximate cause.[107]

For Herschel, therefore, to explain a phenomenon is to account for it in terms of the proximate causes that produce it, and this constitutes the ideal of scientific knowledge, even though the ideal may not be immediately attainable. Such proximate causes, in his understanding, are none other than Newton's *verae causae:*

Experience having shown us the manner in which one phenomenon depends on another in a great variety of cases, we find ourselves provided as science extends with a continually increasing stock of such antecedent phenomena or causes (meaning at present merely proximate causes), competent, under different modifications, to the production of a great multitude of effects besides those which originally led to a knowledge of them. To such causes Newton has applied the term *verae causae*, that is, causes recognized as having a real existence in nature and not being mere hypotheses or figments of the mind.[108]

Herschel's first understanding of cause, as can be seen from this citation, pertains to the phenomenal order and is an antecedent in terms of which something more complex may be explained. A cause, in this meaning, is a simple phenomenon, although Herschel does not always think of causality in such a restricted sense. Moreover, he does not treat simple phenomena as themselves irreducible, but takes the view that any simple phenomenon may, on further investigation, itself turn out to be complex. Thus any phenomenon may be regarded as simple until further analyzed, and when so analyzed can lead to a knowledge of its proximate causes. Herschel has no illusions regarding the possibility of discovering "ultimate phenomena," but he does not see this limitation as an obstacle to the growth of scientific knowledge. Thus he observes that

. . . it would greatly assist us in our study of nature if we could, by any means, ascertain what *are* the ultimate phenomena into which all the composite ones presented by it may be resolved. There is, however, clearly no way by which this can be ascertained *a priori*. We must go to nature itself and be guided by the same kind of rule as the chemist in his analysis, who accounts every ingredient an element till it can be decompounded and resolved into others. So, in natural philosophy, we must account every phenomenon an elementary or simple one till we can analyze it and show that it is the result of others, which in their turn become elementary. Thus in a modified and relative sense we may still continue to speak of causes, not intending thereby those ultimate principles of action on whose exertion the whole frame of nature depends, but of those proximate links which connect phenomena with others of a simpler, higher, and more general or elementary kind.[109]

Herschel is apparently convinced that nature works through "hidden powers" [110] and "internal mechanisms," [111] but "how far we may ever be enabled to obtain a knowledge of the ultimate and inward processes of nature in the production of phenomena, we have no means of knowing. . . ." [112] His own reservations here arise from man's great difficulty in understanding the concept of force, even when he is directly conscious of the power in his limbs to exert it and so to produce motion:

> This one instance of the obscurity which hangs about the only act of direct *causation* of which we have an immediate consciousness will suffice to show how little prospect there is that, in our investigation of nature, we shall ever be able to arrive at a knowledge of ultimate causes, and will teach us to limit our views to that of *laws* and to the analysis of complex phenomena by which they are resolved into simpler ones, which, appearing to us incapable of further analysis, we must consent to regard as causes.[113]

Despite this acknowledged difficulty in the perception of causal influence, however, Herschel insists, somewhat after the fashion of Thomas Reid, that we do feel our own exertion of forces and that this is equivalent to "the direct perception" of a cause.[114] In a celebrated passage in the *Treatise on Astronomy*, reprinted many times in subsequent editions of the *Outlines of Astronomy*, Herschel disagrees with the Humean account of causation as "habitual sequence," and indeed does so in no uncertain terms:

> Whatever attempts may have been made by metaphysical writers to reason away the connection of cause and effect and fritter it down into the unsatisfactory relation of habitual sequence, it is certain that the conception of some more real and intimate connection is quite as strongly impressed upon the human mind as that of the existence of an external world — the vindication of whose reality has (strange to say) been regarded as an achievement of no common merit in the annals of this

branch of philosophy. It is our own immediate consciousness of *effort*, when we exert force to put matter in motion or to oppose and neutralize force, which gives us
this internal conviction of *power* and *causation* so far as it
refers to the material world, and compels us to believe
that whenever we see material objects put in motion
from a state of rest, or deflected from their rectilinear
paths, and changed in their velocities if already in motion, it is in consequence of such an EFFORT somehow exerted, though not accompanied with *our* consciousness.[115]

It is this line of reasoning, reminiscent of Newton's, that leads
Herschel to argue that bodies falling to earth are moved by a
real force that originates from a spiritual agent, which he
implicitly identifies as God. "They are therefore urged thereto
by a force or effort the direct or indirect result of a *consciousness* and a will existing *somewhere*, though beyond our
power to trace, which force we term gravity. . ." [116] And in
the *Preliminary Discourse* Herschel explicitly refers to this
force of gravity as a *vera causa*. He there indicates that

> . . . in the theory of gravitation we suppose an agent —
> *viz.* force, or mechanical power — to act on *any* material
> body which is placed in the presence of *any* other and to
> urge the two mutually towards each other. This is a *vera
> causa;* for heavy bodies (that is, all bodies, but some
> more, some less) tend to, or endeavour to reach, the
> earth and require the exertion of force to counteract this
> endeavour or to keep them up. Now that which opposes
> and neutralizes force *is* force. . . . Moreover, since it is a
> fact that the moon does circulate about the earth, it must
> be drawn towards the earth by a force; for if there were
> no force acting upon it it would go on in a straight line
> without turning aside to circulate in an orbit, and would
> therefore soon go away and be lost in space. This force,
> then, which we call the *force* of gravity, is a real cause.[117]

Other indications of dissatisfaction with Hume are given
by Herschel when discussing regularities that occur in the
order of nature. He admits that there is a constant conjunction of phenomena and that this "impresses us with a strong
expectation" that events will continue in the same manner,[118]
but he sees this as of little help in the discovery of causes:

If everything were equally regular and periodical, and the succession of events liable to no change depending on our own will, it may be doubted whether we should ever think of looking for causes. No one regards the night as the cause of the day, or the day of night. They are alternate effects of a common cause, which their regular succession alone gives no sufficient clue for determining. It is chiefly, perhaps entirely, from the other or contingent class of events that we gain our notions of cause and effect. From them alone we gather that there are such things as laws of nature.[119]

Having thus minimized the importance of constant conjunction and habitual association, Herschel goes further and describes laws of nature in terms that are almost directly opposed to the Humean account. In Herschel's understanding,

Every law is a provision for cases which *may* occur, and has relation to an infinite number of cases that never have occurred and never will. Now, it is this provision, *a priori*, for contingencies, this contemplation of possible occurrences and predisposal of what shall happen, that impresses us with the notion of a *law* and a *cause*. Among all the possible combinations of the fifty or sixty elements which chemistry shows to exist on the earth, it is likely, nay almost certain, that *some* have never been formed; that some elements in some proportions and under some circumstances have never yet been placed in relation with one another. Yet no chemist can doubt that it is *already fixed* what they will do when the case does occur. They will obey certain laws of which we know nothing at present, but which must *be* already fixed or they could not be laws. It is not by habit, or by trial and failure, that they will learn what to do. When the contingency occurs there will be no hesitation, no consultation — their courses will at once be decided and will always be the same if it occur ever so often in succession, or in ever so many places at one and the same instant. This is the perfection of a law, that it includes all possible contingencies, and ensures implicit obedience — and of this kind are the laws of nature.[120]

Elsewhere Herschel speaks of laws of nature as generalizations expressing "in abstract terms, a whole group of particular facts relating to the behaviour of natural agents in proposed circumstances," or "announcing that a whole class of individuals agreeing in one character agree also in another." [121] Such laws have for him the character of general facts, and these are arrived at by a process of induction.[122]

Earlier we indicated that Herschel's concept of causality was not limited to that of a simple phenomenon serving to explain something more complex. As we have now seen, the term "cause" can have at least four different referents for Herschel: the first is a proximate cause, or antecedent phenomenon; the second is man's immediate consciousness of causality in his own muscular exertion; the third is force exerted on or by an inanimate object, such as the force of gravity or, to use another of Herschel's examples, of a coiled spring; and the last is an ultimate cause, probably unknowable in science but intelligible in terms of God's agency as the Author of Nature.[123] In addition to these meanings and the Newtonian *verae causae*, Herschel also speaks of "extraneous disturbing causes," [124] "common causes," [125] and "possible causes" that may prove helpful in the discovery of "real causes." [126] These additional usages may be conveniently discussed in the context of Herschel's evaluation of the role of hypotheses in scientific reasoning, his understanding of "crucial instances" or crucial experiments, and his own "rules of philosophizing," all of which will now be given brief consideration.

Proximate causes and laws of nature, for Herschel, are arrived at by "the first stage of induction" [127] — the process we have been sketching thus far. Apart from this there are "higher degrees of inductive generalization," [128] and these are concerned essentially with the formation of hypotheses and theories and with their verification. Just as laws arise from the consideration of individual facts, "so theories result from a consideration of these laws . . ." [129] The reason for formulating hypotheses and theories, as Herschel sees it, is that man cannot discover proximate causes that serve to explain all the phenomena he observes, and therefore he has to employ his reason in a more imaginative way to speculate about the inner processes of nature than might serve to explain these additional phenomena. His understanding of such theoretical reasoning is as follows:

The immediate object we propose to ourselves in physical theories is the analysis of phenomena and the knowledge of the hidden properties of nature in their production, so far as they can be traced by us. An important part of this knowledge consists in a discovery of the actual structure or mechanism of the universe and its parts, through which and by which those processes are executed, and of the agents which are concerned in their performance. Now the mechanism of nature is for the most part either on too large or too small a scale to be immediately cognizable by our senses; and her agents in like manner elude direct observation and become known to us only by their effects. It is in vain therefore that we desire to become witnesses to the processes carried on with such means and to be admitted into the secret recesses and laboratories where they are effected.[130]

Herschel thereupon enumerates specific dilemmas encountered in man's attempt to comprehend the intimate structure, for example, of "the smallest visible grain of sand," [131] and also the invisible agents "employed by nature to act on material structures." [132] He then raises the question:

Now are we to be deterred from framing hypotheses and constructing theories because we meet with such dilemmas and find ourselves frequently beyond our depth? Undoubtedly not. *Est quodam prodire tenus si non detur ultra.*[133] Hypotheses, with respect to theories, are what presumed proximate causes are with respect to particular inductions: they afford us motives for searching into analogies, grounds of citation to bring before us all the cases which seem to bear upon them for examination. A well imagined hypothesis, if it has been suggested by a fair inductive consideration of general laws, can hardly fail at least of enabling us to generalize a step farther and group together several such laws under a more universal expression.[134]

This is the minimal use to which hypotheses may be put, according to Herschel. In some instances, he seems to feel,

such a weight of analogy and probability may become accumulated on the side of an hypothesis that we are compelled to admit one of two things: either that it is an actual statement of what really passes in nature, or that the reality, whatever it be, must run so closely parallel with it as to admit of some mode of expression common to both, at least insofar as the phenomena actually known are concerned.[135]

It would appear that Herschel evaluates the theory of gravitation as pertaining to the first type of instance, for it is in this context that he argues for the necessity of natural agents being *verae causae*, presenting the arguments already noted to establish that the force of gravity is a real cause.[136] While this is the conclusion to which Newton himself seems to have come, it is noteworthy that Newton did not consider his own reasoning hypothetical, although he apparently regarded it as inductive, not having distinguished, as Herschel does, a difference of stages in the inductive process. Herschel, nonetheless, is quite willing to concede that hypotheses rarely lead to such conclusive explanations, and so he gives this cautious evaluation of them and of the theories in which they result in terms that are quite Newtonian:

> In estimating, however, the value of a theory, we are not to look in the first instance to the question whether it establishes satisfactorily or not a particular process or mechanism; for of this, after all, we can never obtain more than that indirect evidence which consists in its leading to the same result. What, in the actual state of science, is far more important for us to know is whether our theory truly represent *all* the facts and include *all* the laws to which observation and induction lead. A theory which did this would, no doubt, go a great way to establish any hypothesis of mechanism or structure which might form an essential part of it: but this is very far from being the case, except in a few limited instances; and till it is so, to lay any great stress on hypotheses of the kind, except in as much as they serve as a scaffold for the erection of general laws, is to "quite mistake the scaffold for the pile." Regarded in this light hypotheses have often an eminent use: and a facility in framing them, if attended with an equal facility in laying them aside when they have served their turn, is one of the most valuable qualities a philosopher can possess; while on the other hand, a bigoted adherence to them or indeed to peculiar views of any kind, in opposition to the tenor of facts as they arise, is the bane of all philosophy.[137]

Herschel, as we have noted, was a great admirer of Francis Bacon, and runs through all of the latter's "prerogative instances" to provide examples that confer on these a value they otherwise would not possess.[138] Like Newton, he thought that a "crucial experiment" could be used to decide between two alternate hypotheses that seem otherwise equally capable of accounting for the known phenomena. He is not apodictic on this, however, merely noting that "when two theories run parallel to each other and each explains a great many facts in common with the other, any experiment which affords a crucial instance to decide between them, or by which one or other must fall, is of great importance." [139] It is in this setting that Herschel instances Fresnel's experiment to decide between wave and particle theories of light, the result of which "is stated by him [Fresnel] to be decisive in favour of that theory which makes light to consist in the vibrations of an elastic medium." [140] Later on Herschel cites Pascal's celebrated experiment in support of Torricelli's theory of atmospheric pressure, to the effect that the mercury in a barometer is supported by a "definite external cause" [141] rather than being a consequence of nature's "abhorrence of a vacuum." [142] Referring to Pascal, Herschel writes:

> His acuteness perceived that if the weight of the incumbent air be the direct cause of the elevation of the mercury it must be measured by the amount of that elevation, and therefore that, by carrying a barometer up a high mountain and so ascending into the atmosphere *above* a large portion of the incumbent air, the pressure, as well as the length of the column sustained by it must be diminished; while on the other hand, if the phenomenon were due to the cause originally assigned, no difference could be expected to take place whether the observation were made on a mountain or on the plain.[143]

He goes on to note that it was this decisive experiment, more than any other, that convinced scientists of the value of experimentation in deciding between rival theories:

> Perhaps the decisive effect of the experiment which he caused to be instituted for the purpose on the Puy de Dôme, a high mountain in Auvergne, while it convinced everyone of the truth of Torricelli's views, tended more

powerfully than anything which had previously been done in science to confirm, in the minds of men, that disposition to experimental verification which had scarcely yet taken full and secure root.[144]

Herschel's treatment of hypotheses and crucial experiments pertains to his analysis of the higher degrees of inductive generalizations, which he does not develop in such systematic fashion as the procedures used in the first stage of induction. The latter treatment, which occupies all of Chapter 6 of Part II of the *Preliminary Discourse*, contains his "general rules for guiding and facilitating our search, among a great mass of assembled facts, for their common cause. . . ."[145] These rules serve to spell out "that relation which we intend by cause and effect," and are enumerated as follows:

First, invariable connection and, in particular, invariable antecedence of the cause and the consequence of the effect, unless prevented by some counteracting cause. But it must be observed that, in a great number of natural phenomena, the effect is produced gradually while the cause often goes on increasing in intensity; so that the antecedent of the one and consequence of the other becomes difficult to trace, though it really exists. On the other hand the effect often follows the cause so instantaneously that the interval cannot be perceived. In consequence of this it is sometimes difficult to decide, of two phenomena constantly accompanying one another, which is cause or which effect.

Second, invariable negation of the effect with absence of the cause, unless some other cause be capable of producing the same effect.

Third, increase or diminution of the effect with the increased or diminished intensity of the cause, in cases which admit of increase or diminution.

Fourth, proportionality of the effect to its cause in all cases of *direct unimpeded* action.

Fifth, reversal of the effect with that of the cause.[146]

From these general rules Herschel is led to make a series of observations "which may be considered as so many propositions readily applicable to particular cases, or rules of philosophizing," [147] an expression that immediately calls to mind Newton's *regulae philosophandi*. There are ten of these observations, and they are extremely helpful for understanding Herschel's concept of scientific method, although we cannot examine them all in detail.[148] Among his concerns is how to recognize when a peculiarity "cannot be the cause we seek" and when it "may be the cause in question"; here he would caution "that we are not to deny the existence of a cause in favour of which we have a unanimous agreement of strong analogies, though it may not be apparent how such a cause can produce the effect, and even though it may be difficult to conceive its existence under the circumstances of the case." [149] Herschel notes also "that contrary or opposing facts are equally instructive for the discovery of causes with favourable ones," [150] since these can lead to a knowledge of "counteracting and modifying causes" [151] or even to a "concurrent cause." [152] He observes also how complicated phenomena "may be simplified by subducting the effect of all the known causes" so as to leave a "residual phenomenon" [153] whose *vera causa* may then be uncovered.[154] His final observation is that "the detection of a *possible* cause . . . *must* lead to one of two things: either, first, the detection of a real cause . . . or, secondly, the establishment of an abstract law of nature, pointing out two phenomena of a general kind as invariably connected . . ." [155] With regard to the latter he asserts:

> Such invariable connection is itself a phenomenon of a higher order than any particular fact; and when many such are discovered we may again proceed to classify, combine, and examine them with a view to the detection of their causes, or the discovery of still more general laws, and so on without end.[156]

The last words of this citation reveal that, for Herschel, there was little doubt that science progresses through the discovery of laws and causes, that from this results a cumulative growth of knowledge, and that there are no limits to what the mind of man can uncover in his continued search for causal explanations.

b. Applications and Examples

Herschel has been criticized, and with reason, for his defects as a philosopher.[157] Some of his efforts at epistemology are amateurish, his writings on careful analysis reveal ambiguities far more serious than those noted in the works of the philosophers discussed in the preceding chapter, and he does not synthesize his results in any systematic way. All of these defects, however, are more than counterbalanced by Herschel's knowledge of actual scientific practice and by his ability to supply apt illustrations and applications of the principles he attempted to enunciate. Thus his instincts were good, even if he may not have been expert enough as a philosopher to give them proper formulation. It is for this reason that a survey of the applications and examples he uses will serve to flesh out the methodology outlined in the previous section, and may be of value for understanding scientific practice as it developed in the early to mid-nineteenth century.

Herschel's analysis of sound is one of his basic illustrations. He regards sound as a complex phenomenon that can be explained by reduction to the simple phenomena producing it.[158] After enumerating the various factors involved in the production of sounds of all kinds, Herschel reduces these to two principal components, the mechanical or vibratory motion of a medium and the production of sensation.[159] "Thus," he writes, "we see that an analysis of the phenomenon of sound leads to the enquiry, first, of two *causes,* viz. the cause of motion and the cause of sensation. . . ." [160] Concerning the cause of motion, he thinks that light is shed on this through a knowledge of the laws of motion, since from the point of view of acoustics the motions in accordance with these are to be regarded "as ultimate phenomena, and referable to the direct action of causes, viz. an attractive and a repulsive force." [161] As to the cause of sensation, he goes on, "this must be regarded as much more obscure than that of motion," and in this instance he is willing to give up "the enquiry into causes" and to concentrate his attention instead on "the laws which prevail among phenomena." [162]

A more complex example, actually excerpted by John Stuart Mill and used by him in his *System of Logic,* is Herschel's analysis of the cause of dew as worked out by Dr. William Wells.[163] Herschel presents this as an example of an "inductive search for a cause," [164] describing it "as one of the most beautiful specimens we can call to mind of inductive experimental inquiry lying within a moderate compass." [165] Assuming that dew is a phenomenon whose cause is to be investigated, he first distinguishes it carefully from other forms of moisture that can collect on objects. Comparing all of these phenomena he notes that they agree in one point, namely, "the coldness of the object viewed in comparison with the air in contact with it." [166] Then he inquires whether this temperature difference is "a real cause," questioning the truth of the fact "that the object dewed *is* colder than the air," and whether the temperature difference is an effect of the dewing rather than its cause.[167] To answer these questions it is necessary to vary experimentally the factors that may be involved, and so Herschel enumerates tests with a wide variety of surfaces, noting their ability to conduct heat and to radiate it, and also the influence of surrounding objects such as clouds in the sky.[168] All of these tests confirm the fact that dew results from "the cooling of the exposed surface of the body dewed below the temperature of the air." [169] The experimentation, moreover, removes the doubts arising as to whether this is the "real cause" and supplies fuller details on the mechanisms involved in dew's formation:

> Those surfaces which part with their heat outwards most readily, and have it supplied from within most slowly, will . . . become coldest if there is enough opportunity for their heat to escape and not be restored to them from without. Now a clear sky affords such an opportunity. It is a law well known to those who are conversant with the nature of heat that heat is constantly escaping from all bodies in rays, or by radiation, but is as constantly restored to them by the similar radiation of others surrounding them. Clouds and surrounding objects therefore act as opposing causes by replacing the whole or a great part of the heat so radiated away, which can escape effectually without being replaced only through openings into infinite space. Thus, at length we arrive at the general proximate cause of dew, in the cooling of the dewed surface by radiation faster than its heat can be restored to it by communication with the ground or by counter-

radiation so as to become colder than the air, and thereby to cause a condensation of its moisture.[170]

Less felicitous than this account are Herschel's analysis of the phenomena of light [171] and heat,[172] the second of which he recognizes as "one of the chief agents in chemistry," though he also notes that "there is scarcely any physical agent of which we have so imperfect a knowledge, whose intimate nature is more hidden, or whose laws are of such delicate or difficult investigation." [173] Discussing the controversy over phlogiston and oxygen, however, Herschel observes that one can account for the increase of weight that occurs "in the combustion of any substance which is incapable of flying away in fumes" [174] either by the escape of phlogiston, regarded as an essentially light substance, or by the absorption of oxygen, an essentially heavy one. He states in this context that the controversy has resulted from some investigators "involving the subject in a mist of visionary and hypothetical causes in place of the true acting principles." [175] His own preference is not for a mere saving of the appearances, but rather for the identification of the true cause that accounts for the weight increase:

> So far as weight is concerned, it makes no difference whether a body having weight enters or one having levity escapes; but there is a plain difference in a philosophical point of view, that oxygen is a real producible substance and phlogiston is no such thing: the former is a *vera causa,* the latter an hypothetical being introduced to account for what the other accounts for much better.[176]

The examples mentioned thus far are given in the *Preliminary Discourse* as illustrative of scientific method, since this is essentially a methodological treatise. It is in his *Outlines of Astronomy*, however, where he is writing more as a scientist than as a methodologist, that one can examine Herschel's reasoning and see how committed he actually was to this ideal of causal explanation. Already in the first edition (1849), when explaining the adaptation of the work from the Cabinet Cyclopaedia version of 1833, he insists that it is to remain "a work of explanation," [177] even though some of its chapters are addressed to readers with more mathematical knowledge than readers of the *Treatise*. Such chapters, he writes, "may be considered as addressed to students in that university where the *Principia* of Newton is not, nor ever will be, put aside as an obsolete book, behind the age. . . ." [178] He also acknowledges the growth of scientific knowledge since the prepartation of the first work, including "the addition to the list of members of our [solar] system of no less than eight new planets and satellites during the preparation of these sheets for the press." [179] He then goes on, in a significant passage that reveals his own appreciation of the difference between a logic of discovery and a logic of proof, to state:

> Among them [i.e., the new planets] is one whose discovery must ever be regarded as one of the noblest triumphs of theory. In the account here given of this discovery I trust to have expressed myself with complete impartiality; and in the exposition of the perturbative action on Uranus, by which the existence and situation of the disturbing planet became revealed to us, I have endeavoured, in pursuance of the general plan of this work, rather to exhibit a rational view of the dynamical action than to convey the slightest idea of the conduct of those masterpieces of analytical skill which the researches of Messrs. Leverrier and Adams exhibit. [180]

In his preface to the fifth edition (1858), Herschel lists among his additions "Foucault's remarkable pendulum experiments" and some of his own "new speculations," as for example "on the subject of the moon's habitability" and "the cause of the acceleration of Encke's comet . . ." [181] A similar preface to the tenth edition (1869) mentions, among other advances, those in sidereal astronomy where "the application of spectrum analysis has disclosed the amazing fact of the gaseous constitution of many of the nebulae . . ." [182]

In the body of the work, and here we cite the eleventh and penultimate edition (1871), Herschel explains that the method he will be following "is neither strictly the analytic nor the synthetic, but rather such a combination of both, with a leaning to the latter, as may best suit with a *didactic* composition." Its object, he goes on, is not to convince or refute opponents "but simply to *teach* what is *known*." [183] His confidence in being able to so teach arises from his conviction that "there is now no danger of any revolution in astronomy, like those which are daily changing the features of the less advanced sciences, supervening to destroy all our hypotheses and throw our statements into confusion." [184]

With similar confidence, Herschel proposes that "we shall take for granted, from the outset, the Copernican system of the world," and he would do this

> relying on the easy, obvious, and natural explanation it affords of all the phenomena as they come to be described, to impress the student with a sense of its truth, without either the formality of demonstration or the superfluous tedium of eulogy. . . .[185]

Here he refers the reader to Francis Bacon's remark that "the confirmation of theories relies on the compact adaptation of their parts, by which, like those of an arch or dome, they mutually sustain each other and form a coherent whole," significantly adding in a footnote that "this is what Dr. Whewell expressively terms the consilience of inductions." [186] Having made these statements, however, Herschel also admits that the attainment of knowledge such as this is not done overnight, or "without receiving and discarding in succession many crude and incomplete notions. . . ." [187] Even the study of astronomy "is a continual process of rectification and correction — of abandoning one point of view for another higher and better — of temporary and occasional reception of even positive and admitted errors for the convenience they afford towards giving clear notions of important truths whose essence they do not affect, by sparing him [i.e., the student] that contention of mind which fatigues and distresses." [188] The illustration Herschel provides is again striking:

> We know, for example, that the earth's diurnal motion is real, and that of the heavens only apparent; yet there are many problems in astronomy which are not only easier conceived but more simply resolved by adopting the idea of a diurnal rotation of the heavens, it being understood once for all that appearances are alike in both suppositions. [189]

These citations indicate that Herschel was aware of the possibility of error, and even of substantial revolution, in science, but this did not deter him from his conviction that truth would ultimately be discovered and known, and that what was real would be distinguished from what was merely apparent, in the cumulative advance of scientific knowledge.

Moving on to a more substantive account of astronomical science, Herschel directs attention to the earth and raises the question whether it is to be enumerated among the heavenly bodies, despite its apparently not resembling them in any way. The ancients did not so enumerate it, Herschel remarks, and thus "effectually intercepted the progress of all reasoning from what passes here below to what is going on in the [celestial] regions. . . ." [190] He further observes that "under such conventions, astronomy, as a science of cause and effect, could not exist, but must be limited to a mere registry of appearances, unconnected with any attempt to account for them on reasonable principles. . . ." [191] For this reason he feels that the earth itself is one of the principal objects of the astronomer's consideration, and in fact cautions that "the question whether the earth is in motion or at rest, and if in motion, what that motion is, is no idle inquiry, but one on which depends our only chance of arriving at true conclusions respecting the constitution of the universe." [192] With this as a preamble, Herschel proceeds to observe that, "in order . . . to conceive the earth as in motion, we must form to ourselves a conception of its shape and size." [193] He thereupon enumerates all of the arguments, some of which we have already seen presented by Thomas Aquinas,[194] to establish the sphericity of the earth from various phenomena observed on its surface.[195] Then later, when he has dealt with instruments made available for precise measurements, he details how we know that the earth's "true figure is somewhat elliptical, or flattened . . ." and thus that, "speaking strictly, it would be termed, not a globe, but an oblate ellipsoid or spheroid. . . ." [196]

Having given these particulars, Herschel notes the difference between apparent and real diurnal motions and explains how the Copernican doctrine reduces the apparent motions of the heavens to the real motion and diurnal rotation of the earth. He mentions that the alternative Ptolemaic conception, which seems to agree more with common sense, suffices to "save appearances," [197] although it is extremely difficult to reconcile this view with the "general laws which, so far as we know, regulate the motions of all material bodies. . . ." [198] It is here that Herschel draws the following interesting comparison between the Copernican and the Newtonian accounts of the structure of the solar system:

> In this view of the Copernican doctrine it is rather a geometrical conception than a physical theory, inasmuch [as] it simply assumes the requisite motions, without attempting to explain their mechanical origin or assign them any dependence on physical causes. The Newtonian theory of gravitation supplies this deficiency and, by showing that all the motions required by the Copernican conception *must*, and that no others can, result from a *single*, intelligible, and very simple dynamical law, has given a degree of certainty to this conception, as a matter of fact, which attaches to no other creation of the human mind. [199]

Herschel continues to maintain this causal understanding of Newtonian theory, and in a subsequent chapter explains the oblate spheroidal figure in terms of the physical forces that "result from the rotation of the earth on its axis." [200] He takes this opportunity, in fact, to remark how one discovery can lead to other striking and unexpected consequences:

> The confirmation thus incidentally furnished of the hypothesis of the earth's rotation on its axis cannot fail to strike the reader. A deviation of its figure from that of a sphere was not contemplated among the original reasons for adopting that hypothesis, which was assumed solely on account of the easy explanation it offers of the apparent diurnal motion of the heavens. Yet we see that, once admitted, it draws with it as a necessary consequence this other remarkable phenomenon, of which no other satisfactory account could be rendered. Indeed so direct is their connection, that the ellipticity of the earth's figure was discovered and demonstrated by Newton to be a consequence of its rotation, and its amount actually calculated by him, long before any measurement had suggested such a conclusion. [201]

He thereupon details measurements showing the variation of terrestrial gravity on the earth's surface, and explains that this too is a result of the earth's being a spheroid. Such measurements provide, indeed, "a curious and instructive example of the indirect influence which mechanical causes often exercise, and of which astronomy furnishes innumerable instances," for

> The rotation of the earth gives rise to the centrifugal force; the centrifugal force produces an ellipticity in the form of the earth itself; and this very ellipticity of form modifies its power of attraction on bodies placed on its surface and thus gives rise to the difference in question. Here, then, we have the same cause exercising at once a direct and an indirect influence. . . .[202]

Another geographical phenomenon instanced by Herschel as owing its existence to the earth's rotation is that of the trade winds.[203] Unlike Thomas Hobbes, who was content with his exemplification of the winds' causing the rotation of the earth as an instance of a "false cause," [204] Herschel examines all of the mechanisms involved in the production of winds on the earth's surface, instancing these as "the array of evidence by which the rotation of the earth, as a physical fact, is demonstrated," [205] and thereby equivalently identifies the earth's rotation as the *vera causa* of the winds' movement. He goes on to note "another class of phenomena, inexplicable except on the hypothesis of the earth's rotation on its axis, but flowing easily and naturally from the admission of that principle, . . ." namely, the experiments with pendulums and gyroscopes performed a few years previously by Foucault.[206] The behavior of the gyroscope, in a particular, affords "a clear ocular demonstration of the earth's rotation. . . ." [207]

These few samples will supply some idea of Herschel's commitments to the physical astronomy of his day. They do not, of course, give any indication of Herschel's own discoveries, or his success in extending the Newtonian synthesis to include double-star systems and the sidereal universe in general.[208] But they are important nonetheless, not only for the insight they provide into Herschel's own evaluations, but for the fact that these and similar illustrations were cited by Whewell and Mill in their subsequent attempts to clarify the logical processes used by scientists in discovering new truths about the physical universe.

4. William Whewell

Although he never achieved Herschel's fame as a scientist and was insufficiently appreciated for his work as a philosopher, William Whewell nonetheless made substantial contributions to both science and philosophy; moreover, he well deserves the recognition only recently being given him for his pioneering work in the history and philosophy of science.[209] Whewell studied at Cambridge just a few years behind Herschel, and first devoted himself to physics, geology, and astronomy, being made a fellow of the Royal Society at the age of twenty-six. Later he held professorships at Cambridge, first in mineralogy and then in moral philosophy, and enjoyed two terms as vice-chancellor of the university. He was active also in the British Association, serving as its secretary and president at various times. But it was primarily as a systematic scholar that he deserves to be remembered, particularly for his efforts to document the origins and development of classical science and to clarify the methodology by which it achieved its results. The first of his major writings in this field was his three-volume *History of the Inductive Sciences*, which appeared in 1837; this was followed in 1840 by the two-volume *Philosophy of the Inductive Sciences, Founded Upon Their History*. Both sets were revised and enlarged, and in their third and final edition appeared as three separate but related works, *The History of Scientific Ideas* (2 vols., 1858), *Novum Organum Renovatum* (1858), and *The Philosophy of Discovery* (1860).[210]

The titles to which Whewell finally came give some indication of the philosophy he evolved in the process.[211] His focusing on scientific ideas shows the importance he attached to the work of mind or thought in arriving at necessary and universal truths, while his use of a revised version of the title of Francis Bacon's classic reveals his commitment to an empiricist or inductivist methodology based on observation and experimentation.[212] Both were combined, moreover, not in the way of an a priori synthesis, but rather as a philosophy of discovery leading to necessary truths about the physical universe that themselves are open to development and refinement as science progresses.[213] In elaborating this philosophy Whewell had to face the Kantian problem of how such necessary truths can be derived from experience, and here, unlike his British contemporaries, he adopted the elements of Kant's solution. Thus Whewell saw the relation between sensations and ideas as similar to that between matter and form; in this sense the mind at least partially constructs the object of knowledge from the data of sensation:

> Without the relations of thought which we here term *ideas* the sensations are matter without form. Matter without form cannot exist: and in like manner sensations cannot become perceptions of objects without some formative power of the mind. By the very act of being received as perceptions they have a formative power exercised upon them, the operation of which might be expressed by speaking of them not as *transformed,* but simply as *formed* — as invested with form instead of being the mere formless material of perception.[214]

The formative activity of the mind, for Whewell as for Kant, regulates the way in which one perceives events in space, time, and causal sequence. Whewell was likewise sensitive, as was Kant, to Hume's criticism that sense knowledge is incapable of revealing any necessary connection between events, and yet he himself was convinced that the mind could know such connections through a source other than sense experience. Thus, somewhat like Kant, he attributed the necessity and universality of human knowledge to the structuring such knowledge receives from mind itself. He seems to have disagreed with Kant, however, in seeing the function of ideas as not merely regulative but also as constitutive, and therefore as yielding valid metaphysical knowledge of the ultimate structure of reality. Whewell thus attempted to go beyond Kant, while taking his preliminary inspiration from the *Critique of Pure Reason.* The vehicle he used to do this was his doctrine of fundamental ideas, which he held are not grasped by all, but can be seen intuitively by those who work in the sciences, where they can be grasped progressively and clarified, since "intercourse with the external world is necessary for [their] conscious employment . . ." [215]

For Whewell, as for subsequent philosophers of science, facts, laws, and theories are the fundamental components involved in scientific knowing. The frequently encountered dichotomy between facts and theories, however, is not to be found in Whewell's writings, since this is one of the antitheses he attempts to bridge by his theory of knowledge.[216] Indeed, he not only sees laws as arising by induction from a colligation of facts, but he gives a strong causal understanding to theories themselves, claiming that they can yield a superior type of knowing through causes that, while not always attainable, nonetheless constitutes the ideal of scientific explanation. Thus he sees the province of scientific investigation as extending beyond the mere discovery of laws of nature, and argues explicitly for an induction of causes as part of the quest for a true understanding of the universe.[217] In this respect Whewell remarks on Galileo's caution, allowing that he "discovered the true law of the motion of a falling body," but still noting that "he did not insist upon immediately assigning the cause of this law." [218] Kepler, on the other hand, he commends for being "restless and unsatisfied till he had reduced facts to laws, and laws to causes. . . ." [219] And one of the outstanding achievements of Newton, in Whewell's eyes, was that he "discovered, not merely a law of phenomena, but a *cause;* and *therefore* he was the greatest of discoverers." [220] Of Newton's followers Whewell further observes that

> they saw, for the first time, or at least far more clearly than before, the distinction between the inquiry into the *laws* and into the *causes* of phenomena. They were tempted to ask how far the discovery of causes could be carried, and whether it would soon reach, or clearly point to, the ultimate cause.[221]

From these brief indications of concern with causal explanation one might expect that Whewell would be quite opposed to Comte's conception of scientific method, and this turns out to be the case. Whewell wrote a devastating critique of John Stuart Mill's *Auguste Comte and Positivism* in *Macmillan's Magazine* for March, 1866,[222] and in his systematic writings he took up Comte as an adversary, first as a representative of the "Sensationalist School" and then as the object of explicit attack. In the earlier context he writes:

> Since it is thus difficult to know when we have seized the true cause of the phenomena in any department of science, it may appear to some persons that physical inquirers are imprudent and unphilosophical in undertaking this research of causes; and that it would be safer and wiser to confine ourselves to the investigation of the laws of phenomena, in which field the knowledge which we obtain is definite and certain. Hence there have not been wanting those who have laid it down as a maxim that "science must study only the laws of phenomena, and never the mode of production." But it is easy to see that such a maxim would confine the breadth and depth of scientific inquiries to a most scanty and miserable limit. Indeed, such a rule would defeat its own object; for the laws of phenomena, in many cases, cannot be even expressed or understood without some hypothesis respecting their mode of production.[223]

Whewell proceeds to give examples in support of his position, and then makes the telling observation, cited with approval by Herschel in his lengthy review of Whewell's works,[224] to the effect that

> to debar science from inquiries like these, on the ground that it is her business to inquire into facts and not to speculate about causes, is a curious example of that barren caution which hopes for truth without daring to venture upon the quest of it.[225]

Whewell notes also the practical difficulty of attempting to confine oneself to laws of phenomena alone, particularly in a science like geology, where phenomena such as stratification and fossil remains clearly demand causal explanation. "In this and similar cases," he writes, "to proscribe the inquiry into causes would be to annihilate the science."[226]

In his direct attacks on Comte, Whewell ridicules the very idea of a "positive philosophy," maintaining that Comte had concentrated on denials rather than on affirmations and thus that his philosophy should more possibly be labeled "negative."[227] He is particularly critical of Comte's law of the three stages and his attempt to document this law through a study of the progress of human knowing, maintaining that the attempt is "contrary to history in fact, and contrary to sound philosophy in principle." [228] He analyzes in some detail the Comtean interpretation of Newtonian gravitation and attraction, and rejects it as superficial.[229] His own analysis of history, he maintains, shows that "metaphysical discussions have been essential steps in the progress of each science." [230] So he concludes:

> To exclude such inquiries would be to secure ourselves from the poison of error by abstaining from the banquet of truth — it would be to attempt to feed our minds with the meager diet of space and number because we may find too delightful a relish in such matters as cause and end, symmetry and affinity, organization and development.[231]

Whewell's own understanding of cause may be gathered both from his aphorisms, written after the style of Francis Bacon, concerning the idea of cause and from his extensive review of Newton's "rules of philosophizing" and the concept of *vera causa* entailed in them.[232] Whewell's terminology in aphorisms is admittedly quite Kantian, for he writes:

> The idea of cause is not derived from experience, for in judging of occurrences which we contemplate we consider them as being, universally and necessarily, causes and effects, which a finite experience could not authorize us to do. The axiom that every event must have a cause is true independently of experience and beyond the limits of experience.[233]

It is this idea of cause, moreover, "modified into the conceptions of mechanical cause, or force, and resistance to force, or matter," that is the foundation, in Whewell's mind, of all the mechanical sciences.[234] Despite his Kantian terminology, however, Whewell gives a strong realist interpretation to the notions of cause and force that is at variance with the more common interpretation of Kantian philosophy.[235] The conception of force, in his view, involves the idea of cause as applied to the motion and rest of bodies. "The conception of force is suggested by muscular action exerted; the conception of matter arises from muscular action resisted." [236] Again he maintains that "the idea of cause is expressed for purposes of science by these three axioms: every event must have a cause; causes are measured by their effects; reaction is equal and opposite to action." [237] From these axioms he would then deduce Newton's laws of motion:

> The first axiom, that every change must have a cause, gives rise to the first law of motion, that a body not acted upon by a force will move with a uniform velocity in a straight line. The second axiom, that causes are measured by their effects, gives rise to the second law of motion, that when a force acts upon a body in motion the effect of the force is compounded with the previously existing motion. The third axiom, that reaction is equal and opposite to action, gives rise to the third law of motion, which is expressed in the same terms as the axiom — action and reaction being understood to signify momentum gained and lost. [238]

From the viewpoint of history Whewell notes that these laws of motion were established by means of experiment, but that since their formulation by Newton they have been considered by many philosophers as self evident. [239] This offers no particular difficulty for him, although he admits that "it is a paradox that experience should lead us to truths confessedly universal, and apparently necessary, such as the laws of motion are." [240] His resolution of the paradox lies in the fact that these laws are "interpretations" of the axioms of causation:

> The axioms are universally and necessarily true, but the right interpretation of the terms which they involve is learnt by experience. Our idea of cause supplies the *form*, experience the *matter* of these laws. [241]

Whewell sees in Newton's "rules of philosophizing" and in his method of analysis and synthesis an adumbration of his own procedures based on the colligation of facts and the consilience of inductions. [242] He experiences difficulty, however, with the common interpretation placed on Newton's use of the expression "true cause," since this seems to restrict scientific explanation to causes already known and to inhibit the discovery of new causes that could only be identified through some type of hypothetical reasoning. He himself would prefer to reword Newton's first rule, on this account, to assert that

> we may, provisorily, assume such hypothetical cause as will account for any given class of natural phenomena; but that when two different classes of facts lead us to the same hypothesis, we may hold it to be a *true cause*.[243]

Whewell understood the context of Newton's *hypotheses non fingo*, but he believed that his own methodological employment of the consilience of inductions would safeguard against the pitfalls into which Cartesian and other Continental philosophers had fallen. When such a consilience or "convergence of two trains of induction points to the same spot," he writes, "we can no longer suspect that we are wrong." [244] He continues:

> Such an accumulation of proof really persuades us that we have to do with a *vera causa*. And if this kind of proof be multiplied; if we again find other facts of a sort uncontemplated in framing our hypothesis but yet clearly accounted for when we have adopted the supposition, we are still further confirmed in our belief; and by such accumulation of proof we may be so far satisfied as to believe without conceiving it possible to doubt. In this case, when the validity of the opinion adopted by us has been repeatedly confirmed by its sufficiency in unforeseen cases, so that all doubt is removed and forgotten, the theoretical cause takes its place among the realities of the world and becomes *a true cause*.[245]

Whewell's best illustration of such a true cause is Newton's force of gravity.[246] In fact, there is a tendency throughout his writings to identify cause with force, although he explicitly mentions that he does not wish the term force to be taken in a strictly mechanical sense.[247] Apart from mechanical forces, for example, he is prepared to admit the existence of chemical, vital, and any "new kinds of force" as may best render the results of scientific investigation intelligible.[248] In addition to such forces, moreover, Whewell admits that "the discovery of the causes of phenomena may imply the detection of a fluid by whose undulations or other operations the results are occasioned." [249] Thus he is open to the idea of a substrate, or material cause, as a valid principle of scientific explanation. Whewell admits also the importance of final causes, particularly in the biological sciences, and indeed discourses at length on their role in scientific reasoning.[250] Finally, when he comes to outlining his system for classifying the sciences, the various types of cause figure prominently among the "fundamental ideas or conceptions" on which the classification is based, being listed variously as force, matter, element (composition), substance (atom), vital powers, final cause, historical causation, and First Cause.[251]

Causal explanation, on this accounting, plays an important part in Whewell's philosophy of science. It is largely because of this concern with causes, in fact, that he dwells at such length on the consilience of inductions and on further elaborations of consilience such as his inductive tables and criteria of truth. He offers two such tables, the first outlining the inductive process in astronomy by which one arrives at the theory of universal gravitation, and the second, the inductive process in optics leading to the undulatory theory of light.[252] Both tables, in his view, clearly exhibit "the consilience of inductions and the constant tendency to simplicity observable in true theories." [253] The first table reviews most of the matter contained in Herschel's astronomical treatises, showing how, through a series of successive generalizations, universal gravitation is found to account not only for all the manifest appearances of the heavens, but also for the structure of the solar system, the spheroidal shape of the earth, and even the more recondite precession of the equinoxes — the latter striking him as a remarkable example of consilience.[254] In connection with the tables he remarks that they can be used either to display an order of discovery or an order of verification and proof, depending on the direction in which they are read.[255] He maintains also that "such tabular arrangements of propositions as we have constructed may be considered as the *criterion of truth* for the doctrines which they include." [256] Consistent with his general position on facts and theories, he further maintains "that the most general theory is only the assertion of a great body of facts, duly classified and subordinated." [257] So he claims:

126 The Methodologists of Classical Science

When we assert the truth of the Copernican theory of the motions of the solar system, or of the Newtonian theory of the forces by which they are caused, we merely assert the groups of propositions which, in the Table of Astronomical Induction, are included in these doctrines; and ultimately, we may consider ourselves as merely asserting at once so many facts, and therefore, of course, expressing an indisputable truth.[258]

Such confident assertions lead one to wonder whether Whewell could ever have subscribed to the Kantian epistemology that is occasionally attributed to him. In his own lifetime, as is well known, Whewell's views were variously characterized as identical with those of Kant and as misrepresenting the Kantian philosophy.[259] As Ducasse has rightly noted, however, Whewell himself states that he does not profess himself a Kantian and that he regards his main views as very different from Kant's.[260] To obtain confirmation of this all one need do is read Whewell's enthusiastic disquisition on the First Cause.[261] Among his aphorisms he clearly states, moreover, that "the cause of certain phenomena being inferred, we are led to inquire into the cause of this cause, which inquiry must be conducted in the same manner as the previous one, and thus we have the induction of ulterior causes." [262] It is in contemplating various series of causes that are themselves the effects of other causes that "we are necessarily led to assume a Supreme Cause in the order of causation, as we assume a First Cause in the order of succession." [263] From this and from other indications, metaphysics could not be for Whewell, any more than it was for Herschel,[264] a transcendental illusion. Thus Whewell must have rejected the main thesis Kant set out to prove in the *Critique of Pure Reason*, and so cannot be said to agree with the philosophy Kant elaborated during his critical period.

Herschel was not only Whewell's friend, but took an interest in his writings, and so, considering Herschel's status as the outstanding scientist of his day, some brief indication may well be given here of the latter's evaluation of Whewell's thought. In the review already mentioned Herschel is generally favorable and, indeed, laudatory of Whewell's efforts both as a historian and as a philosopher of science. Early in the review, however, he does point out the existence of two current schools of philosophy, viz., (1) "that which refers all our knowledge to experience, reserving to the mind only a high degree of activity and excursiveness in collecting, grouping, and systematizing its suggestions"; and (2) "that which assumes the presence of innate conceptions and truths antecedent to experience, intertwined and ingrained in the very staple and essence of our intellectual being, and commanding as with a divine voice universal assent as soon as understood." [265] He goes on:

> The author of the very striking, profound, and in many important respects original works of which we have undertaken to give some account belongs to the latter of these schools; and, indeed, appears disposed to press its doctrines and assumptions to a very far greater extent, and to place them in an intimately bolder prominence than we have been at all aware of having been before done, except perhaps in the writings of some of the later German metaphysicians. We confess in ourselves a leaning, though we trust not a bigoted one, to the other side. [266]

Much later on in the review, however, after having commented favorably on so many of the points Whewell had made, Herschel sees the difference between himself and his friend as more similar to "the grand antithesis between an ideal and an empirical philosophy" typified in the opposition between Plato and Aristotle. [267] There he states:

> Mr. Whewell, in the work before us, gives a masterly specimen of what may be done to make Platonism a solid and compact body of philosophy, while the views we have attempted to advocate (we are but too conscious of how inadequately), are fundamentally Aristotelian. . . . [268]

Whewell replied to this review in a personal letter written to Herschel on April 11, 1844, which was reprinted in the second edition of the *Philosophy of the Inductive Sciences* (1847). [269] Here he reduces Herschel's main criticism to the fear that his [Whewell's] use of terms such as idea and form "appear to deprive the external world of its reality; to make it, or at least most of its properties, a creation of the observing mind." [270] On this point Whewell is quick to acknowledge that

> if, by calling space an *idea* we suggest any doubt of its reality and of the reality of the external world, we certainly run the risk of misleading our readers; for the external world is real if anything be real: the bodies which exist in space are things, if things are anywhere to be found. That bodies *do* exist in space, and that *that* is the reason why we apprehend them as existing in space, I readily grant. [271]

Still, in his own defense, Whewell does not see this fear as a reason why he should abstain from using the term idea or why such usage need entail any agnosticism on his part concerning the reality attained:

> But I conceive that the term idea ought not to suggest any such doubt of the reality of the knowledge in which it is involved. Ideas are always, in our knowledge, conjoined with facts. Our *real knowledge* is *knowledge* because it involves ideas, *real* because it involves facts. We apprehend things as existing in space because they do so exist: and our idea of space enables us so to observe them and so to conceive them. [272]

From this and other texts already cited, it is difficult of course to ascertain to what extent Whewell, if not a Kantian, was a naïve realist, a Platonist, or even a Cartesian in his epistemology. [273] Perhaps there are elements of all these philosophies in his thought. Yet there can be no doubt that he was convinced that the objective of science is to attain truth about the universe, that he felt that the methodology he had proposed could attain such truth while still being open to the possibility of refinement, exception, and more accurate formulation, and that through its employment there would result a genuine and cumulative growth of scientific knowledge. [274]

5. *John Stuart Mill*

Whewell had the misfortune to publish his main work on scientific methodology in 1840 — an unpropitious date, it has been remarked, "for the next year saw J. S. Mill's *System of*

Logic, which won such popularity that it overshadowed
Whewell's contributions. . . ." [275] Whatever the intrinsic
merits of Mill's classic, there can be no doubt that it soon became the standard textbook of logic in the universities and
was almost universally looked upon, by the latter part of the
nineteenth century, as the authoritative treatment of scientific
methodology. Only recently, in fact, has the adequacy of
Mill's treatment been called into question, and this on practically the same grounds as a criticism voiced by Whewell
himself, namely, that Mill had no knowledge of science's history or of the actual practice of scientists, and thus created
his method, as it were, in a logical vacuum.[276]

The son of James Mill — himself a celebrated philosopher,
psychologist, economist, and historian — John was tutored
by his father to carry on and propagate the latter's empiricist
and utilitarian philosophy.[277] While still a young man John
became acquainted with the thought of Saint-Simon, and
through this was led to a study of Comte. The Comtean line
of thought proved compatible to the younger Mill, fitting in
well with the empiricism of Bacon and Hume to which he
was already committed. Much of his writing was thereupon
directed against seventeenth-century rationalists, the teachings of Kant and his followers, and the views of Reid and the
Scottish realists.[278] In addition to Comte's writings, Mill
found the scientific examples provided by Herschel and Whewell most helpful for elaborating his theory of induction, although the position to which he came was rejected by Whewell and became the subject of prolonged controversy between
them. Mill's more celebrated polemic was directed against
the chief proponent of intuitionist philosophy in his day, Sir
William Hamilton, professor of logic and metaphysics at Edinburgh; the examination of the latter's philosophy that issued
from this in 1865 provides an important supplement to Mill's
thought as expressed in the *System of Logic.*[279]

Mill's contributions to philosophy are not significant for
their originality, but they are important for the fullness of
treatment he accorded to logical problems and for the fact
that he brought these to the attention of an extraordinarily
large and diverse public.[280] The chief subject to which he addressed himself was that of induction, since he believed that

the physical sciences had made considerable progress
through the proper employment of inductive procedures, and
wished to see the "philosophy of experience" extended to
other fields of knowledge through a broader application of
similar methods.[281] There was also a close association, in
Mill's thought, between induction, laws of nature, causation,
and scientific explanation, all of which topics have an important bearing on the point of this study. Surprisingly enough,
Mill regarded the search for causes as essential to the scientific enterprise, and indeed as the foundation of all inductive
reasoning; he also believed, as did Herschel and Whewell,
that "in some cases at least the sciences do achieve complete
and final certainty concerning the laws of nature," [282] although he disagreed with them over the way in which such
belief could be justified.

The *System of Logic* proposed to do for induction what
traditional treatises on logic had done for deduction, namely,
provide rules analogous to those of the syllogism that would
enable one to arrive at general propositions with certainty.
Mill defines induction as "the operation of discovering and
proving general propositions," [283] although his treatment of
the inductive process suggests that he is more intent on the
proof of such propositions than he is on their discovery. He
sees induction, indeed, as the basis of all proof, and ultimately as the source of all nonintuitive knowledge:

> We have found that all inference, consequently all proof
> and all discovery of truths not self evident, consists of in-
> ductions and the interpretation of inductions; that all our
> knowledge, not intuitive, comes to us exclusively from
> that source. What induction is, therefore, and what con-
> ditions render it legitimate cannot but be deemed the
> main question of the science of logic — the question
> which includes all others.[284]

The inductive process, summarily defined as "generalization
from experience," [285] receives its warrant from the "universal
fact" that the course of nature is uniform, and this constitutes
for Mill "the fundamental principle, or general axiom, of
induction." [286] This axiom or principle functions in much the

same fashion as the major premise of a syllogistic argument.
In fact,

> if we throw the whole course of any inductive argument
> into a series of syllogisms, we shall arrive by more or
> fewer steps at an ultimate syllogism, which will have for
> its major premise the principle or axiom of the uniform-
> ity of the course of nature.[287]

The uniformity of nature, in turn, implies that the universe is
governed by general laws, which Mill refers to as "laws of
nature." [288] These apply immediately to phenomena of nature,
which bear a twofold relationship to one another, the first
being the relation of simultaneity and the second that of succession.[289] As a consequence "every phenomenon is related,
in a uniform manner, to some phenomena that coexist with
it and to some that have preceded and will follow it." [290] Of
these, however, "the most valuable to us" are the relations
pertaining to the order of succession, for these are found to
be governed by a universal law, the law of causation.[291] Mill
regards this law or, as he otherwise phrases it, "the truth that
every fact which has a beginning has a cause," as "coextensive with human experience." [292] And in light of the connection of this law, *via* the uniformity of nature, with the very
process of induction itself, he further affirms that "the notion
of cause [is] the root of the whole theory of induction . . ." [293]

Since causality figures so fundamentally in Mill's justification of induction, it is not surprising that he approaches its
definition with some care. He is quite explicit, for example,
that he wishes to keep his discussion at the phenomenal level
and therefore does not wish to speak of ultimate or ontological causes, or even of "true causes" in the sense of those that
actually *produce* an effect. In support of this manner of defining cause Mill falls back on Reid's distinction, which we have
already indicated,[294] between a physical cause and an efficient cause. Mill's clarification of the resulting meaning is
worth citing in full:

> . . . when in the course of this inquiry I speak of the
> cause of any phenomenon I do not mean a cause which

is not itself a phenomenon; I make no research into the ultimate or ontological cause of anything. To adopt a distinction familiar in the writings of the Scotch metaphysicians, and especially of Reid, the causes with which I concern myself are not *efficient* but *physical* causes. They are causes in that sense alone in which one physical fact is said to be the cause of another. Of the efficient causes of phenomena, or whether any such causes exist at all, I am not called upon to give an opinion. The notion of causation is deemed by the schools of metaphysics most in vogue at the present moment to imply a mysterious and most powerful tie, such as cannot, or at least does not, exist between any physical fact and that other physical fact on which it is invariably consequent and which is popularly termed its cause: and thence is deduced the supposed necessity of ascending higher into the essences and inherent constitution of things to find the true cause, the cause which is not only followed by, but actually produces, the effect. No such necessity exists for the purposes of the present inquiry, nor will any such doctrine be found in the following pages. The only notion of a cause which the theory of induction requires is such a notion as can be gained from experience. The law of causation, the recognition of which is the main pillar of inductive science, is but the familiar truth that invariability of succession is found by observation to obtain between every fact of nature and some other fact which has preceded it, independently of all considerations respecting the ultimate mode of production of phenomena and of every other question regarding the nature of "things in themselves." [295]

Thus restricting himself to the phenomenal order, Mill regards the general uniformity of the course of nature as consisting in nothing more than "an invariable order of succession" between phenomena.[296] This notion thus becomes sufficient for his definitions of cause and effect:

> To certain facts, certain facts always do and, as we believe, will continue to, succeed. The invariable antecedent is termed the cause, the invariable consequent, the effect. And the universality of the law of causation consists in this, that every consequent is connected in this

manner with some particular antecedent or set of antecedents.[297]

Mill's objective in so defining cause and effect is to be able, as already noted, to use these terms in setting up rules that will govern inductive reasoning in a manner analoguous to that in which the rules of the syllogism govern deductive reasoning. These rules turn out to be his famous "four methods of inductive inquiry," [298] namely, the methods of agreement, of difference, of residues, and of concomitant variations. Between the third and fourth of these Mill inserts a "joint method of agreement and difference," with the result that his inductive methodology may be summarized in the five following canons:

First Canon [Method of Agreement]: If two or more instances of the phenomenon under investigation have only one circumstance in common, the circumstance in which alone all the instances agree is the cause (or effect) of the given phenomenon.[299]

Second Canon [Method of Difference]: If an instance in which the phenomenon under investigation occurs, and an instance in which it does not occur, have every circumstance in common save one, that one occuring only in the former; the circumstance in which alone the two instances differ is the effect, or the cause, or an indispensable part of the cause, of the phenomenon.[300]

Third Canon [Joint Method of Agreement and Difference]: If two or more instances in which the phenomenon occurs have only one circumstance in common, while two or more instances in which it does not occur have nothing in common save the absence of that circumstance, the circumstance in which alone the two sets of instances differ is the effect, or the cause, or an indispensable part of the cause, of the phenomenon.[301]

Fourth Canon [Method of Residues]: Subduct from any phenomenon such part as is known by previous inductions to be the effect of certain antecedents, and the residue of the phenomenon is the effect of the remaining antecedents.[302]

Fifth Canon [Method of Concomitant Variations]: Whatever phenomenon varies in any manner whenever another phenomenon varies in some particular manner, is either a cause or an effect of that phenomenon, or is connected with it through some fact of causation.[303]

All of these canons, predictably, are formulated in the language of cause and effect. The reason for this is that inductive inquiry, in Mill's view, has for its object to ascertain what causes are connected with what effects, and thus is concerned with searching "into the effects of a given cause, or into the causes of a given effect." [304] Since Mill is insistent that his four methods are the only possible modes of experimental inquiry, "of direct induction *a posteriori,* as distinguished from deduction," causality is effectively made by him to bear the burden of all successful generalization in science and, by extension, in any area of human inquiry that would utilize a scientific methodology.

It should be noted that Mill shows an acquaintance with Aristotelian terminology, and in one place points out the extreme difficulty of distinguishing a condition from a cause, instancing the Aristotelian "material cause, *causa materialis*" [305] as the only condition he is aware of that has "received the name of cause. . . ." [306] In criticizing Sir William Hamilton's theory of causation, moreover, Mill acknowledges that Hamilton was familiar with the teaching of the Aristotelians concerning the four causes, but holds that he confused the material with the efficient cause.[307] The efficient cause, in Mill's expression, is "the only one of these [four causes] which answers either to the common, or to the modern philosophical, notion of cause." [308] But Hamilton, he observes, "ignores *efficiens* altogether, and imagines that when the rest of the world are speaking of *efficiens,* they mean *materia.*" [309] Matter, as Mill sees it, is exempt from his causal law, since "it is *events,* that is to say, changes, not substances, that are subject to the law of causation." [310] So Mill can confidently assert that "nothing is caused but events," [311] and since every event by definition must have a beginning, he feels that he can use this as a justification for his law of causation, namely, that everything that begins to exist must have a cause.[312]

Mill also discourses on hypotheses and concedes them a place in scientific inquiry. He defines a hypothesis as "any supposition which we make (either without actual evidence or on evidence avowedly insufficient) in order to endeavour to deduce from it conclusions in accordance with facts which are known to be real. . . ." [313] Such suppositions are made, according to Mill, "under the idea that if the conclusions to which the hypothesis leads are known truths, the hypothesis itself either must be, or at least is likely to be, true." [314] And, he goes on, "if the hypothesis relates to the cause or mode of production of a phenomenon, it will serve, if admitted, to explain such facts as are found capable of being deduced from it." [315] Scientific explanation is therefore "the purpose of many, if not most, hypotheses." [316] This, at any rate, is how Mill conceives the role of hypotheses in such explanation:

> Since explaining, in the scientific sense, means resolving an uniformity which is not a law of causation into the laws of causation from which it results, or a complex law of causation into simpler and more general ones from which it is capable of being deductively inferred; if there does not exist any known laws which fulfill this requirement, we may feign or imagine some which would fulfill it; and this is making an hypothesis. [317]

Thus, unlike Newton, Mill would "feign hypotheses," and would place no restrictions on the scientist's ingenuity in so doing. Hence he observes that

> . . . there are no other limits to hypotheses than those of the human imagination; we may, if we please, imagine, by way of accounting for an effect, some cause of a kind utterly unknown, and acting according to a law altogether fictitious. [318]

While Mill concedes such latitude in principle, in actual fact he feels that "there is probably no hypothesis in the history of science in which both the agent itself and the law of its operation" are entirely fictitious:

> Either the phenomenon assigned as the cause is real, but the law according to which it acts merely supposed, or the cause is fictitious, but is supposed to produce its ef-

fects according to laws similar to those of some known class of phenomena.[319]

Mill is not content, moreover, to deal with causes that are merely imagined, but would seek some type of verification or proof of a cause's existence. For this,

> I conceive it to be necessary, when the hypothesis relates to causation, that the supposed cause should not only be a real phenomenon, something actually existing in nature, but should be already known to exercise, or at least to be capable of exercising, an influence of some sort over the effect.[320]

It is in this context that Mill raises the question, occasioned by Whewell's criticism of Newton, whether it is ever allowable, in a scientific hypothesis, to assume a cause, or whether one must always ascribe an assumed law to a known cause? [321] Mill replies to this as follows. If one is dealing with a "known cause," then the hypothesis can "be received as true merely because it explains the phenomena." [322] But it is still legitimate to frame a hypothesis with an assumed cause, since this may turn out to be "very useful by suggesting a line of investigation which may possibly terminate in obtaining real proof." [323] Such real proof, however, will result only if the assumed cause can be verified through other evidence. Mill attributes the formulation of this condition to Comte, and offers it as a possible interpretation of Newton's use of the expression *vera causa:*

> But, for this purpose, as is justly remarked by M. Comte, it is indispensable that the cause suggested by the hypothesis should be in its own nature susceptible of being proved by other evidence. This seems to be the philosophical import of Newton's maxim (so often cited with approbation by subsequent writers) that the cause assigned for any phenomenon must not only be such as, if admitted, would explain the phenomenon, but must also be a *vera causa.*[324]

While conceding the difficulty of ascertaining Newton's original meaning, Mill here endorses (though not explicitly) Whewell's suggestion that the Newtonian *vera causa* should in no way be understood uniquely as a "known cause":

It is certainly not necessary that the cause assigned should be a cause already known; otherwise we should sacrifice our best opportunities of becoming acquainted with new causes. But what is true in the maxim is that the cause, though not known previously, should be capable of being detected, and its connection with the effect ascribed to it should be susceptible of being proved, by independent evidence. The hypothesis, by suggesting observations and experiments, puts us on the road to that independent evidence if it be really attainable; and till it be attained, the hypothesis ought only to count for a more or less plausible conjecture.[325]

Closely associated with Mill's views on hypotheses is his account of empirical laws. Following the terminological practice of his day, he defines an empirical law as one that describes "uniformities which observation or experiment have shown to exist," but with which there is hesitation in generalizing beyond the observed cases "for want of seeing any reason *why* such a law should exist." [326] The answer to such a why-question would, for Mill, be preferably in terms of causality:

To state the explanation, the *why*, of the empirical law, would be to state the laws from which it is derived, the ultimate causes on which it is contingent.[327]

This desideratum coheres, moreover, with Mill's understanding of scientific explanation in general. To explain "laws of causation" is for him the same thing as "resolving them into other laws." [328] In moving toward more and more general laws, however, one recedes from familiar phenomena and begins to deal with those that are more mysterious. Thus the process of explanation "resolves a phenomenon with which we are familiar into one of which we previously knew little or nothing, as when the common fact of the fall of heavy bodies was resolved into the tendency of all particles of matter towards one another." [329] Such considerations lead Mill to the following deductivist account of the nature of scientific explanation:

. . . in science, those who speak of explaining any phenomenon mean (or should mean) pointing out not some

more familiar, but merely some more general phenomenon, of which it is a particular exemplification; or some
laws of causation which produce it by their joint or successive action, and from which, therefore, its conditions
may be determined deductively. Every such operation
brings us a step nearer towards answering the question
which was stated in a previous chapter as comprehend-
ing the whole problem of the investigation of nature, viz.,
What are the fewest assumptions, which being granted,
the order of nature as it exists would be the result? What
are the fewest general propositions from which all the
uniformities existing in nature could be deduced? [330]

Here, obviously, is Mill's endorsement of the "covering-law"
model of scientific explanation that is much discussed in recent literature on the philosophy of science. Yet such a
model, as should be clear from the context, was not proposed
by Mill as a substitute for causal explanation, but rather as a
way of articulating such explanation in terms of his more and
more general laws of causation.

Since mention has been made of Comte and his influence on Mill, at least brief notice should be given to Mill's
evaluation of Comte's position on causality. Mill takes
Comte's polemic to be directed not against causes themselves,
but against the practice of substituting supernatural for natural causes, or the practice of conceiving "mental abstractions
as real entities." [331] On this basis he gives the somewhat benign interpretation of Comte's position:

It is often said of him [Comte] that he rejects the study
of causes. This is not, in the correct acceptation, true, for
it is only questions of ultimate origin, and of efficient as
distinguished from what are called physical causes, that
he rejects. The causes that he regards as inaccessible are
causes which are not themselves phenomena. Like other
people he admits the study of causes, in every sense in
which one physical fact can be the cause of another.[332]

Mill does admit, however, that Comte found the explicit use
of causal terminology repugnant, and he sees this prejudice
as seriously limiting Comte's philosophy, depriving it in effect
of any true inductive reasoning. Mill's statement here is actually a good summary of how he conceives causes to func-

tion at the phenomenal level in scientific explanation, and so is worth giving in its entirety:

> [Comte] has an objection to the *word* cause; he will only consent to speak of laws of succession: and depriving himself of the use of the word which has a positive meaning, he misses the meaning it expresses. He sees no difference between such generalizations as Kepler's laws, and such as the theory of gravitation. He fails to perceive the real distinction between the laws of succession and coexistence, which thinkers of a different school call laws of phenomena, and those of what they call the action of causes: the former exemplified by the succession of day and night, the latter by the earth's rotation which produces it. The succession of day and night is as much an invariable sequence as the alternate exposure of opposite sides of the earth to the sun. Yet day and night are not the causes of one another. Why? Because their sequence, though invariable in our experience, is not unconditionally so: those facts only succeed each other provided that the presence and absence of the sun succeed each other, and if this alternation were to cease we might have either day or night unfollowed by one another. Thus there are two kinds of uniformities of succession, the one unconditional, the other conditional on the first: laws of causation, and other successions dependent on those laws. All ultimate laws are laws of causation, and the only universal law beyond the pale of mathematics is the law of universal causation, namely, that every phenomenon has a phenomenal cause, has some phenomenon other than itself, or some combination of phenomena, on which it is invariably and unconditionally consequent. It is on the universality of this law that the possibility rests of establishing a canon of induction. A general proposition inductively obtained is only then proved to be true when the instances on which it rests are such that if they have been correctly observed, the falsity of the generalization would be inconsistent with the constancy of causation, with the universality of the fact that the phenomena take place according to invariable laws of succession. It is probable, therefore, that M. Comte's determined abstinence from the word and the idea of cause has much to do with his inability to conceive an induc-

tive logic, by diverting his attention from the only basis on which it could be founded.[333]

If Mill differed from Comte, however, he more consistently expressed himself as at variance with Whewell also. Mill acknowledges his disagreements with the latter in the prefaces to the first, third, and fourth editions of the *System of Logic;* even in the eighth and final edition, in fact, Whewell's name stands out before all others as the adversary he is combating. The main difference between them centers around the empirical basis of necessary truths.and the role of mind in their formulation.[334] Closely associated with this is their difference over the role of the idea, or conception, in accounting for inductive generalizations.[335] Regarding Kepler's discovery of the ellipticity of a planet's orbital motion, for example, Whewell insists that the conception of ellipse is something added to the facts in order to make the generalization possible, whereas Mill maintains that "the ellipse was in the facts before Kepler recognized it." [336] Mill thought, also, that Whewell was too precipitate in offering the consilience of inductions as conclusive proof of the truth of a theory.[337] These differences have been analyzed in some detail in the recent literature, with results that are generally more partial to Whewell than to Mill.[338] The differences between the two are basic, however, and perhaps irreconcilable, considering the deep-seated disagreements over the epistemic character of scientific knowledge that continue to be voiced down to the present day.

Regarding Mill's philosophy of science as a whole, this too has come in for its share of criticism. Mill's attempt to base induction on the uniformity of nature is generally regarded as circular, and is even seen by many as a wrongheaded attempt to reduce induction to deduction.[339] By his own admission, moreover, Mill equated the philosophy of science with the logic of science,[340] and on this basis can rightly be criticized for not paying sufficient attention to the extralogical factors involved in scientific discovery and in the validation of scientific knowledge generally. With regard to his teaching on causes and laws of nature, Mill's doctrine is open to all the objections that have been directed against Hume.[341]

Ducasse, in fact, charges Mill with even greater inconsistency than Hume in his single-minded attempt to justify scientific knowledge through radical empiricist principles alone.[342] Yet these criticisms should not obscure the fact that Mill's account of the philosophy of inductive science has been, and continues to be, enormously influential. Indeed, of all the methodologists discussed in this chapter, Mill has done the most to create the ambience in which contemporary philosophers of science work, particularly in their attempts to reconcile the discoveries of twentieth-century scientists with the classical methodological ideals that derive from nineteenth-century science.

6. Claude Bernard

Like Mill, Claude Bernard was influenced by Comte; unlike him, he was an experimental scientist of great renown whose methodological views were based on his own practice in science and, as a consequence, gained wide acceptance not only among philosophers but among fellow scientists as well.[343] For this reason alone Bernard would merit inclusion among the methodologists of classical science. There is a further reason for our taking note of his contributions, however, and this is because of his special concern with the methodology of the biological sciences. The assertion has been made that biology did not emerge as a science until the nineteenth century,[344] and if one gives credence to this and focuses only on the experimental aspects of this emerging science, he would have to give credit to Bernard for his documentation of the methodological canons that made such an emergence possible. Indeed, Bernard can be said to occupy much the same position with respect to the life sciences that Herschel, and to a lesser extent Whewell, occupy in the physical sciences. Like them, moreover, he appreciated the role of causal explanation in science, although in a way that is differently nuanced and with reservations dictated by the complexity of the subject matter with which he had to deal.

Bernard's early education was along humanistic rather than scientific lines, and he initially aspired to a career as an author and playwright.[345] He turned from this to medicine,

however, and after an internship in the municipal hospitals of
Paris, found his true interest to lie in experimental pathology.
He quickly achieved fame in this field. Bernard became professor of experimental medicine at the Collège de France in
1855, and was elected a member of the French Academy in
1868. He published numerous papers describing his researches and discoveries, but the best expression of his methodology is to be found in his classic, *An Introduction to the
Study of Experimental Medicine* (1865) and in scattered
jottings in his famous notebook, *Le Cahier rouge* (1850–
1860).[346]

Bernard read Auguste Comte and, while rejecting positivism as a systematic philosophy and strongly repudiating
Comte's atheism,[347] nonetheless preserved some Comtean elements in his philosophy of science. Unlike Whewell, for example, Bernard accepted Comte's law of the three stages,
only replacing the last or positive stage in the law with that
of experimental method. He states of this that "experimental
method is by no means primitive or natural to man, and . . .
only after lengthy wanderings in theological and scholastic
discussion has he recognized at last the sterility of his efforts
in this direction." [348] Further articulating this development,
he writes:

> The human mind has at different periods of its evolution
> passed successively through *feeling, reason* and *experi-
> ment*. First, feeling alone, imposing itself on reason, cre-
> ated the truths of faith or theology. Reason or philoso-
> phy, the mind's next mistress, brought to birth
> scholasticism. At last, experiment, or the study of natural
> phenomena, taught man that the truths of the outer
> world are to be found ready formulated neither in feeling
> nor in reason. These are indispensable merely as guides;
> but to attain external truths we must of necessity go
> down into the objective reality of things where they lie
> hidden in their phenomenal form.[349]

Bernard's apparent disparagement of theology and philosophy was associated with their search for ultimate causes; as
he saw it, experimental science proves to man more and more
every day "that primary causes, like the objective reality of
things, will be hidden from him forever, and that he can

know only relations." [350] The discovery of such relations was
interpreted by Bernard as answering the question "How?,"
whereas concern with ultimates seemed to be answering the
question "Why?" [351] Bernard would readily admit that "the
nature of our mind leads us to seek the essence or the *why* of
things," but he felt that this induces us to aim beyond the
goal that it is given us to reach.[352] "Experience soon teaches
us," he asserts, "that we cannot get beyond the *how*. . . ." [353]
In answering how-questions, however, and here he was unlike Comte, Bernard did not rule out the possibility of causal
knowledge. For Bernard, indeed, answering this type of question will lead us to "the immediate cause or the necessary
conditions of phenomena." [354] Thus, like Harvey and Newton,
he would not discourage the search for the proximate causes
of phenomena, even though he would continue to disclaim
any knowledge of primary or ultimate causes.

Bernard's main concern, predictably, was with experimental method and how this could yield knowledge, as he
puts it, of "the immediate cause determining the circumstances in which a phenomenon presents itself. . . ." [355] He
conceives this method as passing through three stages, those
of observation, hypothesis, and experimentation. Observation
and experimentation are for him the two poles of experimental
reasoning, and they supply knowledge of the facts, but between them and bridging them is the hypothesis, which Bernard also refers to as the experimental idea or the idea a
priori. Describing this intermediary he writes:

> The experimental idea is the result of a sort of presenti-
> ment of the mind which thinks things will happen in a
> certain way. In this connection we may say that we have
> in our minds an intuition or feeling as to the laws of na-
> ture, but we do not know their form. We can learn it
> only from experiment.[356]

Bernard sees this intuition as particularly important in the
life sciences, because of the complexity of their subject matter. Among his notes are the following remarks to this effect:

> There are sciences in which one cannot experiment (as-
> tronomy), in which observation can suffice to reveal the
> nature of the phenomena because their cause is very sim-
> ple. But with more complex facts this is impossible.

> First it is necessary to observe a phenomenon, then, after it has been observed, to make hypotheses about its cause. Then it is necessary to split the phenomenon into its elements; from this comes the experiment.
>
> The experiment is always the termination of a process of reasoning, whose premises are observation. Example: if the face has movement, what is the nerve? I suppose it is the facial; I cut it. I cut others, leaving the facial intact — the control experiment.[357]

And again:

> To experiment is to observe certain natural phenomena in order to establish their nature or cause.
>
> To observe is to examine things as they pass in natural sequence. Whatever means one may use, microscopes, telescopes, one only observes.
>
> Experimentation is, properly speaking, nothing more than the decomposition of a phenomenon into its elements. One removes them in succession, and observes what is lacking, in order to identify the role of each of these elements in the total production of the phenomenon.[358]

The role of the idea in experimentation, for Bernard, is strictly instrumental: our ideas are only "intellectual instruments" that we use to break into phenomena.[359] As such they do not have an absolute character, and "we must change them when they have served their purpose, as we change a blunt lancet that we have used long enough."[360] And although we conceive of such experimental ideas as *a priori*, they are only "reached by investigation, inductive or interrogative reasoning,"[361] and perhaps for this reason they "are at bottom really *a posteriori* ideas."[362] It is this direction of thought that leads Bernard to assert that both induction and deduction must be used in applying the experimental method, and thus to hold that both processes are found in all the sciences:

> I do not believe that induction and deduction are really two forms of reasoning essentially distinct. By nature man has the feeling or idea of a principle that rules par-

ticular cases. He always proceeds instinctively from a principle, acquired or invented by hypothesis; but he can never go forward in reasoning otherwise than by syllogism, that is, by proceeding from the general to the particular.[363]

In so stating his convictions, Bernard felt that he was at variance with Francis Bacon, who in his view did not understand the experimental method and therefore could not possibly be its inventor. He agrees that

Baconian induction . . . has become famous and has been made the foundation of all scientific philosophy. Bacon was a great genius, and his great restoration of the sciences is sublime as an idea. . . . Yet Bacon was not a man of science, and he did not understand the mechanism of the experimental method. To prove this, it would be enough to cite the hapless attempts which he made. Bacon advises us to fly from hypotheses and theories; we have seen, however, that they are auxiliaries of the method, indispensable as scaffolding is necessary in building a house.[364]

Elsewhere Bernard is even more critical of the Baconian canons, claiming that they can only be misleading to those who would be true investigators of nature:

. . . those who make the most discoveries in science know Bacon least, while those who read and ponder him, like Bacon himself, have poor success. . . . As for Bacon and the other more modern philosophers who try a general systematization of precepts for scientific research, they may seem alluring to people who look at science only from a distance; but works like theirs are of no use to experienced scientists; and by false simplification of things, they mislead men who wish to devote themselves to cultivating science. What is more, they embarrass them by burdening the mind with vague and inapplicable precepts that we must hasten to forget if we wish to become true experimenters.[365]

Bernard sees experiment as putting one's ideas to test and so determining their validity. Facts are the criteria that determine such validity, but even these do not have an absolute character, since reason enters into their very constitution to supply the ultimate criterion of truth. Bernard is willing to admit "that facts are the only realities that can give form to the experimental idea and at the same time serve as its control; but this is on condition that reason accepts them."[366] Otherwise expressed:

> A fact is nothing in itself, it has value only through the idea connected with it or through the proof it supplies. We have said elsewhere that, when one calls a new fact a discovery, the fact itself is not the discovery, but rather the new idea derived from it; in the same way, when a fact proves anything, the fact does not itself give the proof, but only the rational relation which it establishes between the phenomenon and its cause. This relation is the scientific truth which we now must discuss further.[367]

Bernard's ensuing treatment of scientific truth divides this into two types, the first mathematical and the second experimental. Mathematical truths, in his understanding, are "conscious and absolute" truths, because the ideal conditions in which they exist are always conscious and known by us in an absolute way.[368] Experimental truths, on the other hand, are "unconscious and relative," but they rest, nonetheless, on principles that are absolute because "they speak to our consciousness and our reason."[369] Bernard is explicit that this "absolute principle of experimental science is conscious and necessary determinism in the conditions of phenomena."[370] Because of his insistence on such determinism, in fact, he used the term "determinism" to characterize his own philosophy of science and thus to distinguish it from the then current and opposed positions of vitalism and mechanism.[371] It is only because such determinism exists, he maintains, and can be known by man with a type of a priori consciousness, that it becomes possible for him to discover scientific truth. Here Bernard's thought has a pronounced kinship with that of Whewell and Kant, as is detectable in the following statement:

> Experiment only shows us the form of phenomena; but the relation of a phenomenon to a definite cause is necessary and independent of experiment; it is necessarily mathematical and absolute. Thus we see that the principle of the criterion in experimental sciences is

fundamentally identical with that of the mathematical sciences, since in each case the principle is expressed by a necessary and absolute relation between things. Only in the experimental sciences these relations are surrounded by numerous, complex and infinitely varied phenomena which hide them from our sight. With the help of experiments, we analyze, we dissociate these phenomena, in order to reduce them to more and more simple relations and conditions. In this we try to lay hold on scientific truth, i.e., find the law that shall give us the key to all variations of the phenomena. Thus experimental analysis is our only means of going in search of truth in the natural sciences, and the absolute determinism of phenomena, of which we are conscious *a priori*, is the only criterion or principle which directs and supports us.[372]

There is further reason to believe that Bernard equates such determinism with causality, and in this way regards causal explanation as actually constitutive of science. So he elaborates:

It follows from the above that, if a phenomenon, in an experiment, had such a contradictory appearance that it did not necessarily connect itself with determinate causes, then reason should reject the fact as non-scientific. We should wait and by direct experiments seek the source of error which may have slipped into the observation. Indeed, there must be error or insufficiency in the observation; for to accept a fact without a cause, that is, indeterminate in its necessary conditions, is neither more nor less than the negation of science.[373]

In the detection of such determinism, which he discusses under the heading "proof and counterproof," Bernard disagrees with the constant conjunction type of analysis advocated by Hume and opts instead for stronger causal connection:

. . . proof that a given condition always precedes or accompanies a phenomenon does not warrant concluding with certainty that a given condition is the immediate cause of that phenomenon. It must still be established that, when this condition is removed, the phenomenon will no longer appear.[374]

Bernard refers to this necessary (as opposed to sufficient) condition as counterproof, and urges its continued employment as a type of systematic doubt, somewhat in the Cartesian tradition. He also sees it as associated with the crucial experiment:

> Counterproof decides whether the relation of cause to effect, which we seek in phenomena, has been found. To do this, it removes the accepted cause, to see if the effect persists, relying on that old and absolutely true adage: *sublata causa, tollitur effectus*. This is what we still call the *experimentum crucis*.[375]

It is by means such as these, in Bernard's view, that experimenters seek to find determinism in nature; "with the help of reasoning and of experiment they try to connect natural phenomena with their necessary conditions, or, in other words, with their immediate causes." [376]

Bernard's frequent use of the term "immediate cause," as in the last quotation, suggests a fuller elaboration of the meaning he attaches to this expression. In one text, where he is establishing a parallel between the physicist and the physiologist, while noting that they differ in the phenomena they study — the former, those taking place in inorganic matter and the latter, those occurring in living matter — he holds that they do not differ in the object they seek to attain. Rather they both set themselves "a common object, viz., getting back to the immediate cause of the phenomena which they are studying." [377] He enlarges on this as follows:

> Now, what we call the immediate cause of a phenomenon is nothing but the physical and material condition in which it exists or appears. The object of the experimental method or the limit of every scientific research is therefore the same for living bodies as for inorganic bodies; it consists in finding the relations which connect any phenomenon with its immediate cause, or putting it differently, it consists in defining the conditions necessary to the appearance of the phenomenon.[378]

In another place, Bernard introduces a distinction between the cause of phenomena and the means of producing them. Here he again identifies the cause with the answer to the

question "How?" since, as we have seen, he had already eliminated why-questions from scientific inquiry:

> In the knowledge that we acquire, we should distinguish
> between two sets of notions: the first corresponds to the
> *cause* of phenomena, the second to the *means* of produc-
> ing them. By the cause of a phenomenon we mean the
> constant and definite condition necessary to existence;
> we call this the relative determinism or the *how* of
> things, i.e., the immediate or determining cause. The
> means of obtaining phenomena are the very processes by
> whose aid we may succeed in putting in action the single
> determining cause which produces the phenomenon. The
> necessary cause in the formation of water is the combina-
> tion of two volumes of hydrogen with one of oxygen; this
> is the single cause which always determines the phenom-
> enon. We cannot conceive of water apart from this essen-
> tial condition. Subordinate conditions or processes in the
> formation of water may be extremely varied; only all
> these processses reach the same result, viz., combination
> of oxygen and hydrogen in invariable proportions.[379]

Bernard here provides another example, concerned with the
transformation of starch into glucose, and then continues:

> The determinism, i.e., the cause of the phenomenon, is
> therefore single, though the means for making it appear
> may be multiple and apparently various. It is most im-
> portant to establish this distinction especially in medi-
> cine, where the greatest confusion reigns, precisely be-
> cause physicians recognize a multitude of causes for the
> same disease. To convince ourselves of what I am urging
> we have only to open a treatise on pathology. By no
> means all the circumstances enumerated are causes; at
> most they are means or processes by which a disease can
> be produced. But the real and effective cause of a disease
> must be *constant* and *determined*, that is unique; any-
> thing else would be a denial of science in medicine. It is
> true that determining causes are much harder to recog-
> nize and define in the phenomena of living beings; but
> they exist nevertheless, in spite of the seeming diversity
> of means employed.[380]

From this discussion Bernard is therefore led to the conclusion that the type of determinism that seeks to identify an ef-

fect with a cause is axiomatic for science and that it "can no more be transgressed in the sciences of life than in the sciences of inorganic matter." [381]

Although Bernard is willing to discourse on "immediate causes," and indeed sees their discovery as essential to the scientific enterprise, he consistently refuses to enter into any search for first, primary, or ultimate causes. "First causes," he writes, "are outside the realm of science; they forever escape us in the sciences of living as well as in those of inorganic bodies." [382] His rejection of this metaphysical type of inquiry was undoubtedly connected with the controversy then raging among biologists over the existence of vital force, for Bernard had made the following entry in his *Cahier rouge:*

> It is not scientific to concern oneself with the vital force, but it is not useful to deny it, because in denying it one affirms something else. The search for primary causes is not scientific (see Newton on this subject).[383]

A few lines later Bernard enumerated various types of force, adding that all of them are unknown:

> The first is the *vital force.*
> The 2nd is the *physical force.*
> The 3rd is the *chemical force.*
> But what is most clear is that all three are unknown.[384]

Bernard took up this topic again in the *Introduction,* where he holds that the word "force" expresses a mere abstraction:

> The experimental method necessarily turns aside from the chimerical search for a vital principle; vital force exists no more than mineral force exists, or, if you like, one exists quite as much as the other. The word, force, is merely an abstraction which we use for linguistic convenience. For mechanics, force is the relation of a movement to its cause. For physicists, chemists, and physiologists, it is fundamentally the same. As the essence of things must always remain unknown, we can learn only relations, and phenomena are merely the results of relations.[385]

Such relations are expressed in scientific law, and it is this alone that is based on causality, understanding the latter in a proximate and non-ultimate sense:

A scientific law gives us the numerical relation of an effect to its cause, and that is the goal at which science stops. When we have the law of a phenomenon, we not only know absolutely the conditions determining its existence, but we also have the relations applying to all its variations, so that we can predict modifications of the phenomenon in any given circumstances.[386]

As further inducement not to delude himself with inquiries into the first cause, Bernard urges the physiologist to imitate the physicist, and here he returns to his example of Newton:

We must imitate the physicists in this matter and say, as Newton said of gravitation: "Bodies fall with an accelerated motion whose law we know; that is a fact, that is reality. But the first cause which makes these bodies fall is utterly unknown. To picture the phenomenon to our minds, we may say that the bodies fall as if there were a force of attraction towards the center of the earth, *quasi esset attractio*. But the force of attraction does not exist, we do not see it; it is merely a word used to abbreviate speech.[387]

Bernard does not give the source of this citation, but he evidently feels that Newton would give support to the conclusion he himself has reached: "To sum up, the object of science is everywhere the same — to learn the material conditions of phenomena." [388]

Bernard's agnosticism with respect to the force concept, his example of hydrogen and oxygen combining to form water, and his frequent references to the necessary "material conditions in which a phenomenon appears," [389] would lead one to believe that scientific explanations, for him, are almost exclusively provided in terms of material causality. From jottings in the *Cahier rouge*, however, it is obvious that Bernard did not regard matter as the sole principle of explanation to be sought in scientific research. He has noted, for example, that "one cannot say that properties result from matter, although they are dependent on its integrity." [390] Then below this he instances the form of a bird's nest as being independent of its matter and the beauty of a monument as independent of the stone from which it is made, considered by itself. In other texts he refers to the "soul" [391] and even to the "Aristotelian entelechy" [392] as instances of this higher principle of explanation. Bernard also emphasizes the importance of final causes in the study of living organisms, while admitting that they have little role to play in the study of the inorganic:

> . . . physicists and chemists can reject all idea of final causes for the facts that they observe; while physiologists are inclined to acknowledge an harmonious and pre-established unity in an organized body, all of whose partial actions are interdependent and mutually generative. We really must learn, then, that if we break up a living organism by isolating its different parts, it is only for the sake of ease in experimental analysis, and by no means in order to conceive them separately. Indeed when we wish to ascribe to a physiological quality its value and true significance, we must always refer it to this whole, and draw our final conclusion only in relation to its effects in the whole.[393]

And, in his notes on the subject of teleology, Bernard makes the following observations about intentionality:

> When we observe in natural phenomena the interrelationships that exist, of such a nature that things seem to have been made with foresight, such as the eye and the stomach, which are formed in anticipation of food and future light, we cannot prevent ourselves from supposing that these things were made intentionally with a determined goal. . . . We ought to recognize, in the totality of natural phenomena and their determined relationships for determined ends, a great intentional intelligence.

> This intentional determination appears especially evident in living creatures which form a finite whole. It appears less so to a physicist and a chemist, who only see fragments of the general phenomena of the great whole. Thus it is these who have fought teleology as furnishing false ideas, and today scientists do not dare admit that they are teleologists, because these are things that cannot be demonstrated. In any event nothing has been put in its place, and the place remains empty.[394]

For himself, after reviewing all the arguments against teleology, Bernard accords them the status of suppositions, compared to which he is content to assert that "teleology is equally valuable, until further notice."[395]

From these brief indications of Bernard's thought on methodology, one can see that his account is related to a variety of philosophical systems, ranging from the Aristotelian through the Cartesian to the Kantian. Personally, however, he disclaimed any philosophy, and declared himself as particularly opposed to attachment to any philosophical system. He saw this as dangerous, as frequently inhibiting the search for truth:

> When a man of science takes a philosophic system as his base in pursuing a scientific investigation, he goes astray in reaches that are too far from reality, or else the system gives his mind a sort of false confidence and an inflexibility out of harmony with the freedom and suppleness that experimenters should always maintain in their researches. We must therefore carefully avoid every species of system, because systems are not found in nature, but only in the mind of man.[396]

Possibly as a result of exposure to a rationalistic scholasticism in his youth, Bernard was outspoken in his denunciation of scholastic philosophy and what he regarded as its a priori methods.[397] In extolling experimental reasoning, in fact, he claimed that this is precisely the reverse of scholastic reasoning.[398] Apparently he extrapolated these excesses of the scholastics to all attempts at systematic philosophical thought; for his own part he simply declares, "I think that the best philosophic system consists in not having any." [399]

But Bernard on this account did not reject philosophy, and he affirmed that "even while avoiding philosophic systems, I like philosophers and greatly enjoy their converse." [400] Again, speaking of philosophy and science, he sees the need for their greater cooperation: "without trying to dominate one another, they must unite." [401] He goes on:

> Their separation could only be harmful to the progress of human knowledge. Striving ever upward, philosophy makes science rise towards the cause or the source of things. It shows science that there are questions beyond it, torturing humanity, which it has not yet solved.[402]

And finally, in Bernard's understanding, what must unite philosophers and true men of science is their ardent desire for knowledge, their search for truth:

. . . truth itself is surely what concerns us and, if we are still in search of it, that is because the part which we have so far found cannot satisfy us. In our investigations, we should else be performing the useless and endless labor pictured in the fable of Sisyphus, ever rolling up the rock which continually falls back to its starting point. This comparison is not scientifically correct: a man of science rises ever, in seeking truth; and if he never finds it in its wholeness, he discovers nevertheless very significant fragments; and these fragments of universal truth are precisely what constitutes science.[403]

On this note, then, let us bring to a close not only our presentation of Bernard's methodological ideas but also our exposition of causality in classical science. It is a good note on which to end, for it accurately reflects the optimism that characterized science's progress from the seventeenth to the nineteenth century, an optimism tempered by some awareness of science's limitations, but confident nonetheless of its ability to acquire knowledge and to attain truth, and this ultimately through its search for the causes that underlie nature's operations.

7. Recapitulation

Since our treatment of classical science began in the latter part of the first volume and has continued through a major portion of the second, a brief summary of the points already made may prove helpful before proceeding to a study of causality in contemporary science. The major conclusion to which our exposition thus far has led is that, contrary to a widespread impression, the passage from medieval and Renaissance science to classical science was not effected by, nor even accompanied by, an abrupt change in methodology as this relates to causal analysis. Aristotle went into eclipse with the rise of modern science, it is true, and with him, the style of analysis and argumentation that characterized peripatetic and scholastic treatises on natural philosophy. The ideal of science also underwent significant changes, as seen in the almost exponential growth of experimentation and of mathematical reasoning applied to the study of nature. Yet, con trary to the general conception, the search for causes was not abandoned, nor did causal knowledge cease overnight to be a goal to which scientists aspired. Moreover, throughout most of the period extending from the seventeenth to the nineteenth century, the term "cause" continued to be understood in a sense broad enough to include all four of the Aristotelian types, and was not immediately restricted, as is commonly supposed, to efficient causality alone. The concept of cause was, however, subjected to close scrutiny from an epistemological viewpoint, and its usage in scientific contexts became more and more a point of controversy. Out of this debate arose a different set of distinctions, or qualificatory adjectives, as applied to causal terminology, and also different interpretations of the meaning and ultimate referents of causal concepts. The setting for this emergence was provided by the founders of classical science, and most of the epistemological issues were raised by those whom we have called the philosophers of such science, but it remained for the methodologists treated in the present chapter to bring these issues to a head, and thus set the stage for the general demise of causal analysis and the rise of contemporary science.

Among the founders of modern science, Harvey stands out as most in continuity with the Aristotelian tradition, for he made explicit use of Aristotle's four types of causes, seeing them as useful in scientific discovery as well as in the codification of its results. He did stress, however, the importance of material and efficient causality, and presented his famous demonstration of the circulation of the blood in terms of the material cause. Also, he made no claims for the complete and ultimate character of his explanations, but rather focused on proximate causes, most of which were discernible to observation and thus led to "ocular demonstration." Gilbert and Kepler, on the other hand, were more open to Platonic influences and so accorded primacy to formal causality. Of the two, Kepler placed the greater stress on quantitative reasoning, understanding form in a mathematical sense, although he also saw the necessity for efficient causes to account for the celestial motions and thus pioneered in the introduction of force concepts into mechanics. Galileo is the most enigmatic of the group, for after fruitless searches for the efficient causes of local motion in his early writings, which he there presented as "true causes," he abandoned this quest and settled instead for knowledge of the laws governing such motions. Yet he gave strong impetus to a mechanistic philosophy, seeking to explain secondary qualities in terms of the material constituents of bodies and the effect of their motion on the senses, and thus implicitly supplying explanations in terms of material and efficient causality. As opposed to Galileo, on the other hand, Newton placed explicit emphasis on causal analysis, making this the basis for his *regulae philosophandi* and setting as the ideal of science the discovery of the "true causes" of natural phenomena. Newton's hope, of course, was that such causes could be discovered through experimentation, and therefore would be phenomenal in character, although it is not easy to see how the causes he claimed to have discovered can be so qualified. The "true cause" uncovered in the *experimentum crucis*, for example, pertains to the order of material causality, whereas gravity, which he used to explain the heliocentric structure of the solar system, may be viewed either as a quality, and thus as a type of formal cause, or as a force, and thus pertaining to the order of efficient causality. Newton disclaimed any knowledge of ultimates such as the nature of light or of gravity, but apparently did not see this as in any way inhibiting his search for the proximate causes of natural phenomena.

Among the modern philosophers we have considered, Descartes, Hobbes, Leibniz, and Kant all subscribed to causal reasoning and saw explanation in terms of causes as essential to scientific knowing. Descartes viewed God as the primary cause of motion and as the ultimate certification of his clear and distinct ideas, thereby claiming for his laws of motion only the status of secondary causes. Consistent with his mechanical philosophy, he initiated the program of reducing formal and final causes to efficient causes, and generally regarded all natural phenomena as causally determined in this sense. Descartes also made much of hypotheses as supplementary to his clear and distinct ideas and, coupled with experimentation, as capable of revealing the "true causes" of phenomena. In somewhat the same vein Hobbes considered science as certain knowledge, focused attention on the "necessary connection" between cause and effect, and at the same time countenanced the use of hypotheses. For him the "entire cause" is made up of efficient and material components, and both formal and final causality are reducible to the operation of efficient causes. Leibniz and Kant were also quite causal in their thinking, although for them the term "cause" was practically equated with force, leading them to develop philosophies that have been correctly characterized as types of dynamism. Leibniz experienced no difficulty with the Aristotelian fourfold structure of causality, explicitly making use of final causes and even seeing them as useful for scientific discovery. His main concern, however, was with mechanical causes, understood in the sense of forces, which themselves required explanation in terms of metaphysical principles, and ultimately in terms of God as First Cause.

With Locke, Berkeley, and Hume, the epistemological problem came into focus; "necessary connection" was subjected to close scrutiny, and generally there was a retrenchment in the claims of science to provide certain knowledge of the real world. Locke's incipient skepticism is traceable to his empiricism, for he experienced great difficulty in verifying any causal explanations, even those of the "corpuscularian philosophy," and so did not see how any demonstrations, or strict science, could arise in the study of nature. Berkeley accorded the status of mathematical hypotheses to mechanical explanations, and saw gravity and force as only "occult qualities." For him, physics is not concerned with efficient causes but merely with the laws that govern phenomena. The real cause behind such laws can be studied only by the metaphysician, and ultimately this cause is God. Hume carried Locke's skepticism to its radical term, while proposing a psychological justification of causality and its impression of "necessary connection." Although his empiricism really did not allow this, Hume implicitly accepted such causes as gravity and elasticity, but like Newton was selectively agnostic with regard to the ultimate causes that produce them. Against Hume, Kant attempted to justify a principle of causality as necessary to make science possible, understanding science uniquely in the sense of Newtonian physics, and thus rejecting traditional metaphysics as a "transcendental illusion."

Finally Reid, juggling the conflicting claims of empiricists and idealists and measuring these against his own common-sense philosophy, proposed two meanings for the word "cause," one physical and the other metaphysical. Physical causes pertain to the phenomenal level, and thus are discernible by the constant-conjunction type of analysis advocated by Hume; whereas metaphysical causes are efficient causes in the proper sense, and these, not being phenomenal, will never yield themselves to a Humean analysis.

Although this diversity of interpretation among philosophers seems hopelessly confusing, certain of their refrains were taken up by those who wrote on the methodology of science and so continued to be called to the attention of scientists. Bacon, closest of all to the founders of classical science and to the tradition of the *Posterior Analytics*, regarded science as true and certain knowledge resulting from the discovery of causes, and was followed in this conviction by Herschel, Whewell, and Bernard. Bacon discounted hypothetical reasoning, however, and placed great stress on induction, holding that by this process one could arrive directly at the causes of phenomena. He tended to equate causes with forms, and forms in turn with laws of nature. Comte, on the other hand, proscribed the search for causes in scientific inquiry as part of his positivist program, maintaining that science should be concerned only with the laws of phenomena. Comte endorsed the use of hypotheses, provided these are open to empirical verification, and stressed prediction rather than explanation as science's primary aim. His views were given a sympathetic hearing by Mill and, to a lesser extent, by Bernard, although neither accepted his interdiction of causal inquiry and indeed made such inquiry the basis of their own methodologies. Mill effectively adopted the positivist program, understood causes as "events," and attempted to formulate their relation to effects in purely phenomenal terms, thus also following Hume. Herschel and Whewell, on the other hand, reacted against the Comtean restrictions and the Humean interpretation, seeing more than succession in causality and insisting on some element of production or efficacy in its exercise. Both regarded gravity as a *vera causa*, and effectively equated cause with force, somewhat in the same way as Leibniz and Kant. Both also saw Newtonian physics as constituting the ideal of science, and gave what some would refer to as its theoretical aspects a quite realist interpretation. Bernard, on the other hand, concentrated almost exclusively on experimental methodology and pronounced himself against force concepts, preferring to search for immediate, phenomenal causes, which he viewed as so many types of determiners. He mentions all four of the Aristotelian causes, but seems to focus more on material, formal, and final, than on efficient causality.

Thus causes, and explanations in terms of causes, continued to be a subject of concern, and dispute, among scientists until late into the nineteenth century. Chief among the topics of controversy was whether causes should be viewed uniquely as events, as discernible only at the phenomenal level, and as expressible in some way in terms of laws regulating phenomena, or whether they should be taken more in the sense of forces, internal mechanisms, latent configurations, or hidden processes that serve to explain phenomenal occurrences. Implicit in the answers to these questions were actually two meanings of causality, neither of which was clearly accepted by the scientific community, nor was the difference between them sufficiently realized. The first may be characterized as a weak or minimal meaning, usually associated with the term "causation," which stresses the phenomenal or eventlike character of cause and effect and therefore holds that causes themselves can be discovered and known; whereas the relation between cause and effect, not being an observable event or occurrence, is best interpreted as a psychological or conceptual projection into reality. The second meaning, on the other hand, is the strong or maximal sense usually associated with the use of the term "cause" in ordinary language. This stresses knowledge of the connection between cause and effect, generally in terms of some agency or efficacy discerned in the effect's production, and seeing this as lodged in some way in the mechanism and conditions necessary for such production.[404] Both of these meanings, as we have seen, were used implicitly by most of the founders, philosophers, and methodologists of classical science, even though in their explicit terminology they repudiated the one or the other. And, regardless of the meaning intended, the notions of cause and causal explanation thus came to be strongly linked to the ideals of classical science, and therefore became vulnerable with the downfall of this science in the closing decades of the nineteenth century.

Part Two
Contemporary Science

CHAPTER THREE

The Changing Status of Causality

In 1958, a year before his death, Friedrich Waismann lectured at Oxford University on the subject "The Decline and Fall of Causality," and pinpointed 1927 as the year that "saw the obsequies" of causality in contemporary science.[1] Explaining the title of his lecture, Waismann observed that these obsequies should not have been totally unexpected. They were, in his view, preceded by a long period of decline, reaching back to the end of the eighteenth century, when Pierre Simon de Laplace had made his famous declaration in the *Philosophical Essay on Probabilities:*

> We may regard the present state of the universe as the effect of its past and the cause of its future. An intelligence which at a given moment knew all the forces that animate nature, and the respective positions of the beings that compose it, and further possessing the scope to analyze these data, could condense into a single formula the movement of the greatest bodies of the universe and that of the least atom: for such an intelligence nothing would be uncertain, and past and future alike would be before its eyes.[2]

With this statement, in Waismann's analysis, Laplace became the modern formulator of a principle of causal determinism that would hold sway as the ideal of scientific explanation for more than a century and a half. But even within the world view of classical mechanics, he went on, such an ideal would turn out to be one that human intelligence and ingenuity could never attain. The obstacles scientists would encounter as they attempted to make measurements with unlimited accuracy, an implicit requirement of Laplace, argued Waismann, already put the concept of causal determinism in jeopardy. So the decline of causality, if not its fall, was an almost inevitable consequence of the Laplacean ideal. But the death-blow, for Waismann, came with Heisenberg's enunciation of the uncertainty principle in 1927, for this showed the radical impossibility of predicting events at the atomic level, with the result that there "causality ceases to operate." [3] The Laplacean mechanical conception of nature, erected by Kant into a metaphysics and enthusiastically embraced by the Enlightenment, was only gradually found to furnish an empty ideal for the physical scientist; lip service was therefore paid to it through a long period of decline, and eventually it was allowed to die a quiet death. But "the end of causality," on the other hand, "came dramatically, with a bang, not a whimper," on the heels of Heisenberg's famous discovery.[4]

Waismann's analysis of the rejection of causal determinism apparently found few objectors in 1958, although even then some might have wondered why causality need be so strongly linked with determinism and predictability, and already there had been proposals for a limited reinstatement of causal concepts among philosophers of science.[5] Indeed, Heisenberg's discovery notwithstanding, causality was never completely without its defenders among philosophers, or even among scientists, whether it was understood in its minimal Humean sense of causation or in its maximal realist sense of causal efficacy. To provide an overview, therefore, of the entire spectrum of attitudes towards causal explanation in contemporary science, this chapter will be divided into three sections. The first will pursue Waismann's theme in more detail, examining the criticisms voiced against causal concepts that led to their gradual retrenchment, if not complete abandonment, in scientific usage; the second will take up Humean justifications for the continued use of such concepts; and the third will sketch the yet stronger claims made by anti-Humeans for causal analysis as an integral part of scientific explanation.

1. *The Decline and Fall of Causality*

It is difficult to treat systematically all the factors that contributed to the de-emphasis of causal notions in contemporary science. Certainly the issue of determinism in nature was primary, and even decisive in the minds of many, and yet there were contributory developments that served to undermine the early nineteenth-century attitudes. Enumerated among these should be: the rise of statistical reasoning and the use of probability notions even prior to quantum physics; the concern with the foundations of mechanics, and particularly renewed attempts to define such entities as mass and force in ways that would preserve for them a purely phenomenal character; the reaction against idealist metaphysics, especially the Hegelian variety; the interest in logic and formalism that attended the extensive work being done in the foundations of mathematics; and a continuing concern on the part of scientists, interested in philosophy but generally lacking formal education in it, with the profound problems arising within their own disciplines. One such series of problems, only touched on by Waismann in his essay, grew directly out of scientists' attempts to follow Mill's lead in abandoning any claims for efficacy or production in the causal nexus, and substituting for this the notion of mere temporal sequence between "events," one of which would be designated as the "cause" and the other as the "effect." In many scientific usages such designations were found to be quite arbitrary, with the result that what was initially considered as a causal relationship turned out to be more safely characterized as one of functional dependence. Other difficulties presented themselves when locating these "events" and their spatio-temporal sequences in different frames of reference, such as those associated with Einstein's special theory of relativity. Yet more serious were the difficulties encountered in trying to conceive of gravity, or force, or any "true cause," for that matter, as an "event" at the phenomenal level. The various enigmas asso-

ciated with force concepts, in fact, and this considering the
tendency of so many classical methodologists to equate force
with cause, proved in the long run to be as harmful to the
ideal of causal explanation as any of the factors already enumerated.

a. Probability vs. Certainty

But at the end of the nineteenth century, determinism in
nature, and the certitude thought to be attained in scientific
knowing because of it, was still the key argument that induced many to seek causal explanations. One of the earliest
attacks on this argument, made not so much against causality
as against the certitude believed to be engendered by it, was
that of the British political economist, William Stanley Jevons.[6] Stimulated by his interest in probability concepts, Jevons studied also the related problem of induction, and did
so with such success that his work has been signaled as "a
bridge from nineteenth-century philosophy of science to current discussions in this field." [7]

Jevons wrote extensively on logic, and in this field was
much influenced by Mill, whose *System of Logic* he summarized and made accessible to beginning students.[8] On one
point he disagreed with Mill, however, and this was the latter's use of the law of causation to justify induction. Jevons's
own concern with probability, and the uncertainty he saw as
characterizing all scientific predictions about the future,
made him suspicious of any attempt to equate causal reasoning with science itself, or to see it as generating the types of
certitude embodied in the Aristotelian and Baconian ideals.
He felt that Mill, whom he otherwise greatly admired, had
fallen under the "noxious power" of causal terminology, and
thereby was led to ascribe an unwarranted certainty to the
results of inductive reasoning. "Not only does Mill treat the
laws of causation as almost coextensive with science," he
wrote, "but he so uses the expression as to imply that when
once we pass within the circle of causation we deal with
certainties." [9] He himself did not see how any conclusion
reached as a result of the inductive process could ever be regarded as absolutely certain, being willing to accord such
conclusions, at best, only a high degree of probability.

Adopting a more cautious attitude towards causality, therefore, Jevons proposed to correct Mill by first rejecting his definition of a cause as an "invariable antecedent of an event." His reason for doing so is the following:

> A cause is defined as the necessary or invariable antecedent of an event, so that when the cause exists the event will also exist or soon follow. If then we know the cause of an event, we know what will certainly happen; and as it is implied that science, by a proper experimental method, may attain to a knowledge of causes, it follows that experience may give us a certain knowledge of future events. But nothing is more unquestionable than that finite experience can never give us certain knowledge of the future, so that either a cause is not an invariable antecedent, or else we can never gain certain knowledge of causes.[10]

Pursuing this line of argument, to get rid of Mill's "invariable sequence" Jevons proposed a new definition of causality that would incorporate the notion of probability and would accent phenomenal succession rather than necessary antecedence:

> To us, then, a cause is not to be distinguished from the group of positive or negative conditions which, with more or less probability, precede an event. In this sense there is no particular difference between knowledge of causes and our general knowledge of the succession of combinations, in which the phenomena of nature are presented to us, or found to occur in experimental inquiry.[11]

Apart from such reservations, Jevons was insistent that he had no objection against the use of causal terminology; his only concern was that this usage not lead us "to imagine that our knowledge of nature can attain to certainty." [12] In discussing causes and their various types, moreover, he did not restrict his understanding of causality to that of efficiency alone. In his logic textbook, for instance, he explained Aristotle's "four kinds of causes for the existence of a thing," [13] and in his examples he frequently cited internal causes such as structures and their functioning. He was even willing to admit that "invariably acting" mechanisms exist in nature, and that scientists in their investigations are witnessing "the productions of a complicated machine"; he did not think, however, that they would ever be allowed "to examine its intimate structure." [14] The ultimate operations of nature, for him as for Harvey and Newton, are thus shrouded in mystery. But at the level of proximate antecedents, he was quite content to speak of oxygen as the cause of combustion, gunpowder as the cause of an explosion, matter as the cause of its own continued existence, and energy as the cause of all motions and changes in nature.[15] And, somewhat surprisingly, Jevons even admitted a general principle of causality, seemingly going so far as to sanction its use in arriving at knowledge of the First Cause:

> Every event must have a cause, and that cause again a cause, until we are lost in the obscurity of the past and are driven to the belief in one First Cause, by whom the course of nature was determined.[16]

Such language, of course, is reminiscent of Herschel and Whewell, and one can only surmise how Jevons could extract such a transcendent result from the sparse content he was willing to concede to his definition of causality.[17]

b. Phenomenalism and Conventionalism

Jevons's strictures on the certainty of causal reasoning contributed to the decline of causality, but not nearly so much as did another type of critique that began with John B. Stallo and reached its culmination in the phenomenalism of Ernst Mach.[18] At first an enthusiastic Hegelian,[19] Stallo later reacted strongly against the philosophical views of his "intellectual infancy" and proposed an analysis of science that was antimetaphysical in the extreme.[20] The main target of his attack was the mechanistic explanations of nature endorsed by most of the physicists of his day, most particularly the kinetic theory of gases. Stallo focused on the arbitrariness of the assumptions underlying kinetic theory, and as a consequence denied it explanatory value, characterizing it as "an unraveling of the simple into the complex, an interpretation of the known in terms of the unknown, an elucidation of the evident by the mysterious, a reduction of an ostensible and real fact to a baseless and shadowy phantom." [21] He unequivocally rejected the reality of atoms or molecules, refusing to see any cogency in the attempts made by Boltzmann, Stefan, and Maxwell to ground the existence of such entities on experimental evidence. In this, Stallo's views were not unlike Mach's, who attempted to work out a consistent philosophy of science that would rest on phenomena alone and would not employ causal reasoning, even at the level of mechanics, to justify its results. Since Mach was more influential than Stallo, and was more explicit in his rejection of causal explanation, it will be profitable to analyze his views here in somewhat more detail.

Like Herschel and Whewell, Mach was a student of the history of science, being early concerned with the origins of the principle of the conservation of energy and with the development of the science of mechanics. Like them also, his interest in philosophy centered around methodological questions raised by the inductive sciences.[22] Many of Mach's ideas were taken up and developed by the members of the *Wiener Kreis*, and his writings exerted an important influence on Einstein and Bridgman. Yet he himself had little appreciation for logic, and his passionate desire to "get rid of metaphysical obscurities" prevented him from accepting the theory of relativity as well as the existence of atoms.[23] His philosophy of science is characterized by its stress on operational definitions, particularly that of mass, and its consequent rejection of Newton's absolute space and time; its view of science as a means of economizing human thought; its substitution of the notion of functional dependence for that of causal explanation; and its emphasis on sense data as the immediate object of the scientist's consideration.[24]

The last-mentioned characteristic serves as a key to the understanding of Mach's phenomenalism. Since the object of science is human sensation and exclusively that, for Mach it is a mistake to speak of objects or things existing independently of man's sense impressions. "Nature is composed of sensations as its elements," not, as taught by traditional epistemologists, of things. "The thing is an abstraction, the name a symbol, for a compound of elements from whose changes we abstract." [25] As a consequence:

> Sensations are not signs of things; but, on the contrary, a thing is a thought-symbol for a compound sensation of

> relative fixedness. Properly speaking the world is not composed of "things" as its elements, but of colors, tones, pressures, spaces, times, in short what we ordinarily call individual sensations.[26]

Consistent with this view, Mach states that the task of science is to analyze human sensations and to organize them into some type of synthesis. Its aim is not theoretical, for the object of science is not to inquire into the causes or meanings of phenomena or to supply explanations for them; rather its end is purely practical, to enable man to adapt himself, with a maximum economy of thought and effort, to the conditions producing the sensations he experiences. "The whole operation," as he summarizes it, "is a mere affair of economy." [27]

It is in such a context that Mach gives his account of the notions of cause and effect:

> In speaking of cause and effect we arbitrarily give relief to those elements to whose connection we have to attend in the reproduction of a fact in the respect in which it is important to us. There is no cause nor effect in nature; nature has but an individual existence; nature simply *is*. Recurrences of like cases in which A is always connected with B, that is, like results under like circumstances, that is again, the essence of the connection of cause and effect, exist but in the abstraction which we perform for the purpose of mentally reproducing the facts. Let a fact become familiar, and we no longer require this putting into relief of its connecting marks, our attention is no longer attracted to the new and surprising, and we cease to speak of cause and effect.[28]

Somewhat like Hume, therefore, Mach sees causal connection as a type of psychological projection into reality arising from man's need to economize his thought. "The ideas of cause and effect originally sprang from an endeavor to reproduce facts in thought." [29] Mach admits that an individual's assurance of the validity of causal concepts is probably associated with his own voluntary movements and the changes they produce externally, but he also sees society and culture as instrumental in their development. In the final analysis, however, cause and effect are things of thought, having an economical office. It cannot be said *why* they arise. For it is precisely by the abstraction of uniformities that we know the question "why." [30]

Mach then inserts at this point an explanatory footnote wherein he affirms his preference for the notion of functional dependence over that of causality:

> The notion of cause possesses significance only as a means of provisional knowledge or orientation. In any exact and profound investigation of an event, the inquirer must regard the phenomena as dependent on one another in the same way that the geometer regards the sides and angles of a triangle as dependent on one another. He will constantly keep before his mind, in this way, all the conditions of fact. [31]

It is this notion of dependence, moreover, that Mach regards as his essential contribution to the epistemology of science, and which he claims as one of his earliest discoveries:

> In a lecture delivered in 1871, I outlined my epistemological point of view in natural science generally, and with special exactness for physics. The concept of cause is replaced there by the concept of function; the determining of the dependence of phenomena on one another, the economic exposition of actual facts, is proclaimed as the object, and physical concepts as a means to an end solely. [32]

Mach thought to avoid the causal connotations of Newton's force concepts by revising the definitions and laws of motion and by constructing a more systematic mechanics on observable phenomena such as accelerations. In particular, he proposed to eliminate Newton's definition of mass as "quantity of matter" (apparently because of its atomistic implications), and would redefine it operationally as "a special and distinct property determinative of accelerations." [33] Mach's revised definition reads:

> All those bodies are bodies of equal mass which, mutually acting on each other, produce in each other equal and opposite accelerations. [34]

Similarly, in place of Newton's other definitions and his laws of motion, Mach would substitute the following:

> a. *Experimental Proposition.* Bodies set opposite each other induce in each other, under certain circumstances to be specified by experimental physics, contrary *accelerations* in the direction of their line of junction. (The principle of inertia is included in this).
> b. *Definition.* The mass-ratio of any two bodies is the negative inverse ratio of the mutually induced accelerations of those bodies.
> c. *Experimental Proposition.* The mass-ratios of bodies are independent of the character of the physical states (of the bodies) that condition the mutual accelerations produced, be those states electrical, magnetic, or what not; and they remain, moreover, the same, whether they are mediately or immediately arrived at.
> d. *Experimental Proposition.* The accelerations which any number of bodies A, B, C . . . induce in a body K, are independent of each other. (The principle of the parallelogram of forces follows immediately from this).
> e. *Definition.* Moving force is the product of the mass-value of a body into the acceleration induced in that body.[35]

Mach concedes that to these principles a few "arbitrary definitions" should be added, although in his view they are not strictly indispensable. With regard to the propositions themselves, however, he is quite satisfied that they meet all of the demands of his epistemology:

> The propositions above set forth satisfy the requirements of simplicity and parsimony which, on economico-scientific grounds, must be exacted of them. They are, moreover, obvious and clear; for no doubt can exist with respect to any of them either concerning its meaning or its source; and we always know whether it asserts an experience or an arbitrary convention.[36]

Despite this avowal, strangely reminiscent of typically Cartesian and rationalist statements of the seventeenth century, and despite the fact that Mach's axiomatization of mechanics is now generally regarded as a viable alternative to Newton's, the principles on which it is based seem vulnerable to many of the criticisms that have been directed against the radically empiricist philosophies of Hume and Mill. It is difficult to see, moreover, how Mach's statements that "bodies of equal mass . . . *produce in each other* equal and opposite accelerations," or "bodies set opposite each other *induce in each other* . . . contrary accelerations," do not implicitly invoke the very notion of causal efficacy he rejects, or how, even according to his own canons, any of his propositions fall uniquely into the category of experienced fact or arbitrary convention.[37]

Mach's use of the notion of convention nonetheless impressed many of his contemporaries, and was not without its effect on the French mathematician, Henri Poincaré, whose philosophy of science is itself generally characterized as conventionalism.[38] Influenced also by Émile Boutroux, Poincaré, somewhat like Jevons, was suspicious of attempts to confer absolute value on science's results, particularly when these would be used to predict the future. He felt that any explanation in vogue at a given time must ultimately give way to a better explanation. While admitting that scientists often speak of their theories as true, he preferred to regard them as merely convenient. Their value is not in the order of truth but in that of utility: they simplify the work of scientists — and here Poincaré's debt to Mach is obvious — and they furnish an aesthetic picture of the universe. The subject matter of science, however, is neither sensations nor things, but rather relations between things; these are knowable by intuition whereas things in themselves are not. Thus Poincaré's epistemological views were not as radical as Mach's but were more akin to those of Kant. He presupposed, for example, an underlying orderliness and rationality in the universe, although this for him was a matter of belief rather than of certain knowledge.

In working out his philosophy of science Poincaré proposed a distinction between sciences that are merely rational and those that are empirico-rational.[39] The merely rational sciences, the paradigm of which is mathematics, are for him free constructions of the human mind; the role of experience is completely extrinsic to their development, merely suggesting possibilities to them and providing instances for their application. The objects of such sciences are beings of reason.

The relationships that obtain among these objects are expressed by axioms; these are postulated as conventions and implicitly define the objects and their properties. Yet they are not completely arbitrary, for they must avoid internal contradiction and be at least convenient, i.e., simple and adapted to the properties of the bodies with which they deal. The empirico-rational sciences, on the other hand, are concerned with the objects of experience, with entities in the real world. Knowledge is attained in such sciences mainly by the discovery of laws that govern as many different facts as possible. Experience provides these single facts, and the human mind uses them to ascend to the universal order by employing principles that are essentially conventional, and thus not determined either by the nature of things or by the mind's own laws of thought. Much of its work is done through the construction of hypotheses, and these, Poincaré again insists, are not merely arbitrary since they must agree both with experience and with experimental laws. Yet they are selected by "free convention," inasmuch as a great number of different possibilities may be thought of to explain the same facts. For this reason, hypotheses (like theories) should not be said to be true or false, but more or less "suited" to describing phenomena.

An obvious difficulty that presented itself to both Mach's and Poincaré's accounts of hypotheses was that of deciding between the Ptolemaic and the Copernican views of the earth's position and movement in the universe. If hypotheses are neither true nor false, it would seem that one could still entertain the Ptolemaic world view without being accused of error. Mach considered this problem, and seemingly endorsed the astronomical arguments for the earth's rotation we have seen elaborated by Herschel, while rejecting that this must be an "absolute rotation," i.e., one taking place in Newton's "absolute space." [40] Mach's explanation of his own position is not completely clear, but it is set forth in the following passage:

> . . . if we take our stand on the basis of facts, we shall find we have knowledge only of relative spaces and motions. Relatively, not considering the unknown and neglected medium of space, the motions of the universe are

the same whether we adopt the Ptolemaic or the Copernican mode of view. Both views are, indeed, equally correct; only the latter is more simple and more practical. The universe is not twice given, with an earth at rest and an earth in motion; but only once, with its relative motions, alone determinable. It is, accordingly, not permitted us to say how things would be if the earth did not rotate. We may interpret the one case that is given us, in different ways. If, however, we so interpret it that we come into conflict with experience, our interpretation is simply wrong. The principles of mechanics can, indeed, be so conceived that even for relative rotations centrifugal forces arise.[41]

The expression "centrifugal forces" in the last sentence refers to the explanatory factors that Herschel and others invoked to account for phenomena associated with the earth's rotation, such as its assumption of an oblate form, the diminution of the acceleration of gravity at its equator, and the rotation of the plane of a Foucault pendulum swinging on its surface.[42] Apparently Mach would like to believe on the basis of such evidence that the earth somehow rotates, but his principles do not allow him to say that Ptolemy's hypothesis is "simply wrong," and thus he makes his decision between the competing views merely on the basis of simplicity and practicality.

Poincaré found himself in much the same quandary, made more acute by the fact that a contemporary, Édouard Le Roy, was interpreting his teaching to mean that the scientist can never attain truth, that he is always dealing with systematized fictions or arbitrary conventions, and that even the so-called facts of science are arbitrary or conventional in character. Among such facts Le Roy listed the earth's rotation, and on this matter Poincaré felt obliged to remonstrate against him and explain more fully his own position vis-à-vis the Ptolemic and Copernican hypotheses.

In his *Science and Hypothesis* (1902), Poincaré had stated that the proposition, "the earth turns round," has no meaning in the sense that it is not capable of experimental verification.[43] Then, rephrasing his thought, he had immediately added: "or rather these two propositions, 'the earth turns round' and 'it is more convenient to suppose that the earth turns round,' have one and the same meaning." Three years later, in *The Value of Science,* Poincaré complained about the interpretations placed on this passage, particularly in the light of the historical Ptolemaic-Copernican controversy and the resulting condemnation of Galileo.[44] By way of clarification, Poincaré drew a comparison between the propositions, "the earth turns round" and "the external world exists." If one were to assert that the propositions, "the external world exists" and "it is more convenient to suppose that the external world exists," have one and the same meaning, then "the hypothesis of the rotation of the earth would have the same degree of certitude as the existence of external objects." [45] Developing this line of thought, and embellishing it further with his thesis that a physical theory "is more true as it puts in evidence more true relations," Poincaré proceeded to give his considered judgment on the subject of the earth's rotation:

> No, there is no absolute space; these two contradictory propositions: "the earth turns round" and "the earth does not turn round" are, therefore, neither of them more true than the other. To affirm one while denying the other, *in the kinematic sense,* would be to admit the existence of absolute space. But if the one reveals true relations that the other hides from us, we can nevertheless regard it as physically more true than the other, since it has a richer content. Now in this regard no doubt is possible.[46]

Here Poincaré enumerates all the phenomena that had been adduced by Herschel and others to prove the earth's rotation, and admits that "for the Ptolemaist all these phenomena have no bond between them; for the Copernican they are produced by the one same cause." [47] Focusing, however, not on the conclusion of the reasoning but on what he regards as the truth of the relationships between the phenomena, Poincaré goes on:

> In saying, the earth turns round, I affirm that all these phenomena have an intimate relation, and *that is true,* and that remains true, although there is not and can not be absolute space.[48]

He then digresses from the question of the earth's rotation to that of its revolution around the sun, and lists the three phenomena that seem to justify such a revolution, viz., the apparent displacements of the planets on the celestial sphere, the aberration of the fixed stars, and the parallax of these same stars. He thereupon inquires whether these phenomena occur simply "by chance," in the sense that they are totally unrelated, and again replies:

> To adopt Ptolemy's system is to answer, yes; to adopt that of Copernicus is to answer, no; this is to affirm that there is a bond between the three phenomena, and that also is true, although there is no absolute space.[49]

Summing up the result to which he has finally come in answering the difficulty proposed by Le Roy, Poincaré concludes:

> In Ptolemy's system, the motions of the heavenly bodies cannot be explained by the action of central forces; celestial mechanics is impossible. The intimate relations that celestial mechanics reveals to us between all the celestial phenomena are true relations; to affirm the immobility of the earth would deny these relations, that would be to fool ourselves. The truth for which Galileo suffered remains, therefore, the truth, although it has not altogether the same meaning as for the vulgar, and its true meaning is much more subtle, more profound and more rich.[50]

Subtle indeed it is, for one can well wonder what kind of "truth" this is that is really only "more convenient" than its denial, and at ground seems based only on a convention that makes celestial mechanics possible.

Although himself neither a phenomenalist nor a conventionalist, Pierre Duhem is frequently grouped with Mach and Poincaré, and with good reason, for he was able to propose a clever way out of their quandary by banishing causal explanation from the realm of science altogether. An extremely able historian of science and a promising physicist as well, Duhem in his studies had covered much the same ground as ourselves in the two volumes thus far.[51] He too had noted the long search for causes throughout the medieval, Renaissance, and early modern periods, the seemingly endless controversies over "true causes" and "occult causes," and the constant intrusion of what he regarded as metaphysical considerations into the deliberations of scientists. Somewhat like Kant, moreover, Duhem was upset over the lack of agreement among metaphysicians, over the changing fashions that produced such variations in the explanations scientists were willing to accept, and over the resulting turmoil in the scientific community. The solution he proposed for all this was simple but radical: following Comte, he would banish causes, explanations, and all matters relating to truth and reality from science, and make it completely "positive" in the Comtean sense. His would be the supreme convention, wherein science itself would be conventionalized to prohibit henceforth all of the embarrassing questioning that has resulted only in controversy throughout its long history.

Duhem's own philosophy is best seen in his evaluation of the aim and structure of physical theory.[52] Many philosophers, he admits, would maintain that a physical theory has for its object the explanation of a group of laws experimentally established, either to guarantee their certainty, as acoustical theories seem to do, or else to provide plausible accounts of phenomena, and thus serve more modestly as hypothetical explanations.[53] In either case, because of the very explanation used, physics becomes subordinate to metaphysics and the value of the particular theory becomes dependent on the metaphysical system adopted.[54] So Duhem asserts:

> When we regard a physical theory as a hypothetical explanation of material reality, we make it dependent on metaphysics. In that way, far from giving it a form to which the greatest number of minds can give their assent, we limit its acceptance to those who acknowledge the philosophy it insists on.[55]

The simplest way he sees to avoid this undesirable consequence is to formulate a different aim for physical theory that will enable it to be "autonomous," in the sense of being free of any metaphysical commitments. This he does by denying the theory's explanatory character:

> A physical theory is not an explanation. It is a system of mathematical propositions, deduced from a small number

of principles, which aim to represent as simply, as completely, and as exactly as possible a set of experimental laws.[56]

Under this formulation the problem of truth is no longer one of judging conformity with reality, but becomes simply a matter of agreement with experimental laws:

> Thus a true theory is not a theory which gives an explanation of physical appearances in conformity with reality; it is a theory which represents in a satisfactory manner a group of experimental laws. A false theory is not an attempt at an explanation based on assumptions contrary to reality; it is a group of propositions which do not agree with the experimental laws. Agreement with experiment is the sole criterion of truth for a physical theory.[57]

Even experimental laws, however, do not attain truth in the same manner as do "the laws of common sense." So Duhem elaborates:

> The laws that ordinary non-scientific experience allow us to formulate are general judgments whose meaning is immediate. In the presence of one of these judgments we may ask, "Is it true?" Often the answer is easy; in any case the answer is a definite yes or no. The law recognized as true is so for all time and for all men; it is fixed and absolute.
>
> Scientific laws based on the experiments of physics are symbolic relations whose meaning would remain unintelligible to anyone who did not know physical theories. Since they are symbolic, they are never true or false; like the experiments on which they rest, they are approximate. The degree of approximation of a law, though sufficient today, will become insufficient in the future through the progress of experimental methods. . . . It is provisional also in that it does not connect realities but symbols, and that is because there are always cases where the symbol no longer corresponds to the reality; the laws of physics cannot be maintained except by continual retouching and modification.[58]

From these brief indications it may be seen that, for Duhem, scientific propositions, whether these be laws or theories, provide only a provisional or schematic knowledge of reality. Their function is essentially symbolic; they do not explain phenomena, they merely represent or symbolize them.[59] Unlike Mach, however, and more in sympathy with Poincaré, Duhem did not deny a physical reality and an ontological order, and in fact asserted that science in its progress more and more approaches knowledge of these:

> Thus, physical theory never gives us the explanation of experimental laws; it never reveals realities hiding under the sensible appearances; but the more complete it becomes, the more we apprehend that the logical order in which theory arranges experimental laws is the reflection of an ontological order, the more we suspect that the relations it establishes among the data of observation correspond to real relations among things, and the more we feel that theory tends to be a natural classification.[60]

Such a conviction, nonetheless, Duhem did not regard as a part of physics. This was for him a type of belief, even akin to a religious belief, which was in no way essential to the nature or practice of physical science.[61] And if such claims for explanation and reality are made to pass out of physics, causality and all of the problems it poses go with them. Thus did Duhem, in his well-intentioned way, put his seal of approval on Mach's sensationalism and Poincaré's conventionalism. His proposal for a sharp line of demarcation between science and philosophy found many supporters, particularly among Catholics, who welcomed this clearcut way of keeping the domain of *philosophia perennis* intact against the encroachments of scientists.[62] Less acceptable were his strictures on what science must or must not do to the new generation of physicists who, even as Duhem was propounding his views, were already wrestling with relativity and would soon be faced with the profound enigmas of quantum mechanics. Their reaction notwithstanding, however, the general thrust of Duhem's critique can only be regarded as antimetaphysical and anticausal, and thus as contributing substantially to the decline of causality in modern science.

c. Logical Positivism

The foregoing discussion of the earth's rotation, with its brief indication of problems of logical consistency and mathematical foundations, in this case relating to the concept of space, hints at the next direction to be taken in discussions of scientific methodology. This saw a burgeoning of interest in mathematical logic and the application of techniques that had proved helpful in clarifying the fundamental concepts of arithmetic and geometry to similar problems in the physical sciences. The center for much of this work was Vienna, where, under the inspiration of Mach, a group of philosopher-scientists collectively identified as the *Wiener Kreis* addressed themselves to these problems. The movement is usually known as logical positivism, a label that correctly reflects its antimetaphysical attitude and its faith in radical empiricism as well as its program for developing a "scientific philosophy" based essentially on formal logic. Later, as the group dispersed under political pressures prior to World War II, the interests of its members broadened, and they became the leaders of the philosophy of science movement in Britain and the United States.[63]

Apart from the empirio-criticism of Mach, the *Wiener Kreis* was markedly influenced by Bertrand Russell's work on the logical foundations of mathematics and by the *Tractatus Logico-Philosophicus* of Ludwig Wittgenstein, who was partially inspired by Russell. Russell's attitude toward causality is somewhat caricatured in his oft-quoted dictum: "The law of causality, I believe, like much that passes among philosophers, is a relic of a by-gone age, surviving like the monarchy, only because it is erroneously supposed to do no harm." [64] Actually Russell's analyses of causality, and particularly its changing status with developments in science throughout his long career, was far more nuanced than this statement indicates. In fact the frequent changes in Russell's philosophy, and particularly his attitude toward the role of causality in man's knowledge of the external world, arose precisely from his attempts to stay abreast of scientific developments and to incorporate these into his own thought.[65] Generally he subscribed to the Humean account of causation, and within this framework concentrated on delineating the differences between common or prescientific usage of the term "cause" and the ways it had come to be understood in classical, relativity, statistical, and quantum physics.[66]

Russell's influence aside, the founder and guiding spirit

behind the *Wiener Kreis* was Moritz Schlick, who succeeded Mach and Boltzmann as professor of the philosophy of inductive science at the University of Vienna. Like Duhem, Schlick was completely unimpressed with the metaphysics of his day, but at the same time was unprepared to accept either Poincaré's conventionalism or Duhem's interdiction of inquiry into the meaning of, and the reality behind, the scientist's symbolic formulations.[67] Rather he saw the object of science to be the attainment "of knowledge concerning all natural events and processes," and this would consist in the formulation "of the most general propositions, as well as an examination of the truth of the hypotheses," whereas the task of philosophy would be "to interpret the meaning of the propositions of natural science."[68] The result at which Schlick aimed was not to develop a new system of philosophy but only to inaugurate a new, scientific way of philosophizing. Since metaphysics, understood in the Hegelian sense, was still anathema, philosophy for him would be identified with "the philosophy of nature," and insofar as science had proved itself to be the only legitimate way of studying nature, philosophy of nature would become essentially the philosophy of science.

Schlick's debt to Mach may be seen, first of all, from the way in which he speaks of cause and effect as events that are functionally related — in the case of laws of nature in terms of mathematical relationships that generally take the form of differential equations:

> The principle of causality, as usually formulated, states that every event is the effect of a cause. The content of the concepts cause and effect cannot be strictly transcribed because natural events cannot be isolated. Hence the words "cause" and "effect" do not occur at all in the laws of nature; instead, we have the interconnection of events expressed by mathematical functions. Every event is interpreted as a change of state; every state is characterized by certain magnitudes, and every law of nature states a relation between these changes in magnitude which describes various events. The changes in magnitude, whenever possible, are assumed to be infinitely small, in which case natural laws are expressed in the form of differential equations.[69]

Explaining the consequences of this way of looking at causality, Schlick admits that it introduces a type of determinism where "the past-future direction has no preferred role in comparison with the future-past direction," which is to say that prediction and retrodiction on the basis of such laws become equivalent.[70] Schlick saw this determinism as implying some type of real connection between cause and effect but, like Russell, he followed Hume in maintaining that the search for any "causal link" is meaningless:

> . . . it is exactly the same whether we say that the past determines the future or the future determines the past. But what does the word "determine" mean? The meaning of both the principle of causality and determinism depends on just this. The causal determination of one event by another is without doubt a real connection between the two; but this only means that between the two, other dependent events can always be discovered. Nevertheless, we must agree with Hume in maintaining that the search for a causal link, or cement of some kind between two events, is a meaningless one.[71]

Because of this Humean commitment, Schlick was forced to see in the principle of causality nothing more than a statement of regularity of sequence among events, and this in turn as equivalent to a natural law statement. Thus, for him, the question of causality's existence became equivalent to that of natural law's existence:

> The inquiry as to whether causality exists can only be interpreted as the inquiry whether a natural law exists. The principle of causality itself is not a law; it only expresses the fact that laws exist.[72]

Despite this implicit admission of causality's existence, Schlick saw insuperable logical difficulties in attempts to formulate a principle of causality, and was content to leave justifications of such a principle at the purely pragmatic level:

> As a matter of fact, the fulfillment of predictions is always the decisive criterion for the existence of causality; it is, however, of a purely practical nature and thus not suitable for a logical formulation of the principle of causality.[73]

Consistent with the foregoing, Schlick held that classical physics is deterministic. The introduction of statistical and probability considerations, for him, did not affect this basic evaluation. Whereas in classical physics, however, causality is viewed as involving a one-to-one relation, Schlick would see statistical reasoning as involving a many-to-one relation, wherein several different events are regarded as effects of the one event viewed as cause. Using this way of analyzing problems in thermodynamics, he was able to show how the law of entropy and the irreversibility of natural processes could still be based on causal concepts. With regard to quantum theory, on the other hand, Schlick was convinced that Heisenberg's uncertainty principle had effectively ruled out causal reasoning at the microlevel. As a consequence of the uncertainty relation, he writes:

> . . . it is impossible to say that the state of a system can ever be accurately determined by measurement. But since a determination of this kind is a prerequisite for the strict application of the principle of causality, it follows that modern science must renounce the exact truth of this principle and be satisfied with predictions that have probability. Science is thus no longer deterministic in character.[74]

Another concern of Schlick, also traceable to Mach, was what he regarded as the mistaken identification of causes with forces. Schlick admitted that, even in his day, there were those who regarded forces as the "real causes of natural events," and this on the basis of the muscular effort that human beings experience when they attempt to set bodies in motion.[75] He sided with Mach, however, in holding that anthropomorphic conceptions such as these, "however easily they may be explained as due to the origin of the concept of force, have nothing to do with physics." [76] He discussed also the changing status of force concepts with the rise of field theories, maintaining that, while "we must not regard the 'forces' as in any sense causes," they are "the expression, nevertheless, of a regularity of the causal process." [77]

Although not an original member of the *Wiener Kreis*, Hans Reichenbach had interests similar to Schlick's and wrote extensively on the problem of causality in modern science, particularly on the changes of causal concepts occasioned by developments in statistical and quantum physics. Like Schlick he saw no reason to reject causality because of the use of probability notions, although he could not accept the truth of principles of causality on an a priori basis, conceding such principles only the status of empirical hypotheses.[78] Causal reasoning could be used in the macroscopic realm, he reasoned, even though it might not hold true at the microlevel, whenever the law of large numbers would effectively transform the probable character of microphenomena into the practical certainty of statistical regularities or laws. Reichenbach took this position even before the promulgation of the uncertainty principle, and regarded his reasoning as vindicated by Heisenberg's discovery.[79] With the enunciation of the uncertainty principle, however, he became further convinced that the existence of causal laws underlying statistical regularities would never be capable of verification, and thus, consistent with the verifiability theory of meaning, would become physically meaningless.[80] Yet, despite this conviction, he remained interested in conserving, and rendering as consistent as possible, the use of causal terminology in the quantum domain. Taking inspiration from Rudolf Carnap, who had proposed the construction of formal languages that would be capable of anomaly-free interpretations, Reichenbach set about interpreting quantum phenomena in terms of a three-valued logic, wherein the normal values of truth and falsity would be implemented by a third, intermediate value which he designated as indeterminacy.[81] Reichenbach envisaged a quantum-mechanical language based on this logic that would avoid the wave-particle dilemmas — a type of *tertium quid* between a wave language and a particle language whose chief merit would consist in its elimination of causal anomalies. As he explains it:

> Quantum mechanical language can be formulated in different versions; we use in particular three versions: the corpuscle language, the wave language, and a neutral language. All three of these languages concern phenomena and interphenomena, but each of them shows a characteristic deficiency. Both the corpuscle language and the wave language show a deficiency so far as they

include statements of causal anomalies, which occur in places not corresponding to each other and therefore can be transformed away, for every physical problem, by choosing a suitable one of the two languages. The neutral language is neither a corpuscle language nor a wave language, and thus does not include statements expressing causal anomalies. The deficiency reappears here, however, through the fact that the neutral language is three-valued; statements about interphenomena obtain the truth value "indeterminate." [82]

The deficiencies in all three languages, in Reichenbach's analysis, arise ultimately from the fact that each is based on the world of ordinary experience, whereas they are being used to describe "the structure of the atomic world, which thus is recognized as intrinsically different from the macro-world, and likewise from the atomic world which classical physics had imagined." [83]

On the basis of reasoning of this type, Reichenbach felt justified in maintaining that probability is more fundamental than causality at the microlevel, and thus can provide a more ultimate explanation of natural processes. In this sense, it can be said that he, like Waismann, saw the decline of causality in probability notions and its decisive fall with the rise of quantum physics. Not all those with positivist leanings, however, came to such a radical conclusion. Richard von Mises, for example, protested against the opinion being expressed in his day that positivism had brought about the destruction of causality.[84] Even more objectionable, in Mises's view, was the allegation that positivists were actually suppressing thought by prohibiting "the search for the *true* causes of the individual occurrences in nature in all fields where a statistical theory is proposed." [85] He would prefer to hold for a less apodictic statement along the following lines:

> The causal concept of everyday life, or better, the causal expressions of everyday language, have not been banished from contemporary physics (they have always played a much less important role in the theoretical structure than one is inclined to think). Only the precise form of deterministic physics (of differential equations) has proved to be too narrow, and a supplementation by other means has become necessary.[86]

On the other hand, true to the principles of his scientific philosophy, Mises would insist that "the vague and changeable causality concept of everyday life" can never be normative in the formulation of "exact scientific theories." [87]

d. Operationalism and the Copenhagen School

The rise of the new physics, and particularly the philosophical problems posed by developments within quantum theory, thus led to a questioning of causality's status as a fundamental category of scientific explanation. As may be seen from the foregoing, however, the rejection of causal reasoning was not as complete as popularizations of the effect of physics on philosophy have suggested. Apart from the writings of conventionalists and positivists, this impression was probably strengthened by another line of thought known as operationalism, which was not without its influence on the Copenhagen School and its interpretation of quantum mechanics. Thus, to complete our account of "the decline and fall of causality," something should be said about these remaining movements and the attitudes they engendered toward causality.

Operationalism is the term usually applied to the thought of Percy W. Bridgman, a distinguished physicist and Nobel prize winner, who also addressed himself to problems in the epistemology of physics. Bridgman explicitly acknowledged his debt to Stallo, Mach, and Poincaré, while avowing that the fundamental attitude behind his work, in epistemology as in experimental physics, was that of empiricism.[88] The label attached to his thought comes from his proposal to identify any physical concept with the set of operations used to define or measure it. As he put it:

> In general, we mean by any concept nothing more than a set of operations; the concept is synonymous with the corresponding set of operations. If the concept is physical, as of length, the operations are actual physical operations, namely, those by which length is measured; or if the concept is mental, as of mathematical continuity, the operations are mental operations, namely those by which we determine whether a given aggregate of magnitudes is continuous.[89]

This mode of operational definition, suggested to Bridgman by Einstein's handling of the concept of simultaneity in his special theory of relativity, he proposed to generalize and extend to all the concepts of physical science. The advantages Bridgman saw in developing such a method would include its commitment to a pure empiricism, unimpeded by any a priori principles that would determine or limit the possibilities of new experience; the clarity and distinctness of definitions given in terms of unique sets of physical operations; and the grounding of concepts in actual experience in a way that would be valid only for the experimental range in which they had been verified, thereby eliminating the need for revision with further advances in science.[90]

Among the concepts Bridgman chose to define operationally, oddly enough, was that of causality, which he took up immediately following his treatment of space and time because of its "spatial and temporal implications."[91] The difficulties Bridgman saw in so defining causality stemmed from the fact that the definition would have to be concerned with events within a system, where such events would be themselves connected but the system sufficiently isolated so as to preclude connectivity with extraneous events. Assuming that such notions as isolation and connection could be suitably defined in terms of the behavior of the system itself, Bridgman formulated his operational definition of causality as follows:

> If now the connectivity or correlation between phenomena is of a special kind, we have a causal connection; namely, if whenever we arbitrarily impress event A on a system we find that event B always occurs, whereas if we had not impressed A, B would not have occurred, then we say that A is the cause of B, and B the effect of A. By suitably choosing the event A, we may find the effect of any event of which the system is susceptible.[92]

A typically causal connection, in his view, is the phenomenon of propagation of a mechanical disturbance, for here the spatio-temporal implications of causality are readily seen, since, "when a disturbance is propagated to a distant point, the effect follows the cause in time, as time is usually measured."[93]

It is experiences such as these, Bridgman continues, that lead us to think that the effect necessarily follows the cause, a result having for him important consequences in the special theory of relativity.[94]

Bridgman was at his best when discussing technical applications of his operational definitions, but he otherwise was quite guarded in extrapolating his results to the general case. An instance in point is his discussion of the notion of Laplacean determinism:

> The conviction, arising from experience, that the future is determined by the present and correspondingly the present by the past, is often phrased differently by saying that the present causally determines the future. This is in a certain sense a generalization of the causality concept. It is one of the principal jobs of physics to analyze this complex causal connection into components, representing as far as possible the future state of the system as the sum of independent trains of events started by each individual event of the present. How far such an analysis is possible must be decided by experiment. It is certainly possible to a very large extent in most cases, but there seems to be no reason to expect that a complete analysis is possible.[95]

Bridgman anticipated no problems with systems that could be described in terms of linear differential equations, but he did express doubt whether all the phenomena of nature could be so described. With respect to causal sequences generally, Bridgman agreed in principle that the search for their origins "is equivalent to finding the ultimate elements in a scheme of explanation." [96] He saw no theoretical difficulty with this, although he did acknowledge that it would have practical limitations arising from the fact that an operational definition of causality requires the possibility of variation within a system, and as sequences and systems become more extended such variation becomes more and more an impossibility.

Among other physical concepts, Bridgman discussed operational definitions of force and mass. Like Mach and Schlick he saw the force concept as arising "from the muscular sensations of resistance experienced from external bodies," [97] and so he first proposed a static definition of force wherein a spring balance would initially be used to replace the human muscles, and then, more generally, an elastic body whose deformation would be measurable under the force's influence. Bridgman then would extend these operational procedures to dynamic systems, considering first those isolated from all gravitational fields and only subsequently taking into account the effects of gravity. Even in the isolated laboratory in empty space, of course, he recognized that the dynamic consideration of force would require a new concept, that of mass, with which it was "entangled," but he held that it could "later be disentangled by a process of successive approximations." [98] Bridgman admitted that the resulting definition of force "is highly academic, involving as it does hypothetical experiments in laboratories situated far out in empty space." [99] This example, in fact, illustrates the difficulty encountered in attempting to restrict operational definitions to experiments that have actually been performed, and the tendency to include also imaginary or thought experiments (*Gedankenexperimenten*) in their formulation. It is interesting to note, in this connection, that Bridgman himself saw many limitations in the operational approach, and never wished to erect it into a systematic philosophy or otherwise give it the dogmatic overtones that the term "operationalism" would suggest.[100] Others, however, lured by the attractiveness of Bridgman's ideas, have explored the possibilities of converting operationism into a consistent philosophy of science.[101]

As an experimental physicist working in the area of high pressures, Bridgman was concerned mainly with the conceptual analysis of classical mechanics. The year of publication of his *Logic of Modern Physics*, however, saw also the enunciation of Heisenberg's indeterminacy principle, and thus it is not surprising that his ideas quickly found application in the quantum domain. Among the philosopher-physicists who concerned themselves with such applications, Niels Bohr and Max Born are especially noteworthy, not only for the fact that their interpretations show a kinship with Bridgman's, but also because the Copenhagen School, with which they were intimately associated, is frequently cited as having contributed to the demise of causal determinism in contemporary physics.

Heisenberg's principle, as commonly explained in textbooks of modern physics, allows for the application of classical concepts to the phenomena studied in quantum mechanics, but at the same time it defines certain limits for the measurement or quantitative determination of such concepts. For example, according to the principle, the velocity and position of a particle can never be measured simultaneously with complete accuracy; if the particle's position is accurately specified, its velocity or momentum will be left undetermined, whereas if the latter is accurately specified, the former will not be. The principle is also related to the wave-particle anomaly and the problems it raises,[102] for it specifies the limits within which one can reconcile the concept of a particle localized at a point in space and time with that of a wave field precisely determined in momentum (or energy), whose space-time extension is infinite. In the case of light, for example, there are certain phenomena that can only be explained by regarding it as corpuscular in character, whereas there are other phenomena that can only be understood by ascribing to it an undulatory or wave character. If, on the basis of such phenomena, one asserts simultaneously that light is both localized as a particle and spread out as a wave, he falls into explicit contradiction. Heisenberg's principle would eliminate such simultaneous assertions by prohibiting the precise assignation of these wave-particle determinations as mutually exclusive, while allowing both to be used concurrently, within the limits stated in the principle, in probability statements that correctly describe the observed phenomena.

Bohr's contribution to an understanding of indeterminacy was made in this setting. Using an operational approach analogous to Bridgman's, he asserted that the procedures of measurement and observation integral to the detection of the phenomena being studied must enter into the ascription of such characteristics. Attributes at the microlevel, he insisted, are at least partially defined by the measuring apparatus used to detect them, and therefore they cannot be completely ascribed unless the measuring process as a whole be taken into account. He readily admitted that, depending on the experimental situation used to observe it, light appears to have either particle or wave properties; he also saw, however, that once the conditions of observation are completely specified, the properties that are to be observed become quite predictable. Taking account of all these factors, therefore, Bohr arrived at the insight that the wave and particle aspects of light (and of matter also) are not contradictory, but complementary. This complementarity, in his words, derives from "the impossibility of any sharp separation between the behaviour of atomic objects and the interaction with the measuring instruments which serve to define the conditions under which the phenomena appear." [103] He goes on:

> In fact, the individuality of the typical quantum effects finds its proper expression in the circumstance that any attempt at subdividing the phenomena will demand a change in the experimental arrangement introducing new possibilities of interaction between objects and measuring instruments which in principle cannot be controlled. Consequently, evidence obtained under different experimental conditions cannot be comprehended within a single picture, but must be regarded as *complementary* in the sense that only the totality of the phenomena exhausts the possible information about the objects.[104]

The "principle of complementarity" enunciated in this passage hence stresses that, despite the mutual exclusivity of classical concepts when applied to the quantum domain, such concepts are indispensable for a full account of the phenomena being studied, when all of the operational procedures involved are made explicit.[105]

The precise effect of these principles of indeterminacy and complementarity on causal thinking is difficult to ascertain. Bohr himself made no extravagant claims, and indeed stated that "the viewpoint of complementarity may be regarded as a rational generalization of the very ideal of causality." [106] He did feel, however, that some revision would be called for, and that causal accounts of microphenomena would henceforth only be valid in statistical form.[107] In his view, therefore, causality and probability had come to be inseparably linked in explanations within quantum mechanics. This also was the view of Bohr's colleague, Max Born, who had contributed heavily to the formulation of the Copenhagen position, and who subsequently developed his ideas in the Waynflete Lectures given at Oxford in 1948, published under the title of *Natural Philosophy of Cause and Chance*.[108] In this work, as we will now detail, Born proposed to retain causality as integral to the scientific enterprise while at the same time denying it the status of an ultimate category, for in his analysis, chance, or probability, had been found to be more fundamental.

In Born's understanding the concept of causality is closely allied with that of determinism, although the two are not identical.[109] The characteristic note of causality is dependence, and by this Born does not mean "logical dependence" but rather the "dependence of real things of nature on one another." [110] Such dependence, moreover, need not always be conceived in a spatio-temporal way but can have an abstract, timeless character. When events are viewed as fixed in space and time, however, and when one is seen as the cause of the other, then causality implies principles of antecedence and contiguity, the first stating that the cause precedes the effect and the second that cause and effect must be in either immediate or mediate spatial contact. Compared to this, determinism is a more restricted concept involving the additional note of predictability. As Born defines it:

> Determinism postulates that events at different times are connected by laws in such a way that predictions of unknown situations (past or future) can be made.[111]

Causality, on the other hand, is to be understood only in the sense of lawlike dependence, and thus has broader scope:

> Causality postulates that there are laws by which the occurrence of an entity B of a certain class depends on the occurrence of an entity A of another class, where the word "entity" means any physical object, phenomenon, situation, or event. A is called the cause, B the effect.[112]

Only when this definition is applied to single events, adds Born, do the notions of antecedence and contiguity come to be entailed with that of causality.

It is the more general understanding of causality that undoubtedly lies behind Born's affirmations that causal explanation must remain an integral part of scientific method:

The statement, frequently made, that modern physics has
given up causality is entirely unfounded. Modern physics, it is true, has given up or modified many traditional
ideas; but it would cease to be a science if it had given
up the search for the causes of phenomena.[113]

Again, in a somewhat lengthy passage wherein he stresses the
influence of causality and the principles of antecedence and
contiguity on the development of classical physics, Born asserts that causality itself remains unaffected by the latter's
downfall and is still integral to the scientific enterprise:

Contiguity is closely bound up with the introduction of
contact forces, pressures, tensions, first in ordinary material bodies, then in the electromagnetic ether, and thus to
the idea of fields of forces; but the systematic application
of contiguity to gravitation exploded Newton's theory,
which was superseded by Einstein's relativity. Similar
was the fate of the postulate of antecedence; it is closely
bound up with irreversibility in time, and found its first
quantitative formulation in thermodynamics. The recon-
ciliation of it with Newton's laws was attempted by
atomistics and physical statistics; the idea being that ac-
cumulations of immense numbers of invisible Newtonian
particles, atoms, or molecules appear to the observer to
have the feature of irreversibility for statistical reasons.
The atoms were first hypothetical, but soon they were
taken seriously, and one began to search for them, with
increasing success. They became more and more real,
and finally even visible. And then it turned out that they
were not Newtonian particles at all. Whereupon the
whole classical physics exploded, to be replaced by
quantum theory. Looked at from the point of view of our
principles, the situation in quantum theory is reversed.
Determinism (which is so prominent a characteristic of
Newton's theory) is abandoned, but contiguity and antecedence (violated by Newton's laws) are preserved to a
considerable degree. Causality, which in my formulation
is independent of antecedence and contiguity, is not affected by these changes: scientific work will always be
the search for causal interdependence of phenomena.[114]

These statements notwithstanding, Born also wished to
leave a large part for chance to play in contemporary physics,

conceding it a yet more fundamental role than causality. He first introduced this idea in an observational context, stressing the need for probability laws even to discern cause-effect relationships:

> The first use of probability considerations in science was made by Gauss in his theory of experimental errors. . . . It has a direct bearing on the method of inference by induction which is the backbone of all human experience. I have said that in my opinion the significance of this method in science consists in the establishment of a code of rules which form the constitution of science itself. Now the curious situation arises that this code of rules, which ensures the possibility of scientific laws, in particular of the cause-effect relation, contains besides many other prescriptions those related to observational errors, a branch of the theory of probability. This shows that the conception of chance enters into the very first steps of scientific activity, in virtue of the fact that no observation is absolutely correct. I think chance is a more fundamental conception than causality; for whether in a concrete case a cause-effect relation holds or not can only be judged by applying the laws of chance to the observations.[115]

Later, Born returned to the same theme, only this time not in the context of observation but rather in that of the interpretation of the formalism of quantum theory. Here he again affirms the predominance of chance over cause:

> From the standpoint of these lectures on cause and chance it is not the formalism of quantum mechanics but its interpretation which is of importance. Yet the formalism came first, and was well secured before it became clear what it really meant: nothing more or less than a complete turning away from the predominance of cause (in the traditional sense, meaning essentially determinism) to the predominance of chance.[116]

Here, it is true, chance is held to be more fundamental than a deterministic type of causality and not a generalized type as Born has defined it. In a still later reflection, at the conclusion of the treatment of chance, even this seems called into question:

With this statement the circle of our considerations about cause and chance in physics is closed. We have seen how classical physics struggled in vain to reconcile growing quantitative observation with preconceived ideas on causality, derived from everyday experience but raised to the level of metaphysical postulates, and how it fought a losing battle against the intrusion of chance. Today the order of ideas has been reversed: chance has become the primary notion, mechanics an expression of its quantitative laws, and the overwhelming evidence of causality with all its attributes in the realm of ordinary experience is satisfactorily explained by the statistical laws of large numbers.[117]

Immediately following this, by way of confirmation, Born adds a chapter entitled "Metaphysical Conclusions" wherein he describes his considered position as the "statistical interpretation" of quantum mechanics, and wherein he cites two letters he has received from Einstein expressing the latter's disagreement with that interpretation because it invokes a "dice-playing god." [118] Born comments on the fact that in Einstein's letters the words *ich glaube* appear repeatedly, underlining the fact "that even an exact science like physics is based on fundamental beliefs." [119] Born admits that the physicist's most fundamental notions have to be accepted by an act of faith, and for him, both causality and probability are among these. So he concludes:

> Causality is such a principle, if it is defined as the belief in the existence of mutual physical dependence of observable situations. However, all specifications of this dependence in regard to space and time (contiguity, antecedence) and to the infinite sharpness of observation (determinism) seem to me not fundamental, but consequences of the actual empirical laws.

> Another metaphysical principle is incorporated in the notion of probability. It is the belief that the predictions of statistical calculations are more than an exercise of the brain, that they can be trusted in the real world. This holds just as well for ordinary probability as for the more refined mixture of probability and mechanics formulated by quantum theory.[120]

With this conclusion we must end our account of "the decline and fall of causality." [121] Is Waismann's statement, with which we opened this chapter, essentially correct? As we have now seen, it is difficult to extract such a definitive result from even the most positivist of the expositions we have recounted. And yet the impression created by current interpretations of quantum theory, and particularly those of the Copenhagen School, give credence to Waismann's analysis. Surely, after 1927, there was no longer the confidence in, and enthusiasm for, the search for causes that characterized so much of nineteenth-century science. More specifically, to sum up and hence simplify a complex situation: causal principles had ceased to be accepted as themselves certain or as the guarantors of certainty for science's results; the Laplacean identification of causality with determinism and predictability had come to be uniformly rejected; and the suspicion, indeed in many quarters the conviction, that causality could no longer function as an ultimate category of explanation and would have to be replaced by chance or probability was being voiced by many distinguished philosophers of science. Yet, in spite of all this, the notion of causality was itself still viable and its use in scientific reasoning would continue to be discussed, as we are now about to see.

2. *The Concern With Explanation*

Attention has just been drawn to the questioning of causal explanation as the ultimate to which science can attain. The long-standing association of explanation with causality implied by such questioning continued to be recognized in the early part of the twentieth century. The two concepts were, in fact, never completely disassociated; what did happen was that they were gradually seen as not convertible, with the result that, as restrictions were placed on the causal concept, the notion of explanation was broadened to include types other than causal explanation. Yet there were some, as already noted, who denied any explanatory value whatever to the laws and theories of science; just as they would withdraw truth and causality from the scientist's purview, so they would prohibit him from offering any explanations of physical reality. Although such thinkers were in the minority, they were sufficiently vocal to gain a hearing and, somewhat paradoxically, by this very circumstance provoked a reaction against their extreme position.

It is such a reaction, centering around the notion of explanation, that will occupy us in this and the following section.[122] In the present section we shall be concerned with those who subscribed to the weaker, Humean notion of causation, whereas in the following, the emphasis will be on attempts to go beyond Hume and make stronger claims in terms of causal efficacy. The aim of the exposition will be to show the extent to which the concentration on explanation has led to a progressive reinstatement of causality among recent philosophers of science; first in the context of the explanatory value of scientific theories and laws, then in the broader context of answers to the question "Why?," and finally in terms of more basic commitments that would again concede some type of ultimacy to causal explanations.

a. Theories as Explanations

At a time when Stallo, Mach, Poincaré, and Duhem were retrenching on the ontological claims of their predecessors, denying truth or falsity to laws and hypotheses, insisting on the "economic" or "symbolic" value of scientific knowledge generally, and telling scientists that they need no longer be concerned with explanations, it would take a strong personality to rise against them and assert a firm *sed contra*. Such personalities have not been lacking in any period of science's history, and the early twentieth century proved no exception. The protagonist here was Norman Robert Campbell, an English physicist who was concerned from 1904 onward with the foundations of science, and who published his definitive study of this subject shortly after World War I.[123] Like many experimental scientists, Campbell does not fit readily into any philosophical school or category; he probably would have resented being called a metaphysician, and he surely did not think that causality was the answer to the scientist's difficulties. He did, however, express a strong conviction that scientific knowledge had to be explanatory in character, and that the strength of its explanations would reside, not in its laws, but in its theories. The distinctive note of Campbell's thesis is summed up in the epigram, written in Greek, with which he began his classic: "It is not the facts, but the explanation of them, that matters."

Like Jevons, Campbell disagreed with Mill's use of causality to justify induction; unlike him, he had no respect for the great English methodologist, ridiculing him as "an awful warning to those who would pronounce sweeping judgments about science without studying it themselves," [124] and again as someone who "never knew a law when he saw one" [125] and "whose views are often suggestive just because they are erroneous." [126] On the other hand, Campbell held Mach and Poincaré in high regard, and indeed located his own writing in the same genre as theirs, while noting that they were not physicists but "mathematicians by profession," hence disagreeing with their views on the role of explanation in physics.[127] Mach's doctrine that the object of science is to attain "economy of thought," in particular, he found "utterly intolerable." His rejection of this is forthright and unequivocal:

> The best way to attain economy of thought, a way only too successfully followed by the vast majority of mankind, is not to think at all. Science is a branch of pure learning; thought is its object. To engage in science in order not to think would be as sensible as to engage in commerce in order not to make money.[128]

Campbell was well acquainted with the ideas of Bertrand Russell, whom he also admired, while again disagreeing with his emphasis on logic as important for clarifying science's methodology. So he observed that

> . . . the province and power of logic have been very greatly extended in recent years, but some of its essential features . . . have remained unchanged; and any process of thought which does not show those features is still illogical. But illogical is not synonymous with erroneous. I believe that all important scientific thought is illogical, and that we shall be led into nothing but error if we try to force scientific reasoning into the forms prescribed by logical canons.[129]

With regard to philosophy and metaphysics, on the other hand, and particularly the latter's concern with problems of reality and existence, Campbell showed himself more sympathetic. While recognizing that many scientists of his day were antimetaphysical, he nonetheless argued:

> If it is found that propositions and conceptions which are distinctively scientific are based on other propositions and conceptions and derive from them their truth and significance, then, even though some people choose to term them metaphysical and not scientific, it remains the fact that these other propositions are essential to science.[130]

And again:

> . . . we are all metaphysicians, physicists included. We are all interested in problems which the metaphysician attempts to solve. . . . The world is not divided into those who do and those who do not hold metaphysical doctrines, but rather into those who hold them for some reason and those who hold them for none.[131]

Despite such declarations of interrelation between science and philosophy, Campbell pursued a course somewhat like Duhem's wherein he attempted to keep their provinces separate and distinct. This is clear in his remarks concerning their respective attitudes toward reality, existence, and truth — terms, he holds, which have quite different meanings for the scientist and for the philosopher — and it is also discernible in his treatment of causality. Campbell did not deny the existence of cause and effect, and even conceded that scientists employ "propositions, which may be regarded as laws, which do state undeniable relations of cause and effect." [132] On the other hand, he maintained that most scientific laws do not assert causal relations, and moreover

> that such relations are by no means essential to science and that they play a much less important part in it than is often imagined. So little is it our object to order our external judgments in terms of cause and effect that our efforts are consistently directed to ridding ourselves of the necessity for employing cause and effect at all.[133]

Campbell was a firm believer in induction, however, and although he rejected Mill's canons and their dependence on the law of causation, admitted that they could lead to the discovery of "particular causes." [134] Again, when discussing probability, he found it convenient not only to treat of the "probability of events" but also of the "probability of causes." [135] Thus, while far from the mentality of Herschel and Whewell, basically he was no more anticausal than he was antimetaphysical in his attitudes.

What is distinctive about Campbell's teaching, however, is his emphasis on the role of theories in science, and particularly their explanatory character. A theory, as he conceived it, is made up of two components: a set of propositions, which he termed "the hypothesis," that considered in itself is incapable of proof or disproof; and another set of propositions, which he called "the dictionary," that relates the terms of the hypothesis to scientific laws, the latter being true or false. Using these components, Campbell proposed a striking illustration of the explanatory power of a theory by considering alternate ways of deducing known scientific laws. First he took the law that the resistance of a metal is directly proportional to its temperature, constructed a formal system of mathematical propositions from which this could be deduced, spelling out in detail its hypothesis and dictionary, and thereby offered a rigorously correct account of the experimental law. In contrast to that procedure, he then took the kinetic theory of gases, as maligned by Stallo, again spelled out its hypothesis and dictionary, and showed how it could be used to explain Boyle's and Gay-Lussac's gas laws. The first example Campbell regarded as trivial and valueless: admittedly it presented a logical structure for deducing a law, and yet it had no explanatory power whatsoever. The second he regarded as the correct ideal of a theory, insofar as it provided an analogy in terms of which the mechanisms behind the gas laws could be visualized and thus understood. In Campbell's view, a theory must provide an analogy or a model, not necessarily mechanical, for otherwise it will not explain. A purely formal system does not satisfy this requirement:

> Any fool can invent a logically satisfactory theory to explain any law. There is as a matter of fact no satisfactory physical theory which explains the variation of the resistance of a metal with the temperature. It took me about

a quarter of an hour to elaborate the theory given [to deduce the resistance-temperature law]; and yet it is, I maintain, formally as satisfactory as any theory in physics. If nothing but this were required we should never lack theories to explain our laws; a schoolboy in a day's work could solve the problems at which generations have labored in vain by the most trivial process of trial and error. What is wrong with the theory [I have given], what makes it absurd and unworthy of a single moment's consideration, is that it does not display any analogy; it is just because an analogy has not been used in its development that it is so completely valueless.[136]

As opposed to this, the kinetic theory of gases displays an analogy and so has value and explanatory power. Whether this assertion would entail him in a commitment to the "reality" of gas particles or molecules, or in assent to the proposition that the impacts of the molecules on the walls of a container "cause" the pressure on them, presented a considerable epistemological problem for Campbell. In attempting an answer he found it necessary to fall back on the differences of terminological usage between scientists and philosophers, and otherwise left the question open. Typical of his attitude is the statement: "It would be troublesome and superfluous to analyze all of the senses in which cause and effect are occasionally used; so long as we recognize that they are used in different senses . . . we are not likely to be led into error." [137]

b. The Covering-Law Model
Despite the force of Campbell's objections against mere logical deducibility, they were not immediately effective and had to wait some decades before being considered seriously by philosophers of science.[138] In the interim, the interest of the *Wiener Kreis* in formal logic led to an extensive development of a view similar to that Campbell was opposing — Rudolf Carnap's conception of a theory as a partially interpreted formal system.[139] The explanatory aspect of theories was thus not stressed in the way Campbell had envisaged, although the explanatory idea of science was not itself abandoned. Rather, the stress on explanation passed from theories to laws, and the latter came to be seen as the main factor in

scientific explanation. The object of this development is usually referred to as the covering-law model of scientific explanation, with which the names of Carl Hempel, R. B. Braithwaite, and others are associated. Since Braithwaite's study, *Scientific Explanation,* addresses in its title the very problem we are considering, it may profitably be the subject here of a brief exposition.[140]

Braithwaite sees it as the essential function of science to establish general laws covering the behavior of empirical events, since in this way a science "provides explanations of the facts which it investigates." [141] This he regards as true whether one seeks general explanations of classes of phenomena or raises historical questions about the causes of particular events, since

> . . . the statement that some particular event is the effect of a set of circumstances involves the assertion of a general law; to ask for the cause of an event is always to ask for a general law which applies to the particular event.[142]

As can be seen from this citation, Braithwaite associates causality with general laws, or laws of nature, and he interprets both in terms of Hume's constant-conjunction analysis. Consistent with the Humean view he denies that there is any such thing as nomic universality, holding "that universals of law are objectively just universals of fact, and that in nature there is no extra element of necessary connexion." [143] The expression "natural law" has for him an honorific connotation, which he believes derives from the explanatory power of general propositions that are so named; indeed, even "true hypotheses containing theoretical concepts" may be regarded as natural laws if they are thought to explain their instances.[144] Speaking generally,

> a true scientific hypothesis will be regarded as a law of nature if it has an explanatory function with regard to lower level hypotheses or its instances; vice versa, to the extent that a scientific hypothesis provides an explanation, to that extent will there be an inclination to endow it with the honourable status of natural law.[145]

Among natural laws, moreover, there are some that may be designated as "causal laws," and these will specify relationships between events that are spoken of as cause and effect. Braithwaite is intent on showing, however, that there need be no special ontological nexus behind such laws, and that they can all be accounted for on Humean principles in terms of combinations of constant conjunction and spatio-temporal relationships.[146]

Within this context Braithwaite regards both causal and teleological explanations as valid in science.[147] Sometimes when a causal explanation is sought the inquirer may be merely demanding a sufficient condition for the event to be explained, whereas at other times he may be seeking a necessary condition. When causal chains involving spatio-temporally continuous series of events are being investigated, the demands of explanation will usually not be satisfied until the first member of the chain has been identified. Teleological explanations differ from causal explanations in that the latter are given in terms of a cause that either precedes or is simultaneous with the effect, whereas the former is given in terms of a goal that is either future or as much future as present or past. Such explanations present a special problem for Braithwaite, as for empiricists generally, since the future reference of goal-directed activities might seem to imply the existence of "final causes" or other nonphysical entities. One type of solution which he countenances is to reduce teleological explanations to physico-chemical explanations of the ordinary causal sort, although admittedly this can be done only in cases where considerable biochemical and biophysical knowledge is available. In the remaining cases Braithwaite proposes to identify a teleological system through its "plasticity," a characteristic which he defines as follows:

> Plasticity is not in general a property of one teleological causal chain alone: it is a property of the organism with respect to a certain goal, namely that the organism can attain the same goal under different circumstances by alternate forms of activity making use frequently of different causal chains.[148]

By studying this feature of goal-directed systems, he maintains, one may reason from what has happened in the past to what will occur at the terminus of the operation, and then he will be explaining the system teleologically. As Braithwaite describes the situation:

> It is when our knowledge of the relevant variancy has been obtained independently of any knowledge of the causal laws concerned that a teleological explanation is valuable. For in this case we are unable, through ignorance of the causal laws, to infer the future behavior of the system from our knowledge of the causal laws; but we are able to make such an inference from knowledge of how similar systems have behaved in the past.[149]

Therefore, although such explanations are inferior to those of the mechanical or physico-chemical causal type and are to be replaced by them whenever the latter become available through the progress of science, they nonetheless are legitimate and constitute a valid explanatory mode.

Since covering laws play such a large role in scientific explanation for Braithwaite, the question arises whether laws themselves can be explained, and in what their explanation will ultimately consist. Braithwaite considers this question, only to reply that their explanation will be found in one's being able to deduce them from higher level laws or hypotheses. So he writes:

> To explain a law is to exhibit an established set of hypotheses from which the law follows. It is not necessary for these higher level hypotheses to be established independently of the law which they explain; all that is required for them to provide an explanation is that they should be regarded as established and that the law should logically follow from them. It is scarcely too much to say that this is the whole truth about the explanation of scientific laws. . . .[150]

Such a deduction, in Braithwaite's estimation, provides "intellectual satisfaction," and it is absurd to suppose otherwise, "even if no explanation is known of the higher level law itself." [151] Thus the sum and substance of all explanation in science is deducibility from a covering law:

> Any incorporation of a fact — be it a particular instance of a law or the law itself — into a deductive system in which it appears as a conclusion from other known laws

is, by virtue of that incorporation, an explanation of that fact or law.[152]

As may be noted even in this sketch, Braithwaite has views quite different from Campbell's, although he was aware of the latter's work on the role of models in theories and studied "Campbellian hypotheses" in some detail, contributing to their understanding and fuller elaboration.[153] What is important for our purposes, however, is that both men, the one stressing theoretical models and the other covering laws, were intent on restoring an explanatory function to science where others had been content to concede it merely a descriptive role. In so doing, moreover, they were not adverse to employing the terminology of cause and effect, and thereby helped to restore to causal explanations the respectability they had begun to lose with the advent of the new quantum theory.

c. Answers to the Question "Why?"

Braithwaite concludes his book with two chapters devoted to "Why?"questions and the ways in which answers to these constitute scientific explanations. The next author we will consider, Ernest Nagel, begins his treatment on the note with which Braithwaite ends. While also endorsing Hume and the empiricist tradition, however, Nagel broadens the discussion considerably by introducing Aristotelian elements into his presentation, thereby rejoining some of the themes discussed in our first volume. His chief work, one of the few systematic expositions of philosophy of science currently available, is entitled *The Structure of Science: Problems in the Logic of Scientific Explanation*.[154] The fact that this has been highly influential, together with its stress on explanation in a context broad enough to include causal inquiry, makes it of capital importance for our study.

To delineate the province of the scientific enterprise, Nagel finds it convenient first to differentiate science from common sense. Among distinguishing factors, the first he notes is that science tries to give explanations as to why facts occur, whereas common sense and ordinary knowledge rarely attempt this. Such an endeavor, therefore, may be taken as the hallmark of scientific knowing:

> It is the desire for explanations which are at once systematic and controllable by factual evidence that generates science; and it is the organization and classification of knowledge on the basis of explanatory principles that is the distinctive goal of the sciences. . . . To explain, to establish some relation of dependence between propositions superficially unrelated, to exhibit systematically connections between apparently miscellaneous items of information, are distinctive marks of scientific inquiry.[155]

Other differentiating factors are that science is more aware of the limits of its validity than is common sense; that science is more consistent and eliminates conflicting statements which common-sense judgments may sustain; that science fosters clear-cut meanings and has greater precision than ordinary language; that science is usually more remote from experience, more abstract, and more theoretical than common-sense knowledge, which is generally concrete and practical; and finally that science deals with propositions that are genuinely testable, whereas common-sense statements are frequently not. These characteristics define many problems relating to the cognitive claims and the logical methods of modern science, but foremost among these for Nagel, are the patterns and structures exhibited in scientific explanations. Thus he focuses on such explanations as a major, if not the exclusive, concern of the philosophy of science.

To discern the patterns that underlie such explanations, Nagel provides ten different illustrations for analysis, each formulated as a question beginning with the word "Why." His list is as follows:

1. Why is the sum of any number of consecutive odd integers beginning with 1 always a perfect square?
2. Why did moisture form on the outside of the glass when it was filled with ice water yesterday?
3. Why did a smaller percentage of Catholics commit suicide than did Protestants in European countries during the last quarter of the nineteenth century?
4. Why does ice float on water?
5. Why does the addition of salt to water lower its freezing point?
6. Why is it that in the progeny of inbred hybrid peas, obtained by crossing round and wrinkled parents,

approximately ¾ of the peas are always round whereas the remaining ¼ are wrinkled?

7. Why did Cassius plot the death of Caesar?
8. Why did Henry VIII of England seek to annul his marriage to Catherine of Aragon?
9. Why do human beings have lungs?
10. Why does the English language in its current form have so many words of Latin origin? [156]

Noteworthy is the inclusion in the list of examples from all areas of scientific and empirical investigation, ranging from the mathematical through the physical to the biological, behavioral, and social sciences. Answers to these questions, as Nagel sees it, constitute explanations, and these fall into four different patterns, each of which constitutes a distinctive type. The four types he identifies as deductive, probabilistic, functional or teleological, and genetic. So, in the above list, the first six questions may be answered on the deductive model, whereas the seventh requires a probabilistic, the eighth and ninth a functional or teleological, and the tenth a genetic explanation. Moreover, within the deductive category the first question seeks the explanation of a necessary, analytical truth whose denial would be self-contradictory. The second and third, on the other hand, ask for the explanation of historical facts — the second an individual event (the formation of moisture on the glass) and the third a statistical phenomenon (the numbers of suicides in particular samples). The next three queries are concerned with what Nagel refers to as universal laws. They differ among themselves in that the fourth (ice floating on water) may be explained in terms of experimental laws, whereas the fifth (the depression of the freezing point of water) requires theoretical principles also, and the sixth (the progeny of inbred hybrid peas), explanation in terms of a statistical law. The seventh example (Cassius plotting the death of Caesar) is probabilistic in the special sense that the explanation must proceed from probable principles. The eighth and ninth questions, both seeking teleological or functional explanations, differ in that the eighth (Henry's annulment) is an historical event whose explanation is sought in terms of an intended goal, whereas the ninth (human beings having lungs) inquires about a distinctive feature present in all systems of a certain kind. The tenth and final example (the occurrence in English of words of Latin origin) seeks a genetic account, i.e., how a certain system has developed from an earlier stage.[157]

Since causal explanation, for Nagel, is situated within the deductive type, a few observations on his treatment of this category are further in order. When the *explicandum* is an individual event, he maintains, the *explicans* will contain at least one universal law, and indeed a law of this kind may even be implicit, such as those that "affirm that there are distinct kinds of substances, each of which exhibits certain fixed concatenations of traits and modes of behavior." [158] In addition there will be "statements of initial conditions" which show how the law is to be applied to the individual case. When the *explicandum* is a law (as opposed to an event), there must be more than one premise, and they must be universal; to prevent circularity in argumentation, moreover, taken either singly or conjointly they must not follow logically from the *explicandum*. Again, at least one premise must be "more general" than the law being explained, although Nagel admits to difficulty in formulating a precise logical definition of such generality. His discussion of this problem, however, leads him into a detailed examination of Aristotle's epistemic requirements for an explanation, namely, that the premises in a deductive account "must among other things be true, that they must be known to be true, and that they must be 'better known' than the *explicandum*," with results that are of considerable interest.[159]

Nagel experiences no difficulty on Aristotle's first point, that the premises must be true, but he finds the second quite unsatisfactory from the viewpoint of modern science:

> The Aristotelian requirement that the premises must be *known* to be true . . . provides an apparently effective criterion for eliminating many proposed explanations as unsatisfactory. But this requirement is much too strong. Were it adopted, few if any of the explanations given by modern science could be accepted as satisfactory. For in point of fact, we do *not* know whether the unrestrictedly universal premises assumed in the explanations of the empirical sciences are indeed true; and, were the re-

quirement adopted, most of the widely accepted explanations in current science would have to be rejected as unsatisfactory.[160]

In place of this Nagel would substitute a weaker requirement
permitting hypothetical premises that are in accord with the
observed facts and still are not solely dependent upon them,
somewhat along the lines of Whewell's consilience of inductions and allied proposals:

> A reasonable candidate for such a weaker condition is
> the requirement that the explanatory premises be com-
> patible with established empirical facts and be in addition
> "adequately supported" (or made probable) by evidence
> based on data other than the observational data upon
> which the acceptance of the *explicandum* is based.[161]

On the other hand, Aristotle's final stipulation is seen by
Nagel as based on the view, inspired by the example of geometry, that first principles can become ultimate premises
"because their necessity is intrinsic and transparent to the
intellect" and thus are "better known." [162] Nagel rejects this
requirement as completely unrealistic for the explanations
advanced in contemporary science:

> This conception is true of nothing that can be identified
> as part of the asserted content of modern empirical sci-
> ence. Accordingly, Aristotle's requirement that the ex-
> planatory premises be better known than the *explicandum*
> is entirely irrelevant as a condition for anything that
> would today be regarded as an adequate scientific expla-
> nation.[163]

Since laws play a key role in deductive explanation for
Nagel, as they do for Braithwaite, he considers them in some
detail, focusing principally on their logical character.[164] In
terms of formal logic, laws are generalized or universal conditionals of the form, "For any x, if x is A then x is B." Nagel
starts with this and then proceeds to show, first, that not all
universal conditionals are laws and, secondly, that not all
laws are causal laws. His justification for the first position is
based on the contrast between accidental universality, or
universals of fact of the type "All the screws in Smith's car are
rusty," with nomic universality, or universals of law of the

type "All crows are black" or "Copper expands when heated."
Since laws of nature are quite obviously of the second type,
Nagel questions if they actually do assert more than accidental
universality and if, this being granted, they can be said to involve some element of necessity, whether this be conceived
as logical or as causal, physical, or real. He answers "yes" to
the first question and "no" to the second, adopting "an essentially Humean interpretation of nomic universality," [165]
and this despite contemporary criticisms of Hume, of which
he is well aware. So Nagel maintains that nomic universality
is distinct from accidental universality but denies, as a basis
for this distinction, any element of necessary connection. In
place of such necessity he would substitute the following four
conditions as determinants of nomic universality:

1. The universal statement must be unrestricted, not
   dealing with individuals or objects that are spatio-
   temporally localized;
2. it must not be merely vacuously true;
3. the evidence in its support cannot be known to co-
   incide with its scope of predication; and
4. on the basis of indirect and apparently negative evidence one would be disposed to retain the statement,
   because its rejection would require a serious reorga-
   nization of a substantial part of one's knowledge.[166]

Having stated these requirements, which effectively define a scientific law, Nagel proceeds to enumerate its various
kinds so as to locate causal laws among them. The first is "a
basic and pervasive type of law" that enables one to hold that
there are certain "natural kinds" or "substances"; [167] the
second and third types describe relations among events or
properties, the second stating "an invariable sequential order
of dependence" and the third "invariable statistical (or probabilistic) relations"; [168] while the fourth type asserts a functional dependence between variable magnitudes associated
with properties or processes, after the fashion of concurrent
variations or of magnitudes varying with time.[169] In this
division causal laws will appear as a species of the second
type, but in order to see this it is first necessary to distinguish
a causal sequence from another related species.

The word "cause" has a variety of meanings and a wide spectrum of uses, Nagel admits, but he thinks it possible to identify a sense that can characterize causal laws and at the same time corresponds to usages "in many areas of science as well as in ordinary discourse." [170] He describes this sense as follows:

> The sense of 'cause' we wish to identify is illustrated by the following example. An electric spark is passed through a mixture of hydrogen and oxygen gas; the explosion that follows the passage of the spark is accompanied by the disappearance of the gases and the condensation of water vapor. The disappearance of the gases and the formation of water in this experiment are commonly said to be the effects that are caused by the spark. Moreover, the generalization based on such experiments (e.g., "Whenever a spark passes through a mixture of hydrogen and oxygen gas, the gases disappear and water is formed") is called a "causal law." [171]

Utilizing this meaning, Nagel then lists four conditions that a law must usually satisfy to be referred to as causal. The first is that there be an invariable and uniform relation between the events designated as cause and effect, with the first event constituting both a necessary and a sufficient condition for the occurrence of the second, although sometimes the sufficient condition may not be completely specified. The second and third requirements relate to the spatio-temporal relationships between the events, the second delineating them as spatially contiguous and the third as continuous in time but with the cause preceding the effect. Nagel's fourth condition is that the relation be asymmetrical in the sense that the first event is the cause of the second but the second is not the cause of the first.[172] All four conditions thus serve to define a causal law, and some of them serve to distinguish it from the other species of sequential order of dependence among events, to which we have referred, which Nagel identifies as a developmental or historical law. The latter, an example of which might be "The consumption of alcohol is always followed by a dilation of the blood vessels," is not in accord with the first and third requirements for a causal law, since they prescind from sufficient conditions and state only necessary ones, and they apply to events that are separated by a time interval of some duration. Developmental laws, however, are obviously similar to causal laws, and so they are both treated by Nagel as classes of the invariable sequence type.

With Braithwaite, Nagel admits the existence of teleological explanations, likewise holding that these need not be limited to activities involving conscious agents and that they need not assert that the future acts causally on the present or the past.[173] Nagel also rejects Aristotle's teaching on final causes and generally holds that teleological explanations "can be reformulated, without loss of asserted content, to take the form of non-teleological ones, so that in an important sense teleological and non-teleological explanations are equivalent." [174] The difference between a teleological explanation and its nonteleological counterpart, for him, "is one of selective attention rather than of asserted content." [175] The selectivity of attention he spells out as follows:

> Teleological explanations focus attention on the culminations and products of specific processes, and in particular upon the contributions of various parts of a system to the maintenance of its global properties or modes of behavior. They view the operations of things from the perspective of certain selected "wholes" or integrated systems to which the things belong; and they are therefore concerned with characteristics of the parts of such wholes, only insofar as those traits of the parts are relevant to the various complex features or activities assumed to be distinctive of those wholes.[176]

The foregoing is only a summary statement of Nagel's very full analysis of scientific explanation, but it shows how well the author is able to reinstate the notion of causality, albeit in a Humean understanding, within the context of such explanation. In the detailed working out of his thesis he is further able to apply these explanatory categories throughout the entire range of the physical, biological, behavioral, and social sciences, and to take up specific topics relating to each. Among such topics he treats causality and indeterminism in contemporary physics, and in so doing provides his answer to the questions raised by Heisenberg, Bohr, and Born, which were discussed at the end of the previous section.

In his analysis, Nagel gives a detailed account of wave-particle duality and, in particular, of the probabilistic interpretation of the wave equation in quantum mechanics.[177] The latter interpretation was first suggested around 1928 by Born, who proposed it to reconcile the conflicting views that electromagnetic radiation is energy flowing continuously as a wave and that it is energy traveling in discrete packets or photons. Born found that he could account for all the observed phenomena by supposing that the energy itself is not distributed continuously but is carried by photons, while the probability of finding a photon at a particular place is determined by wave considerations, with the result that the statistical distribution of the energy packets is also dependent on a continuous wave function. Thus the particle and wave accounts are both necessary to reconstruct all details of the phenomena. In the quantum theory of matter the equation analogous to that for the propagation of electromagnetic radiation is the Schrödinger wave equation, and its solution is known as the wave function or psi-function. According to its probabilistic interpretation, the square of the absolute value of this function for a particular system gives the probability that the elementary constituents of that system will be found at various points in space. It is in such a context that Nagel offers his critique of the role of probability in quantum theory. Although the square of the amplitude of the wave function is construed as a probability distribution, he observes, the psi-function itself is no more a probability function than are the state descriptions employed in Fourier's theory of heat conduction or in Maxwell's theory of electromagnetism.[178] Moreover, "the interpretation of the square of psi's absolute magnitude as a *probability* function is intelligible only on the assumption that certain subatomic processes form statistical aggregates, to which the notion of probability as a relative frequency is applicable."[179] On these grounds Nagel rules out the radically indeterministic implications that some have seen in the new quantum theory:

> In short, if the interpretation associated with the psi-function is a statistical one, then all predictions based exclusively on that interpretation must also be statistical, and cannot be predications of non-statistical properties

to individuals. There is therefore no warrant for the conclusion that because quantum theory does not predict the detailed individual behaviors of electrons and other subatomic elements, the behavior of such elements is "inherently indeterminate" and the manifestation of "absolute chance." [180]

Nagel also argues against the related inference, occasionally drawn, that because the behavior of subatomic objects exhibits only statistical regularities, and since the behavior of macroscopic objects is compounded out of the behavior of their subatomic constituents, the regularities of all physical objects can only be statistical. He analyzes the assumptions underlying this claim, and particularly the circularity involved in assigning macroscopic properties to subatomic objects and then using these to negate the very properties on which they are based, and concludes:

> In consequence, the statistical content of quantum mechanics does not annul the deterministic and non-statistical structure of other physical laws. It also follows that conclusions concerning human freedom and moral responsibility, when based on the alleged "acausal" and "indeterministic" behavior of subatomic processes, are built on sand. Neither the analysis of physical theory, nor the study of the subject matter of physics, yields the conclusion that "there is no strict causal behavior anywhere." [181]

Nagel finally concerns himself with the formulation of a law or principle of causality, and is intent to show that, when properly formulated, there need be no question of the decline and fall of such a law. He admits that the principle as stated by Laplace and Mill no longer can find application throughout the entire range of physical phenomena. His own reformulation of the principle would stress its character as a methodological rule expressing "the general objective of theoretical science to achieve *deterministic* explanations, in the now familiar sense of 'determinism' according to which, given the state of a system for some initial time, the explanatory theory logically establishes a unique state for the system for any other time." [182] So understood, in Nagel's view the principle sets the ideal for what he calls "theoretical science," without whose guidance the latter would cease to exist:

> . . . the actual pursuit of theoretical science in modern times is directed towards certain goals, one of which is formulated by the principle of causality. Indeed, the phrase "theoretical science" appears to be so generally used that an enterprise not controlled by those objectives would presumably not be subsumed under this label. It is at least plausible to claim, therefore, that the acceptance of the principle of causality as a maxim of inquiry (whether the acceptance is explicit or only illustrated in the overt actions of scientists, or whether the principle is formulated with some precision or only vaguely) is an *analytical consequence* of what is commonly meant by "theoretical sciences." [183]

Nagel admits that formulations of the principle will change from time to time, and that some formulations will have to be abandoned as different types of phenomena are investigated, but that theoretical science could not surrender the general ideal expressed by the principle "without becoming thereby transformed into something incomparably different from what that enterprise actually is." [184]

As an overall presentation of the structure of science Nagel's work has received well-deserved praise as a masterful synthesis. Its strength derives from its effort to transcend the order of sense, to give reason its rightful role in scientific inquiry. It is Nagel's insistence on rationality, in fact, that leads him to return to so many traditional themes, reaching all the way to Aristotle, and to incorporate these into a general empiricist program wherein science is characterized as a superior type of explanatory knowledge enabling man to understand and know the truth about the world in which he lives. The strength of Nagel's synthesis, however, proves also to be its weakness. For in attempting to locate his endeavor within a logical empiricist framework, he has declared his basic allegiance to Hume, and particularly to the Humean account of causality, with its many limitations. Thus the lofty ideal he sets for science proves to be beyond the reach of the conceptual apparatus he is willing to concede it. Noting this inconsistency in his work, a reviewer has remarked:

One may wish to render a general description of scientific enquiry on the assumption that nothing is given in experience but contiguity and succession. But when one affirms that science is explanation, and that to give an explanation is to assign a reason why, not merely to describe with a view to prediction, then the assumption is that some connection has been perceived. Seemingly, the nature and source of this connection ought to be explored. . . . Avoiding such an enquiry, Nagel has reduced the principle of causality to advice to look for regularities. If the principle of causality is so conceived, it is difficult to see how Nagel has avoided the "descriptivist" view of science which he wishes to avoid. This seems to be the fundamental ambiguity in Nagel's concept of science, namely, that he wishes to claim more for science than his Humean commitment will consistently allow.[185]

The defect is there, but fortunately it is not fatal. Indeed, its very presence awakens curiosity as to what one might do when armed with Nagel's enthusiasm for causal inquiry but not handicapped by his allegiance to Hume. Attempts have not been lacking from this perspective also, and to these we now direct our attention.

3. *The Anti-Humean Turn*

It would be a difficult and thankless task to canvass all of the adverse reactions to Hume, even were one to limit oneself to twentieth-century authors and concentrate only on criticisms of his constant-conjunction analysis of causation. Kantians and Neo-Kantians, idealists of every sort, Thomists and partisans of other scholastic philosophies, linguistic and analytical philosophers — even experimental psychologists questioning the theory of knowledge behind Hume's account — all have contributed to a substantial critical literature on this subject.[186] Since our major concern is with explanation and related problems in contemporary philosophy of science, we shall have to be even more selective than usual and restrict our consideration to a few key efforts at transcending Hume's teaching in this immediate context.

a. Process and Metaphysics

Perhaps the most radical of all these attempts is one that rejects practically every explanatory category that has been discussed up to this point and focuses instead on process or "becoming" as a central notion in understanding the material universe. Hume was not the immediate target of this movement, although it developed in reaction to the schools he fathered; its more positive inspiration came from vitalist and evolutionary philosophies. One of the principal formulators of process thought was Henri Bergson, whose early training had been in mathematics and physics, but who had reacted against the latter's spatio-temporal categories and what he regarded as its conceptual distortions of reality.[187] In their place he substituted an immediate "intuition of duration," which he claimed puts one in contact with the inner dynamism of being. Rather than rule out introspection and explain movement and life in terms of categories appropriate to inert matter, as mechanistic philosophers had done, Bergson proposed to reverse the order and explain matter in terms of life or consciousness, which he regarded as the primordial reality grasped in intuition. Reality then would not be passive and inert, like matter, but in ceaseless flux or "becoming," and so essentially dynamic, creative, and unpredictable. Bergson saw this dynamic process well exemplified in "creative evolution," which he attributed to a life impulse, an *élan vital,* that penetrates into matter, insinuates itself into physico-chemical systems, endows them with life, and carries them forward into ever higher complexities of organization. Such a causal mode of explanation, as is obvious, is well adapted to the interpretation of evolutionary theories, but it has also been used by Bergson's followers to supply a coherent philosophical basis for relativity and quantum theories. They would see, in fact, in the downfall of mechanism, the revision of space-time concepts, the formulation of mass-energy equivalence, and the principles of indeterminacy and complementarity vindications of Bergson's insights and affirmations of "becoming" and its associated dynamic causation as basic to a proper understanding of the physical universe.[188]

It is not Bergson, however, but rather a thinker partially

inspired by him, Alfred North Whitehead, who is the more significant for purposes of our study.[189] Himself a distinguished mathematician, teacher of Bertrand Russell and collaborator with him on the *Principia Mathematica*, Whitehead also was well acquainted with the classical authors we have discussed in this volume and attempted a radical reconstruction of their philosophies in the light of contemporary physics. In so doing he explicitly addressed himself to Hume's epistemology, analyzed its shortcomings, and reinstated causal efficacy as a primary explanatory factor for the world of science. The systematic metaphysics Whitehead erected in the process is extremely technical and does not lend itself to summarization; the following, therefore, touches only on the main stages in the evolution of his thought as these relate to the problems of causality and scientific explanation.

Whitehead's intellectual development may be conveniently divided into three periods: during the first of these, up to 1910, he was concerned mainly with the logical foundations of mathematics; in the second, to about 1924, he dealt mainly with problems in the philosophy of science; and in the final phase, from 1925 onward, he was intent on elaborating a systematic metaphysics. Even in the first period there are signs of Whitehead's dissatisfaction with the Newtonian world of discrete atoms situated in absolute space and absolute time. Influenced by vector and field concepts and by theories of atomic and molecular vibration, he regarded lines of force as more ultimate than atoms, and so thought of particles not as discrete entities but as elements in a field. Similarly he saw mathematical points not simply as locations in space but as elements in linear polyadic relations, with the result that, for him, points and particles took on the characteristics of vector quantities. This led into what he referred to as the "method of extensive abstraction," a topological way of defining geometrical points and lines as relations between converging sets of overlapping volumes of distinctive shapes.[190] The value Whitehead saw in this type of definition was that it permitted a clearer understanding of the thing defined. For example, no one can perceive Euclidean points or lines, but volumes can be perceived as extending over other volumes, and thus relations such as "overlapping" and "extending over" can become topological aids that render points and lines perceptible.

Whitehead then adapted this method of extensive abstraction to a critique of the Humean account of sensation, wherein, analogous to the Newtonian world, everything is reduced to distinct sense impressions or to atoms of sensation. As opposed to this, Whitehead saw human experience as characterized by a spatio-temporal spread, which should be thought of not as discrete and enduring atoms of sense data but rather as happenings that are themselves events extending over other events. Applying this insight further, Whitehead maintained that in normal experience perception takes place in two distinct modes that are closely linked. The first he referred to as that of "presentational immediacy" and the second that of "causal efficacy." The first mode is concerned with the rather obvious elements in sensation, the sense data of shapes, sounds, and colors, on which Hume built his theory of knowledge. Less obvious is the second mode of perception, sharing in the overlapping character of the perceptive event, which lacks distinctness but is more primitive and makes us aware of how things really affect us. It is in discussing this mode, that of causal efficacy, that Whitehead makes his most telling criticism of Hume. The latter stressed an important element in perception, he admits, but mistook the part for the whole; he denied any genuine causal connection between things precisely because he considered sense data in the mode of presentational immediacy alone, and it is true that no such connection can be justified from this mode of perception. Both Hume and Kant, in fact, overlooked completely perception in the mode of causal efficacy, and thus regarded it as a psychological or conceptual projection into experience. Both were in error, for causal connections exist in nature at all levels and are actually perceived in man's most primitive experiences. Indeed, perception in the mode of causal efficacy is antecedent to that in the mode of presentational immediacy. So Whitehead asserts:

> The sense data are "given" for presentational immediacy. This givenness of the sense data, as the basis of this perceptive mode, is the great doctrine common to Hume

and Kant. But what is already given for experience can only be derived from that natural potentiality which shapes a particular experience in the guise of causal efficacy. Causal efficacy is the hand of the settled past in the formation of the present.[191]

In Hume's account there is an implicit awareness of the role of such efficacy in perception, Whitehead notes, for "in asserting the lack of perception of causality, he implicitly presupposes it." [192] The source of his error, as Whitehead sees it, was not that he was unaware of causal efficacy but that he neglected to take explicit account of it in his theory of knowledge:

> Hume with the clarity of genius states the fundamental point, that sense data functioning in an act of experience demonstrates that they are given *by* the causal efficacy of actual bodily organs. He refers to this causal efficacy as a component in direct perception. Hume's argument first tacitly presupposes the two modes of perception, and then tacitly assumes that presentational immediacy is the only mode. Also Hume's followers in developing his doctrine presuppose that presentational immediacy is primitive, and that causal efficacy is the sophisticated derivative. This is a complete inversion of the evidence.[193]

Moreover, if one follows Hume in restricting attention to presentational immediacy alone, then it is quite true that he will perceive nothing in the present moment that has any inherent reference to past or future, and will be continually mystified as to why there seems to be an order in nature and even general laws from which predictions can be made. Such generalizations, like causality, will either be regarded as something imposed on experience by our ways of looking at things, or will be left as unexplained residues in the "problem of induction." [194]

It is from this type of critique that Whitehead moves into his distinctive themes of the "bifurcation of nature," the "fallacy of misplaced concreteness," and the doctrine of internal relations. The latter is of particular importance, for out of it grows Whitehead's fully developed philosophy of organism. Everything in the universe is related to every other thing, and these relations are not external to the thing itself but

enter into its very being and become essential to its definition. On this account, Whitehead would prefer to talk of
events or happenings rather than of things, with relationships
between events being for him intimate parts of the events
themselves. Such a doctrine has important ramifications for
the understanding of scientific law. Whitehead is openly critical of the positivist and conventionalist attempts to reduce
physical laws to mere descriptions; he sees the aim of science
as not merely to describe but to explain, to make nature intelligible. Such explanations would be impossible if each existing thing were sufficient unto itself, if laws were not immanent in its relationships to, and its power to affect, other
things.

Even this brief sketch will serve to show that Whitehead, like Bergson, is proposing a philosophy wherein causality enters as an integral component in scientific explanation.
Many of the notions he utilizes are based on the concepts of
relativity theory and of wave mechanics, and so are not for-
eign to contemporary physics; indeed they find ready application in the solution of the philosophical problems it has
generated. Unfortunately, however, Whitehead's systematic
metaphysics is difficult, his terminology is strange even to
those with long training in philosophy, and his ideas have
found only limited acceptance among those interested in the
epistemological problems of modern science.

b. Beyond Phenomenalism

Any account of reactions to the positivist interpretation
of science would be incomplete without mention of Émile
Meyerson.[195] Like Whewell, Mach, and Duhem, Meyerson
had a lifelong interest in the history of science and addressed
himself, in his major writings, to its epistemology and to
problems associated with a realist interpretation of its laws
and theories. His thought was influenced by Descartes and
Kant, and it also shows similarities with the philosophies of
Boutroux and Bergson, but its chief characteristic is its opposition to Comte and Mach and particularly to their insistence
that the discovery of the laws of phenomena constitutes science's main object. Meyerson reacted strongly against this
thesis, maintaining like Whitehead that the aim of science is

not to describe but to explain and that such explanation necessarily entails the scientist in the use of causal concepts.

Meyerson proposed his systematic elaboration not as a philosophy of phenomena or of sense but rather as a philosophy of the intellect. He felt that there are both a priori and a posteriori elements involved in science, and that the documentation for this is readily found in its history. Scientists have never been content simply with registering phenomena and summarizing them in laws that make possible the prediction and control of further phenomena. Quite to the contrary, insists Meyerson, they search for something more substantial and real behind the phenomena that will enable them to understand the "Why" of things. Phenomenalism and legalism are therefore not the ultimates toward which the scientific enterprise tends, although they mark provisional stages in its elaboration; the more fundamental tendencies that govern the activities of scientists are realism and causalism. The scientists's ultimate goal is explanation, and this in terms of the ontological factors that make things be as they are.

Hume's error, in Meyerson's view, is that he completely assimilated the concept of cause into that of law, seeing causation as only the lawlike succession of phenomena.[196] From this assimilation it is, of course, an easy step to a positivist or phenomenalist interpretation of science. But cause and law cannot be made equivalent, Meyerson affirms, for "the principle of causality is profoundly different from that of lawfulness." [197] This does not prevent the search for a law being included in that for a cause; indeed, "the establishment of the first is always a step in the way which leads to the second." [198] The search for causes thus goes beyond the detection of lawlike regularities; it is basically the search for explanations. To explain, and this is Meyerson's distinctive thesis, is to identify. The grasping of a causal relationship is a form of identity: "The principle of causality is none other than the principle of identity applied to the existence of objects in time." [199] A person understands a physical change when he is able to identify an effect as already being present in its cause. "What can be the determining reason for that which is conditioned in time?" asks Meyerson. He replies: "One only is possible: that of pre-existence. Things are thus because they were already previously thus." [200]

Yet Meyerson was not naïve in the way in which he applied this identity analysis to the evolution of science. He recognized that reality is resistant to man's attempts to understand it, and argued that man only finds intelligibility through his own constructions, as exemplified in the use of conservation principles, the elimination of time's passage, and the assimilation of matter to the concept of space. Reality rejects these a priori attempts to oversimplify it, and so in terms of his principles the scientist finds that it is only partly intelligible, that it contains an irreducible element, that it is at ground irrational. It is this very irrationality, however, that serves to define the real in opposition to the structures erected by the scientist for its understanding, and that unmasks the pretensions of rationalist and idealist philosophies in their facile attempts to give a clear and distinct account of reality.

One of the best summaries of this progression of thought is given by Meyerson himself in his preface to *Identity and Reality*. There he outlines the work as follows:

> We begin by investigating whether it is true, as Comte and, later on, Mach affirm, that all science is established only for the purpose of action and prediction. We prove that the principle thus put into play, the principle of lawfulness (*légalité*), is not enough, that science attempts equally to *explain* phenomena, and that this explanation consists in the identification of the antecedent and the consequent. It is from this second principle, the principle of *scientific causality*, that the atomic theories are derived. It enters also into the part of science devoted to law by creating the principles of conservation, and by bringing about the elimination of time. An extension of this same principle creates the concept of the unity of matter, which leads to the assimilation of this latter with space, and from that to the annihilation of the external world. These conclusions are not a result of science, they come from the *a priori* elements which science conceals; science reacts, and this action is expressed by Carnot's principle. After having determined more precisely the limits of causal explanation, to which is opposed the concept of the irrational, we show that nonmechanical theories are also evolved from the principle of causality. We

then state that the world of common sense is created by a process strictly analogous to that which produces scientific theories. We end with certain conclusions relative to the philosophy of science, during which we again examine, with the help of the results attained, the problem of the relation between the two principles of lawfulness and of causality.[201]

The distinction between lawfulness and causality was therefore the dominant factor in Meyerson's epistemology; he started with it, was preoccupied with it throughout his exposition, and returned to it at the end of his work. Still his was never a simplistic view, for he admitted to great difficulties in defining the term "cause," [202] allowed for different types of causality and attempted to explain their interrelations,[203] and withal was well aware of the limits of causal analysis.[204]

Meyerson's vigorous rejection of positivism and his stress on explanation helped counteract the Comtean influence in French science and philosophy, making a favorable impression on Louis de Broglie, among others. His views enjoyed popularity around 1930, when they were taken as a viable alternative to the Copenhagen interpretation of quantum theory, which Meyerson himself regarded as a passing aberration. Yet he never seriously influenced philosophers of science in the Anglo-Saxon tradition, who fell more under the domination of the *Wiener Kreis* and so continued to reformulate logical positivist positions. Thus Hume's account of causation remained the prevailing one in England and the United States, although even in these countries the influence of analytical and linguistic philosophies led to its questioning and to at least a partial rejection. We now shall consider briefly one such attempt to go beyond phenomenalism within an analytical framework that is sympathetic to Humean methodology while being critical of its results, that, namely, of Curt J. Ducasse.

Ducasse's early education was in France and England, but all his higher studies were made in the United States and his professional career as a philosopher was spent entirely on the American scene.[205] He may be regarded as a scientific philosopher in the sense that he conceived philosophy as a science, differing from other sciences not in its methodology but only in virtue of its particular subject matter. The analysis of causation was one of his enduring interests, and he published extensively on it throughout his lifetime. His main thesis was that causality and the causal relationship are directly perceptible in experience, and can only be explained, contrary to Hume, by positing some type of nonlogical or physical necessity as actually existent in nature.

Ducasse continually refined his definitions of causality so as to bring out these features. Generally he regarded it as a triadic relationship between events and utilized Mill's method of difference to specify the content of that relationship as follows: If, in a given state of affairs S only two changes are known to occur, one the change C at time t_1 and the other the change E at time t_2, then C is known as the cause of E. Ducasse felt that Hume implicitly used such a differential method to arrive at the idea of causal connectedness, and that this is particularly notable in the way in which he thought cause and effect could be discerned in the single experiment.[206] In his own more precise formulations Ducasse in fact uses the term "experiment" to describe the state of affairs in which only two such changes occur. So he writes:

> Causation is the observable relation which obtains between the three terms of any strict experiment: If, in a given state of affairs S, *only two* changes (whether simple or complex) occur during a given period, one of them E occurring immediately after and adjacent to the other C, then, *eo ipso*, C proximately *caused* E, and E was the proximate *effect* of C.[207]

The expression "strict experiment" here designates a situation in which the method of single difference can be applied, and since the elements of S and the changes are all observable, the causal relationship they define may be said to be directly perceivable also. Moreover, habitual association and regularity of sequence need not be invoked to define the causal relationship, à la Hume, for the only point in repeating any experiment is to check whether all the factors are indeed as they have been perceived to be. Therefore regularities are not causal simply because they are regular, although it is true that they will be regular when they are causal. So it is causality that explains regularity, and not the other way around.

Ducasse was aware of the difficulty of isolating the factors involved in any strict experiment, as well as the dangers of making categorical assertions about them, but he still felt that ordinary experience was sufficient to justify his mode of definition. His emphasis on such experience, and the language we use to describe it, is clearly seen in the following example he provides:

> When any philosophically pure-minded person sees a brick strike a window and the window break, he judges that the impact of the brick was the cause of the breaking, *because* he believes that impact to have been the only change which took place in the immediate environment of the window. He may, indeed, have been mistaken, and acknowledge that he was mistaken, in believing that impact to have been the only change in the environment. But if so he will nevertheless maintain that *if* it had been the only change, it would have been the cause. That is, he will stand by the definition of cause, and admit merely that what he perceived was not a true case of what he meant and still means by cause.[208]

Ducasse was convinced that his definition was the only one "faithful to the manner in which the word 'cause' is actually used by every person whose English has not been contaminated by Hume." [209] Thus he was impatient with what Russell referred to as the "intolerable circumlocution" involved in attempts to avoid saying that one event causes another event, and urged a return to the plain language that states what we precisely do mean in our continued use of causal terminology.

Ducasse's rejection of Hume has stimulated Edward H. Madden and others to comment on his thought in considerable detail and to develop non-Humean views of causality and nonlogical necessity along lines that are implicit in his writings.[210] In this and other ways Ducasse's teachings have been influential in the United States; they have evoked renewed interest in the problem of causality; and they have contributed in no small measure to the anti-Humean turn within the analytical tradition.[211] The net effect of his work has thus been to foster a withdrawal from empiricism and a return to realism, and so prepare for the next development within contemporary philosophy of science relating to causality and explanation, with which we will conclude our exposition.

c. The Return to Realism

The term "realism" is much abused and has taken on a variety of meanings in recent philosophy. In the context of a philosophy of science it has been used by J. J. C. Smart, Wilfred Sellars, and others to describe what Edward MacKinnon refers to as a "new materialism." [212] Linguistic analysis figures importantly in this development, for in it knowledge of the real, based as it is on sense experience, is seen as only partially interpreted and synthesized in a variety of linguistic systems. Each such system has its own explanatory entities, moreover, and the reality of these, it is generally agreed, cannot be judged apart from the linguistic system in which they are embedded. On the basis of these suppositions Sellars examines the competing claims of ordinary language, with its use of "men," "animals," etc., as explanatory entities, and the language of modern physics, where "molecules," "atoms," and "fundamental particles" play the same role. To discriminate between the two languages, Sellars employs a type of reductionism wherein the acceptance of an explanatory theory as more basic furnishes good reason to accord ontological priority to the entities postulated by it. It is in this sense that the acceptance of the theories of modern science as ultimate explainers entails for him a new realism, i.e., an acceptance of the entities with which they deal as existentially real.[213]

Sellars's thought is representative of but one type of scientific realism based on the analysis of theories as linguistic systems.[214] Other types of realism have also been developed within the contexts of Thomistic and Marxist philosophies, and these too have pointed out the inadequacies of Humean and logical positivist accounts of causality, stressing, albeit in radically different ways, the role of matter as a real and causal factor in scientific explanations.[215] More directly associated with contemporary science, however, are the distinctive realist interpretations advanced by three recent writers, all of whom have addressed themselves explicitly to the problems of causality and scientific explanation, and all of whom end up by making strong claims for realism. They are David Bohm, Mario Bunge, and Rom Harré, whose analyses now merit exposition.

David Bohm had already secured his reputation as a quantum physicist before he entered the philosophical arena and questioned the "orthodox" Copenhagen interpretation of quantum theory in his *Causality and Chance in Modern Physics*.[216] Introduced by Louis de Broglie, who lauds its "arguments in favor of a causal reinterpretation of quantum physics," [217] the work is directed against attempts to root quantum theory in absolute chance and proposes instead to indicate how both causality and chance are required for its full understanding. Bohm shows himself knowledgeable in the history of science, tracing its evolution through the classical period and concentrating particularly on the factors that led to the downfall of mechanism. The assumptions on which mechanism was based, he concludes, were "essentially philosophical in character" and did not follow from any specific scientific developments.[218] Similarly, the finality of the orthodox interpretation of Heisenberg's indeterminacy principle is itself a philosophical assumption. Precisely as an assumption, it cannot legislate against causality, and it ought not impose arbitrary restrictions on scientists' efforts to seek ever deeper explanations, even for quantum phenomena. Bohm states this thesis in the following way:

> We shall see . . . that the indeterminacy principle necessitates a renunciation of causality only if we assume that this principle has an absolute and final validity. . . . On the other hand, if we suppose that this principle applies only as a good approximation and only in some limited domain . . . , then room is left open for new kinds of causal laws to apply in new domains. For example, as we shall see, there is good reason to assume the existence of a sub quantum-mechanical level that is more fundamental than that at which the present quantum theory holds. Within this new level could be operating qualitatively new kinds of laws, leading to those of the current theory as approximations and limiting cases in much the same way that the laws of the atomic domain lead to those of the macroscopic domain. The indeterminacy principle would then apply only in the quantum level, and would

have no relevance at all at lower levels. The treatment of the indeterminacy principle can then be criticized as constituting an arbitrary restriction on scientific theories, since it does not follow from the quantum theory as such, but rather from the assumption of the unlimited validity of certain of its features, an assumption that can in no way ever be subjected to experimental proof.[219]

As an alternative to the imposition of restrictive principles such as those of mechanistic philosophy and of the Copenhagen position, Bohm proposes a more general concept of nature that would be open to "an unlimited variety of additional properties, qualities, entities, systems, levels, etc.," to which would apply "correspondingly new kinds of laws." [220] Bohm refers to this as the "qualitative infinity of nature" and enumerates its advantages in providing systematic interpretations of the new physics.[221] One such would be "that fields and particles are closely linked in an even deeper way, in the sense that both are probably opposite sides of some still more general type of entity, the detailed character of which remains to be discovered." [222] Similarly, causal laws and laws of chance both have a place in science "as effectively furnishing different views of any given natural process . . ." [223] The ultimate explanatory factor to which Bohm's analysis concludes is "the infinite totality of matter in the process of becoming," which he regards as "the basic reality." [224]

More prolific than Bohm as a philosopher but like him also a theoretical physicist, Mario Bunge comes to conclusions that are compatible with Bohm's in his *Causality: The Place of the Causal Principle in Modern Science*.[225] Bunge's study is broader in scope than Bohm's and traces in greater detail the development of causal terminology and its application throughout science's history. Bunge also manifests a more explicit ontological commitment, being particularly forceful in his rejection of Hume's constant-conjunction formula for causation, which he criticizes as too weak and as overlooking the all-important element of causal efficacy. His own specifications for a definition are the following:

What we need is a statement expressing the idea — common to both the ordinary and the scientific usage of the word — that causation, far more than a relation, is a category of genetic connection, hence of change, that is, a way of *producing* things, new if only in number, out of other things. This efficacy or productivity of the efficient cause, this dynamic character of the causal connection left aside in the Humean formula, is what we shall try to express.[226]

The formulation that Bunge comes to as a result of this attempt is the following: "If C happens, then (and only then) E is always produced by it." [227] In this formula he interprets both C and E as events, and otherwise maintains that his wording preserves all of the essential components of causality, namely, "conditionalness, uniqueness, one-sided dependence of the effect upon the cause, invariability of the connection, and productivity, or genetic nature of the link." [228] In this definition, it should also be noted that Bunge is focusing solely on efficient causality, since, following modern usage, he has already agreed to "restrict the meaning of the term 'cause' to *efficient cause*, or extrinsic motive agent, or external influence producing change — in contrast to other kinds of cause. . . ." [229] One of his distinctive theses, however, is that the causal determinism implied in his formula is incomplete, in the sense that it is inadequate to explain completely why changes occur. Thus he comments:

> The act of releasing a bow is usually regarded as the *cause* of the arrow's motion, or, better, of its acceleration; but the arrow will not start moving unless a certain amount of (potential elastic) energy has previously been stored in the bow by bending it; the cause (releasing of the bow) triggers the process, but does not determine it entirely. In general, efficient causes are effective solely to the extent to which they trigger, enhance, and damp inner processes; in short, extrinsic (efficient) causes act, so to say, by riding on inner processes.[230]

The externality of causation, so conceived, is what prevents efficient causes from determining their effects completely, and thus causation is not to be identified with determinism. On the other hand, "an adequate picture is provided by a synthesis of self-determination and extrinsic determination, in which external causes are conceived as unchainers of inner processes rather than as agents molding a passive lump of clay." [231]

In treating of causality and scientific law Bunge takes the position that these are not equivalent, despite the fact that the notion of causation frequently enters into law statements. Among noncausal laws he lists as types the taxonomical or morphological, the kinematical, the statistical, and the socio-historical.[232] The increasing diversification of these law types with the progress of science, as Bunge sees it, arises from a growing awareness "that several categories of determination contribute to the production of every real event.[233] And just as Bunge would not identify causation with complete determinism, nor with lawlike regularity, so he would not equate it with prediction. "Unlike causation, which is an ontological category," he writes, "predictability is an epistemological category . . ." As such, the latter depends on our knowledge of general laws and of specific situations, and so "is grounded in *all* types of lawful determination, including causation." [234]

From the foregoing, it is easy to see why Bunge maintains that explanations in science can be causal, but that causality need not enter into every explanation. "Answers to why-questions need not be causal in order to be scientific, although causal explanation does constitute an important ingredient of scientific explanation in many cases." [235] As examples of causal explanation Bunge lists the following categories: (1) inclusion in a sequence of events or of states; (2) tracing of genesis and evolution; (3) connection with different facts; and (4) analysis of complex into simpler facts of the same nature.[236] Categories of noncausal explanation, on the other hand, include the following: (1) recognition, identification, or inclusion in a class; (2) description; (3) explanation in terms of static structure laws; (4) reference to a lower level; (5) reference to a higher level; (6) statistical explanations; (7) teleological explanations; and (8) dialectical explanations.[237] These categories, it may be remarked, differ in some respects from those proposed by Nagel, but the similarity of classification is also impressive considering the different philosophical orientations of the two men.

Although Bunge wrote his book as a defense of the causal principle, he does not regard this principle as a panacea that can replace every form of determinism. Rather he attempts to locate it in the broader context of general determinism, with the result that, for him, "every failure of causality *stricto sensu* can be regarded as the victory of a different principle of determination, and it simply marks the breakdown of outdated ontologies that are too narrow to make room for the unlimited richness of reality, as progressively disclosed by the sciences." [238] The broader principle of determinacy that he urges, moreover, envisages the widest possible range of ontological factors "to afford a truer account of being and becoming." [239] Thus it is not surprising that Bunge avows finally that the "peripatetic norm [*cognitio per causas*] may still be regarded as the paradigm of science," while conceding that terminological and other revisions have to be made in it to keep abreast of developments since the "early stage of rational knowledge" represented by Aristotelianism.[240]

Despite his allowing this wide range of ontological factors as determiners and generally rejecting logical empiricism, Bunge retains some Humean vestiges in his treatment of causation, such as basing his formulation of the causal principle on an event ontology. The last writer whom we shall consider, Rom Harré, parts with even this remnant of logical empiricism and reasserts a traditional type of realism as the philosophy most in accord with scientific practice. In his major systematic work thus far, *The Principles of Scientific Thinking*, [241] Harré in fact launches a full-scale attack on what he refers to as the "myths" that have dominated the philosophy of science literature to date, the principal of which are event ontology and the logico-mathematical ideal of deductive explanation. It is these myths, in his analysis, that give rise to the problem of induction and the problem of causation, which can only be solved by renouncing the exclusive concern with events and by attributing a proper role to causal efficacy in scientific explanation. The germ of Harré's reasoning is contained in the following passage:

> If statements describing the succession of events with which we have some acquaintance exhaust our knowledge of nature, then no general statement including in its subject matter so far unobserved events of similar kinds can be known to be true. There will always be insuffi-

cient evidence for it. Since to predict we need to generalize our past knowledge to new as yet unobserved cases,
we arrive very simply and swiftly at the *problem of induction*. How do we justify logically our entirely practically justified confidence in the continuance of certain,
carefully distinguished, event "patterns"? Events are, it is
alleged, entirely independent of one another. One event
must have ceased to exist before another in the sequence
can be. There can be no carry over. If an event of a certain kind has happened it seems that an event of any
other kind whatever *could* succeed it, no matter what
had come before. Yet we know that this is not so. We do
distinguish an accidental succession of events from a causal succession. This leads to the *problem of causation*.
The universe as we know it is *characterized* by the striking phenomenon of causation. It is not the case that an
event of any logically possible kind follows one of a
given kind. Provided we ensure, or are satisfied of the
stability of the conditions in which the events occur, just
one kind of event follows one of a certain kind, in most
situations. Even when the outcome is not fully known, a
determinate range of probabilities for the likely outcomes
can be found. This is so striking as to lead one to the
idea that events are generative, that one happening generates another, and also that things have quite determinate and characteristic powers to produce definite kinds
of events. But this could not be if it is believed both that
events are all that there is and that events are independent one of another.[242]

Harré's working out of the details of his thesis is too involved to be summarized here, although we shall have the occasion to return to some of its features in our subsequent
exposition. Central to this thesis, however, is his understanding of laws of nature and how these are related to scientific
explanation. Harré's analysis of such laws is based on the
conviction "that the aim of science is to try to find the structures, states and inner constitutions from which the phenomena of nature flow." [243] Stated otherwise, it is the scientist's
task "to look for the causal mechanisms of which the patterns
and regularities of phenomena are the effects." [244] This being
so, the discovery of constant conjunctions and confirming instances in itself does not supply an adequate ground for as-

serting a law of nature, even though it may provide the basis for proposing a generalization as a candidate for lawlike status. The ground for holding any generalization to be a valid law will then not be the observed events and confirming instances, but rather the conviction that there exists "some generative mechanisms, structures and powers in the internal constitution of matter, pervasive fields and so on, which are responsible for the patterns and regularities observed in nature and noted in the instance-statistics."[245] On this understanding causal laws differ from other types of natural law only in the fact that they explicitly assert "the generative connection of cause and effect."[246] Put otherwise:

> Causal laws are those which state the permanent or enduring conditions under which a certain kind of phenomenon will occur; in short they describe the modes of generation or mechanisms of production of phenomena.[247]

A distinctive feature of Harré's analysis of laws of nature is his association of the causal efficacy behind them with the concept of "power."[248] He regards this concept, together with those of "capacity," "liability," "tendency," etc., as of the utmost importance in establishing a realist conception of natural law. He claims also:

> The differentiation and identification of things and materials in terms of their powers, rather than their qualities, leads to an epistemology and metaphysics closer to the realities of scientific thought. To say of a thing or material that it has a power to do, or to be, or to effect something or other, is to say specifically what would happen under appropriate conditions, *and* to say that these effects occur in virtue of the nature of the thing or material, whatever that may be. It is to say specifically what a thing can do, but only unspecifically what nature it has, because it is to say only that it is in virtue of *whatever* nature it has that it can affect things, materials, and observers the way it does.[249]

If this procedure is followed, the study of phenomena as effects leads to an increased knowledge of the entities that cause them, which is reflected in the very way one accords the status of laws to resulting generalizations:

To accord a statement the status of a law is to treat it as describing a process having an associated generative mechanism, but not to describe what that mechanism is. . . . On this view the laws of nature can be seen as describing the powers (and capacities, liabilities, and tendencies) of things and material substances. These may be powers to act upon each other, or to affect observers and instruments in various ways. It is just because these effects are the effects of powers, that observation and experiment can inform us of the natures of things and materials.[250]

Moreover, for Harré such power statements lie at the base of all true explanation. In his mind scientific knowledge consists of two main types of information: (1) knowledge of the internal structures, constitutions, natures and so on of persisting things and materials; and (2) knowledge of the statistics of events, of the behavior of such things and materials, wherein one discerns patterns among these events. A scientific explanation consists essentially in accounting for the second type of information in terms of the first:

In an explanation we show how the patterns discerned amongst events are produced by the persisting natures and constitutions of things and materials. Taken together these two kinds of items of knowledge amount to knowledge of the powers of things and materials.[251]

With this summary of Harré's thought we have now come full circle from Waismann's negative view of causality with which we began this chapter. Harré's declared intention has been to set out a "systematic exposition of the realist point of view in the philosophy of science" that will also constitute a treatment of "conceptual change" and wherein causality will play a major role.[252] To such a project Waismann would probably not have been sympathetic. Waismann had served as Moritz Schlick's assistant in the early days of the *Wiener Kreis*, and would not have found it easy to relinquish the convictions of his youth. Later, it is true, he had come more under the influence of Wittgenstein, whose inspiration is discernible in the linguistic philosophy he developed while lecturing at Oxford. And, by a curious irony, Harré himself is now Waismann's successor at that university, in which capacity he has been the editor of two of the latter's posthumous works.[253]

We have also come full circle in another, more profound sense, for the mention of Oxford should remind us that it was with that venerable university, and with the important work done there by Robert Grosseteste and his school, that we began our historical account of the relationship between causality and scientific explanation. The account has been understandably lengthy; during its course we have seen that relationship variously affirmed, revised, interpreted and reinterpreted, dissolved, and, in the end, reaffirmed once again. It is perhaps time to reflect on such a curious cycle, to extract from it lessons that bear on current philosophy of science, particularly on the vexing problem of the cumulative growth of scientific knowledge, and it is to these tasks that we now turn.

CHAPTER FOUR

The Varieties of Causal Explanation

THE problem of the cumulative growth of scientific knowledge may be put into focus by contrasting the views of two
contemporary historians of science as to what constitutes scientific knowing and how it is acquired. The first is Charles C.
Gillispie, editor-in-chief of the *Dictionary of Scientific Biography,* in process of publication at this writing, which when
completed will be the definitive encyclopedia of the history of
science.[1] Gillispie is also the author of *The Edge of Objectivity,* a study in the history of modern science whose very title
conveys the impression that, with science's advance, the cut-
ting edge of objectivity clears out hazy and confused areas of
thought, eliminates subjective and idiosyncratic judgments,
and contributes to the cumulative growth of knowledge.[2] Gillispie's view of the historiography of science, which sees it as
documenting such advances in knowledge, has been implicitly accepted by the major philosophers of science discussed
in the preceding chapter, who tend to regard science as rational, critical inquiry that is productive of a publicly verifiable type of knowledge, now growing more or less continuously, although contributing to human understanding on an
appreciable scale only within the past few centuries.

The other historian of science is Thomas S. Kuhn, whose

The Structure of Scientific Revolutions has made, consciously
or not, a significant attack on the "cumulative growth of
knowledge" thesis.[3] Kuhn asserts that the larger part of scientific activity, which he calls "normal science," is essentially
puzzle-solving within the context of a paradigm or set of
rules that first comes to be generally accepted, and then is
tenaciously held, within a scientific community. At rare inter-
vals, in his view, scientists break out of this normal pattern
and institute a revolution, which is equivalent to a conceptual retooling within the community and the adoption of a
new paradigm. The latter, once painfully acquired, in its turn
is found to work effectively in solving yet further puzzles.
Through a series of such scientific revolutions, however, and
this is Kuhn's key contention for our purposes, there is not
necessarily linear progress or cumulative growth. Scientific
revolutions may in fact be more accurately characterized as
generating different ways of looking at things, somewhat akin
to Gestalt switches, and one should be wary of regarding
them as productive of new truths, or even of seeing them as
tending asymptotically to objective truth as the limit of a
knowledge-acquisition process.[4]

Kuhn's attack on the concept of truth has elicited a reaction from Karl Popper and some of his disciples, most notably Imre Lakatos, who, while sympathetic to certain aspects
of Kuhn's thesis, feel that he fails to take adequate account of
the results of rational inquiry in furthering human knowledge.[5] Popper focuses on the method of falsification and sees
this as a way of approaching truth, at least as an ideal.[6] He,
however, disagrees with the main line of empiricist thought
in the United States, and another of his disciples, Paul K.
Feyerabend, has attacked the prevalent empiricist doctrine of
scientific theories and the observational-theoretical dichotomy
it implies as inadequate characterizations of actual scientific
practice.[7] Particularly in questioning certain technical developments in the philosophy-of-science literature, such as the
coherence condition for successive theories and the concept
of meaning-invariance for observational terms, Feyerabend
seems to have joined forces with Kuhn, since both effectively
question the "cumulative growth of knowledge" view of the
scientific enterprise.

The apparently antithetical viewpoints of Gillispie and Kuhn both have much to commend them, and the stance to be taken in this chapter owes something to each. While agreeing with Kuhn and Feyerabend in their dissatisfaction with current accounts of science and how it achieves its results, we disagree with the alternatives they provide on the ground that these overly relativize the work, and the resulting advances, of the scientific community.[8] The history of science can be utilized to show how subjectivity and relativism have to some extent attended every stage of science's development, but history can be used also, in accordance with Gillispie's ideal, to illustrate the progressive growth of man's knowledge concerning the world of nature. Yet the latter view of the history of science, we also agree, is difficult if not impossible to justify in terms of a philosophy of science that conceives scientific explanation on the model of formal deducibility alone. Even proposals to think of explanations as answers to the question "Why?," we would further maintain, do not go far enough in broadening out the scope of scientific inquiry. Aristotle, it may be recalled, had conceived of four different types of questions, only one of which was the why-question, and each of these he thought could be answered in causal terms.[9] The varieties of causal explanation he proposed, and which we have seen time and again appearing in different guises throughout this historical account, in our estimation are able to provide more powerful instruments for the acquisition of truth than has been acknowledged in the recent past. Indeed, it is this link between causality and explanation, variously asserted and defended in the West for close to eight centuries, that we will now propose as a ground for the solution of the "growth of knowledge" problem.

To develop these requisite varieties of causal explanation and at the same time to detail the richness of their development since first being proposed in classical antiquity, we here utilize an expository device conceived and developed by Gerald Holton, who refers to it simply as "thematic analysis." [10] In Holton's view, the practice of science in any period of its history is accompanied by certain themata or themes that are usually not stated in the scientific literature of the period but are nonetheless requisite for its full understanding. The same is true of the work of the individual scientist, whose personal views and convictions about nature and the ways to study it generally remain unexpressed, although they may be a governing factor in his discoveries and resulting contributions.[11] To isolate, and thus illustrate, themes of this type, Holton suggests an analysis of science into three components, based on an analogy with the Cartesian coordinate system. Two of these components, which in his usage define the *x-y* plane, are universally recognized as essential to scientific discourse: the first is the experimental or empirical component and the second is the mathematical or analytical component, which he projects along the *x-* and *y-*axes respectively. They correspond roughly to the experimental and the theoretical aspects of science, and accord well with the logical empiricist view of science, with its matters of fact expressed in observational terms and its formal or logical analyses requiring the further use of theoretical terms. They also accord well with the practice of historians of science who generally document both experimental and mathematical contributions, and these a practice not only of the founders of modern science and their followers, but also of their precursors in the Middle Ages and Greek antiquity. In fact, the way in which such a precursor is usually identified — and this is the practice we have followed in our first volume — is in terms of one or other of these components, now regarded as essential for labeling any contribution "scientific."

Holton further maintains that, notwithstanding the claim of positivists that statements are scientifically meaningless unless they have components in this *x-y* plane, such projections are themselves made from a fuller body of knowledge that may be represented by a three-dimensional *x-y-z* space. Here the new element is the *z-*dimension, or projection along the *z-*axis, which Holton refers to as the thematic component of scientific discourse. This dimension is that of the fundamental presuppositions, methodological judgments and decisions, philosophical convictions, ideological and even theological views, all of which may be grouped under the rubric of themata or themes, and none of which is derived from, or resolvable into, empirical observation on the one hand or formal analysis on the other.[12] Holton goes on to illustrate this

thematic component in terms of a concept that is closely associated with the subject of our inquiry, that, namely, of force.
The concept of force, he explains, may be considered as a
point in the x-y plane whose projection on the x-axis "corresponds to the empirical meaning of 'force,'" i.e., its detection
and measurement through, say, the distortion experienced by
standard objects," and whose projection on the y-axis corresponds to "its analytical meaning," i.e., its vector properties
whereby it obeys the parallelogram law of composition.[13]
Similarly, a law statement such as that for gravitational attraction can be analyzed in the x-y plane, since the possibility
exists of verifying the experimental component, e.g., "whether
two masses do move closer in a Cavendish experiment," as
well as the theoretical component, e.g., "whether the analysis
in terms of vectors in Euclidean space is more appropriate
than, say, in terms of scalars." [14] As distinguished from these
components in the x-y plane, however, Holton points to a thematic dimension also associated with the concept of force,
which he identifies as "the persisting theme of an active potency principle that stands behind the whole sequence of concepts from which our idea of force has developed: *energeia,
anima, vis, Kraft.*" [15] Holton does not elaborate on the example, but from our foregoing exposition it should be quite clear
that thematically the resulting idea of force had taken on
very different meanings for Newton, Leibniz, Herschel, and
Mach, even though they all might well have agreed on methods of measuring it and manipulating it mathematically as
the equivalent of a vector quantity. It is, in fact, precisely
these differences along the z-axis that turn out to be most significant for understanding the various opinions of these men
on the role of forces and causes in scientific explanation.

To generalize Holton's analogy further, we now propose
to add time as an additional dimension and so regard scientific thought as developing within a four-dimensional manifold. Within this manifold, and considering the tendency towards specialization within the scientific community itself, we
may also propose the various axes as focuses of special
interest: thus, the x-axis constitutes the domain of the experimentalist and the y-axis that of the theoretician; the z-axis, on
the other hand, is the province of the philosopher of science,

whereas the *t*-axis defines the area of concern for the historian of science.[16] No one specialist, of course, can do his work in isolation from the total thought complex whose particular dimension he is investigating, and indeed, as one proceeds beyond the *x*-axis to the higher orders of dimensionality (implicitly replacing *x, y, z, t* by the indices *1, 2, 3, 4*), a fuller knowledge of the entire manifold becomes more and more essential.

The thematic analysis that we here undertake focuses, in our extension of Holton's analogue, along the *z*- and *t*-axes. Continuing with the chronological divisions that have been regulative throughout our account, we now consider themes relating to causality and scientific explanation that characterize, respectively, the preclassical, the classical, and the contemporary periods of science's history. The themes are representative of these chronological periods, but they are also chosen in such a way as to contribute to an understanding of how causal explanation itself functions as a key factor in the cumulative growth of scientific knowledge. Again, so that our exposition may serve comparative as well as synthetic purposes, it ranges freely along the *t*-axis, thereby allowing the juxtaposition of ideas, however diverse on a chronological scale, that may prove mutually illuminating and so contribute to a fuller understanding of the knowledge-acquisition process.

1. Preclassical Themes

From a methodological viewpoint the preclassical period was dominated by the *Posterior Analytics* and its ideals of demonstrative certitude, although some elements of hypothetical reasoning, usually associated with mathematical premises that could "save the phenomena," were also consistently present. Considering the varieties of answers to Aristotle's four scientific questions, the fourfold structure of causality together with the many meanings that could be subsumed under each of its categories, and the dialectical possibilities of hypothetical argument, this period saw a richness of explanatory modes that has no parallel in either the classical or the contemporary periods. At the same time there was a pov-

erty of materials on which to use this abundance of methodological techniques, with the result that the literature of the
period often creates an impression of hairsplitting rather than
of intelligent utilization. With the burgeoning of materials
open to scientific inquiry, however, and the reopening of
questions relating to the types of explanation available to the
scientist, the earlier concerns can assume a new importance.
Two themes around which discussion of this importance may
conveniently be centered are: first, the classification of various types of explanation; and second, the role of causal definitions in certain of these types, the latter theme being a natural outgrowth of the first, as will become apparent in what
follows.

a. Types of Explanation

Ernest Nagel's list of ten different types of why-questions offers a convenient starting point for our comparative
analysis (see p. 207). In view of Nagel's acknowledgment of
the stringency of the epistemic requirements set down in the
Analytics, it should not be surprising that his list has its defects when studied in the light of the Aristotelian canons. An
obvious limitation, connected with the preclassical meaning
of *epistēmē* or *scientia,* is that it asks questions for which no
"scientific" answers are possible and at the same time omits
other questions, that, if answered, could be productive of true
"science." This limitation notwithstanding, when the former
questions are eliminated and the term "cause" understood in
the four different senses of *aitia* as explanatory factors, it
turns out, somewhat surprisingly, that all of the scientific explanations Nagel offers are actually causal explanations, in
the sense of being reducible to one or other of these four.

For example, the first question, concerned with a mathematical property, may be answered in terms of a formal *aitia;*
the fourth question (why ice floats on water) elicits a re-
sponse in terms of efficient factors such as forces; the fifth and
sixth questions (the depression of water's freezing point by
the addition of salt and the hereditary characteristics of
inbred hybrid peas) require answers in terms of material factors, such as ionic components in solution and genetic materials being transmitted; while the ninth question (human

beings having lungs) calls for a reply in terms of the final cause or purpose of these organs, such as conveying oxygen to the blood. The questions concerned with historical phenomena (3 and 10), even when statistically described, permit of no apodictic replies and thus are not strictly scientific. Similarly, the questions relating to single events or individual persons (2, 7, and 8) would be ruled out in accordance with peripatetic canons as too singular or contingent for scientific judgment, since *de singularibus non est scientia.*[17]

Questions relating to singulars and to historical phenomena were apparently included by Nagel in his list because of the fairly general acceptance of the covering-law model for scientific, and even historical, explanation. From a preclassical viewpoint, however, one may seriously question the sense in which such a covering law or similar generalization may be said to explain. Answering a query as to why moisture formed on the outside of a glass that was filled with ice water yesterday by stating that this *always* happens under those particular conditions, would appear to a peripatetic as really no explanation at all.[18] To shed light on the phenomenon and generate an understanding of it, one would have to detail the factors that caused the moisture to form, somewhat along the lines of Herschel's account of the cause of dew (p. 110). But then the covering law becomes merely an interim device that stimulates one to think out what factors make the generalization itself true, and this ultimately elicits a causal explanation.

Bunge's classification of explanations, while similar in some respects to Nagel's, is more easily assimilable to preclassical categories. The reason for this is his insistence, similar to Claude Bernard's, on seeking out all the "determiners" of phenomena. A determiner, in his understanding, is not really different from the *aitia* of the Greeks or the *causa* of the medievals. Thus all one need do is add to his account of causal explanation further accounts in terms of "inner determiners" and teleological factors, and the complete causal apparatus of the preclassical period comes to be implicit in his analysis.[19]

This is not the place to argue the semantics of terms like "cause," "determiner," and "explanatory factor," but it may be remarked that during both the preclassical and the classical periods these terms were roughly equivalent, and only in the contemporary period has causality generally been narrowed to its Humean understanding. Explanations in terms of material factors were implicitly sought by Galileo, Newton, and Hobbes, and explicitly sanctioned by Harvey and Bernard in their biological studies. The focus on forms as explainers is notable in the work of Gilbert and Kepler, and assumes a key importance for Francis Bacon, who saw it as the terminus of all inductive understanding. Efficient agents, similarly, were searched for by Galileo, Kepler, Newton and Harvey; they assumed the role of principal explainers for Descartes, Hobbes, Locke, and Hume; and, in the guise of forces, they became the ultimate "true causes" for Herschel, Whewell, and Mill. In the classical period final causality was generally not accorded explanatory power within the physical sciences, although Leibniz saw it of use even there; for the biological sciences, of course, Harvey and Bernard continued to insist on its importance. It goes without saying that in the preclassical era all four types of explanatory factors were invoked, as exemplified in the analyses of thunder and lightning by Grosseteste and Aquinas, of the magnet by Peter of Maricourt, of the rainbow by Theodoric of Freiberg, and of local motion by Richard Swineshead in the manuscript attributed to him.[20] Also noteworthy is the fact that these medieval uses of causality did not always occur in the context of demonstration, but in fact more frequently appeared in attempts to find a definition of a phenomenon or essential nature, which definition was also viewed as having explanatory power, as will become clear in our subsequent treatment of causal definition.

To return to Nagel's categories, it will be recalled that he, like Braithwaite, endorses the use of teleological explanations in scientific contexts, although both state their opposition to the use of peripatetic "final causes." One such explanation already appears in Nagel's list, e.g., the case of lungs supplying oxygen to the blood. Another example, which he subjects to fuller analysis, is the assertion that "the function of chlorophyll in plants is to enable plants to perform photosynthesis (i.e., to form starch from carbon dioxide and water in the presence of sunlight)." [21] Such a statement may obviously be viewed as an answer to the why-question, "Why do plants contain chlorophyll?" Nagel's way of eliminating final causes from this explanation is to take the photosynthetic operation as something to be achieved and then inquire into the necessary conditions that make such achievement possible. Thus a teleological statement about chlorophyll, in his analysis, may be replaced without loss of meaning by the nonteleological statements, "Plants perform photosynthesis only if they contain chlorophyll," or "A necessary condition for the occurrence of photosynthesis in plants is the presence of chlorophyll." [22]

This technique, it may be observed, is not unlike that proposed by Aquinas for demonstration *ex suppositione finis*, which was taken up by Buridan, Paul of Venice, and others, and came to be regarded in the preclassical period as the normal way of demonstrating in natural science.[23] Aquinas's concern was to show, in the context of Grosseteste's concern with eternal truths, how demonstrative knowledge could be attained with respect to processes that are directed to an end, but are sometimes impeded from attaining that end through defects of material or efficient factors — in this case, say, the absence of water or sunlight. There was nothing mysterious or obscurantist about Aquinas's methodological use of final causality in this context, nor did his general endorsement of teleology bespeak an intrusion of anthropomorphism or of theologism into his science.[24] He and his mentor, Albert the Great, no less than modern empiricists, wished to put physical science on the strongest observational base possible. Indeed Aquinas would have found little to quarrel with in Nagel's maintaining that:

> The difference between a teleological explanation and its equivalent non-teleological formulation is . . . comparable to the difference between saying that Y is an effect of X, and saying that X is a cause or condition of Y. In brief, the difference is one of selective attention, rather than of asserted content.[25]

Noteworthy here, however, is Nagel's use of "cause" in the sense of a material factor or condition and of "effect" to des-

ignate an end attained, or a process or natural function ful-
filled, which is clearly what preclassical methodologists
would have designated as a final cause. Hence, even in his
own employment of "cause" and "effect" in a teleological context, Nagel must allow these terms to take on broader meanings than in their Humean sense of efficient causation.

Nagel's why-questions, as already observed, relate only
to knowledge of the reasoned fact (*to dioti*, or *propter quid*),
and thus leave untouched Aristotle's other three categories in
which scientific questions may be located. Among these are
that-questions or questions of fact (*to hoti*, or *quia*), as in the
modern example, "Is it a fact that all sulphur is yellow?";
questions of existence (*ei esti*, or *an sit*), e.g., "Is there a
planet in the solar system beyond Neptune?"; and questions
of nature or essence (*ti estin*, or *quid*), e.g., "What *is* sulphur?" Some of these questions, furthermore, may themselves
be associated with why-questions, or focus on refinements
that are necessary to render the answers to such questions
fully intelligible. So one might ask why sulphur is an element,
or why it is yellow, or why there is a perturbation in Neptune's orbit around the sun, and in each case when answering
he will be forced to clarify his own thought on a question of
nature, of fact or property, and of existence, respectively.

Nagel does not take up these questions explicitly, but
significantly he makes allowance for laws that are related to
them, which he sees as involved in answers to why-questions.
They are not causal laws, in his terminology, although in the
preclassical period they would have been seen to contain
causal components. In what follows we shall refer to what he
has in mind as taxonomic laws or taxonomic generalizations.
Nagel describes them in these terms:

> Other laws that easily escape notice because they are so
> familiar lurk in the characterization of various things as
> water, glass, and so on. These latter laws in effect affirm
> that there are distinct kinds of substances, each of which
> exhibits certain fixed concatenations of traits and modes
> of behavior. For example, the statement that something is
> water implicitly asserts that a number of properties (a
> certain state of aggregation, a certain color, a certain
> freezing and boiling point, certain affinities for entering

into chemical reactions with other kinds of substances, etc.) are uniformly associated with each other. The discovery and classification of kinds is an early but indispensable stage in the development of systematic knowledge; and all the sciences, including physics and chemistry, assume as well as continue to refine and modify distinctions with respect to kinds that have been initially recognized in common experience.[26]

Since such laws define specific kinds, they embody formal determiners or formal causes, and to the extent that they resolve properties into various aggregates and components, to say nothing of affinities and powers, they may involve material and efficient factors as well. Taxonomic generalizations are therefore closely associated with the methodological devices of distinction and definition so effectively employed by the Greeks and medievals, and to the extent that these both may employ causal analysis, they lead us into our next theme characteristic of the preclassical period, that, namely, of causal definition.

b. Causal Definitions

The mention of substance and its various kinds recalls a marked thematic difference between the classical and preclassical periods, brought into prominence by the Lockean critique. Translated into the language of causes, this difference reveals itself in a concern that more or less dominated the classical period, namely, whether the causes that count in a scientific explanation must themselves be phenomenal or whether they can also involve, or refer to, hidden powers and mechanisms. The former requirement would be consistent with an empiricist theory of knowledge, which then seemed a good guarantee of truth and certitude, but the latter was attractive also in that it seemed to offer unique opportunities for the growth of knowledge, particularly by way of discovering previously unknown types of entities. While not explicitly answering this question, medieval and Renaissance Aristotelians made a contribution towards an eventual answer, which may be worth examining here. This arose in the context of definitions of accidents, which for the peripatetics related to the phenomenal order, and thus themselves might be thought of as entailing phenomenal causes.

For an Aristotelian such accidents, which include the sensible qualities of sound, heat, and color, must be defined differently from substances.[27] Substances are defined through intrinsic principles, such as their matter or component parts and their form or internal structuring; accidents, on the other hand, are defined through reference to something extrinsic to the accident itself, namely, the subject or substance in which it is found. Thus the matter or material cause of a substance is part of the substance, while the matter or material cause of an accident is not part of the accident but rather its appropriate subject. The formal cause of an accident, in parallel fashion, is the precise effect or modality that the accident introduces into this appropriate subject by its presence. To investigate this, one may first consider the subject without the accident, then determine the proper extrinsic agent or efficient cause that produces the accident in the subject, and from this ascertain precisely what new effect or modality exists in the subject as a result of the accident's presence. The resulting method is one of defining an accident through its proper effect, "effect" being taken here in the sense of primary formal effect or modality that accompanies the accident as a determining form.

To define accidental being, then, the medieval would not begin by considering the accident statically, in a state of existence, but rather by considering it dynamically, as it comes to be, in order to isolate its proper causes. This was the technique used by Theodoric of Freiberg to give a causal definition of the rainbow, which he regarded as an accidental modification of the atmospheric region of the heavens.[28] When this procedure is used, and when a causal analysis is made not of the sensible accident but of the process of its production, the method of reasoning *ex suppositione finis* may be utilized, and from this the identification of all four of its causes readily follows. For example, if sound is being investigated, the final cause of the production of sound is its generation in some subject, and ultimately its sensation in a hearing subject, while the efficient cause is the agent that produces this sound where it was previously not present. Similarly, the

material cause is the medium or substance capable of sup-
porting sound, while the formal cause, the precise quality
being defined, is the modality that sound introduces, as its
formal effect, into the medium in which it comes to exist.
Aquinas used this mode of analysis to define sound in his
commentary on Aristotle's *De anima,* and similar techniques
were utilized in attempts to define thunder and its relationship to lightning.[29]

Generally, the medievals thought that the medium
would have to be motionless to support sound, for otherwise
its background movement might mask the undulatory motion
being generated. In terms of our present-day knowledge of
the various motions within media, it would be necessary to
revise this condition, and moreover to specify what might
serve to distinguish the movement typical of sound from
movements characteristic of other phenomena such as heat.
Here Francis Bacon's inductive canons could be applied, but
they would have to yield information considerably beyond
what Bacon regarded as heat's defining characteristic. A basic
difference between sound and heat might be that sound is
primarily associated with regular undulatory movements of
macroscopic domains of the medium in which it is subjected,
whereas heat is essentially a random molecular movement
within particular domains of the medium. The motion associated with heat, on this accounting, would be more irregular
and of smaller amplitude than that associated with sound. It
might be either a translational motion of entire molecules or
vibratory and rotary motions within molecules themselves on
the part of their constituent atoms. A body having parts susceptible to one or another random motion of this type would,
on this analysis, be the material cause of heat, while its formal cause would be the actuation of this particular suscepti-
bility.

Continuing with this preclassical theme of causal definition, and applying it to information only become available in
the twentieth century, one might propose an analogous definition of color. To simplify the discussion, let us restrict the
analysis to color seen by the eye in opaque surfaces. Such
color is directly sensible to sight, just as sound is sensed by
the ear and heat by touch. The efficient agent that renders

color existent and visible is electromagnetic radiation, or light, which results from the acceleration or deceleration of electric charges known as electrons. The light rays of which this radiation is composed, according to Newton's analysis in the *experimentum crucis*, are not themselves colored, at least not in the same sense that surfaces are colored, but they have the ability to make visibly colored any body containing surface color at least virtually.[30]

The material cause, or proper subject in which color is found, is a surface capable of selectively scattering and reflecting radiation of some particular wavelength or frequency distribution to the eye. In classical physics, the capacity of a surface to absorb and reflect incident radiation is explained by the existence within the medium of electric oscillators. From the viewpoint of quantum mechanics one might say that such oscillators are basically electrons located within atomic and molecular systems that are capable of existing at various energy levels, and that a system of this type may be raised to a higher energy level when light of a characteristic wavelength or frequency falls on the surface. When radiation containing such light impinges on the surface, these oscillators absorb and reradiate it. If the density of oscillators is sufficiently high, the net result is that a large portion of the incident light within the particular wavelength or frequency range is reradiated in a direction away from the surface. This selective radiation of light by the surface is what accounts for its color manifestation.

Such an analysis can be helpful for answering philosophical questions about the reality of color,[31] but for our purposes it raises other interesting questions relative to the growth of scientific knowledge. For example, in discussing the proper subjects of sound, heat, and color, material components such as molecules, atoms, and electrons are found to enter the discussion as explanatory factors. Now, although sound, heat, and color are directly observable, and lend themselves readily to incorporation into an empiricist theory of knowledge, molecules, atoms, and electrons are not so observable, and immediately raise questions of transempirical import. From a "growth of knowledge" perspective, moreover, they immediately suggest the possibility of hidden mechanisms, à la Herschel, made up of types of entities unknown in the seventeenth and eighteenth centuries, but which in their own right can be the objects of scientific enquiry. Each of Artistotle's four questions, in fact, may be asked of these entities, to say nothing of the more recondite types discussed in elementary-particle theory.

A related consequence of this preclassical method of causal definition, and one that directly concerns its explanatory power, bears on the limits one quickly encounters when offering such explanations of qualitative phenomena. The reduction entailed in searching out a proper subject automatically leads one in the direction of greater and greater indeterminacy, with the prospect of terminating ultimately with an explainer that is itself a completely indeterminate substrate. For example, we have stated that the proper subject of sound is a medium or entity with parts susceptible to regular vibratory motion; this requirement automatically limits the existence of sound to subjects large enough to include macroscopic domains of molecules that can support such motion. Similarly, the proper subject of heat is an entity with parts susceptible to random motion in one or more degrees of freedom; under this requirement heat can exist only in aggregates of atomic particles and not in the individual atom as such. Again, the proper subject of color is an entity whose electronic parts are capable of a special type of resonance; it is therefore fruitless to seek color in an entity that does not possess such electronic parts, as, obviously, the electron itself.

The relevance of this defining procedure to the philosophical problems of contemporary science is readily seen. If one cannot speak of a "loud molecule," or a "hot atom," or a "blue electron," on the basis of the very definitions of these qualitative attributes, then one must be even more wary of assigning conventional properties to entities at the level of the so-called fundamental particles. The implied restriction suggests a somewhat novel interpretation of Heisenberg's indeterminacy principle, to be presented in the next chapter. More generally, however, if phenomenal attributes cannot be assigned to ultimate or quasi-ultimate explainers, then the empiricist program would itself seem to be compromised, and other epistemologies that allow stronger ontological claims become of interest to the scientist. The incompatibility of a radical empiricism with preclassical methodological thought is, of course, not totally unexpected, but to pursue this matter further we shall have to turn to other themes that are more distinctive of the classical and contemporary periods.

2. Classical Themes

Newton is the colossus who stands astride the entire modern period, but of parallel thematic importance are Descartes and Bacon, each of whom symbolizes an important ingredient of the classical scientific mentality. Prior to the seventeenth century almost all of the discoveries now regarded as scientific were made in the context of applied mathematics, but it was not until Descartes arithmetized the continuum with his analytic geometry that mathematics came into its own as the queen of the sciences. Similarly, some experimental work had been done before Bacon's *Novum Organum,* but the latter became the rallying point for those who would break away from a sterile scholasticism and embark on systematic programs of experimental discovery.[32] In Holton's analogue, the x-y plane was itself the creation that most typifies classical science, and its two components, the x- and y-axes, are best symbolized in the ideals of Bacon and Descartes respectively. Newton's genius combined both ideals, of course, and the mathematical physics he created gave inspiration to everyone who followed, while also bequeathing to them philosophical and methodological problems of great magnitude that have not yet been completely unraveled.

The joint contribution of Descartes and Newton is generally referred to as the "mechanical philosophy," and it is this philosophy that suggests the two themes we here expound as characteristic of the classical period. These relate to the use of causal reasoning, understanding this in the sense of mechanical causes, to provide explanations of the system of the world, and the use of mechanisms or models, patterned on that of the world system, to explain all of the other phenomena of nature. Although defective in many particulars, both of these themes proved enormously powerful and suggestive, and are generally regarded among the key ideas that brought about the Scientific Revolution, with its great advances in knowledge of the cosmos.[33]

a. Causal Reasoning

The first theme, the use of mechanical causes to replace the "occult qualities" of the medievals, emerged only gradually through the successive contributions of the founders of classical physics, namely, Gilbert, Kepler, Galileo, and Newton. The dominance of a Neoplatonic mathematicism, linked in some ways to Grosseteste while incorporating elements from the hermetic and world-soul traditions of the Renaissance, impeded the early stages of this development. Gilbert's stress on form, Kepler's concern with regular solids and world harmonies, and Galileo's conviction that the book of nature is written in the language of mathematics, all tended to emphasize the mathematical over the physical when seeking explanations of the cosmos. Yet Kepler did effect the breakthrough to physical causes, inspired by Gilbert's explanations of magnetic phenomena, and Newton culminated the development with his analysis of force, particularly that of gravity. The mathematical component was strong even in Newton's thought, however, for when discussing gravitational forces he stated that it was his design "only to give a mathematical notion of those forces, without considering their physical causes or seats," and he further maintained that when speaking of attractions, impulses, and so on, he was considering the forces of which he wrote "not physically, but mathematically." [34] Similarly, Newton's teaching on "absolute space" reflected an almost unconscious merging of physical and mathematical concepts that would vitiate, for Mach and Poincaré, the efficacy of his proofs for the earth's rotation and the heliocentric structure of the solar system.

Contrasted with medieval evaluations of mathematical reasoning and the minimal ontological claims made in the preclassical period for "mathematical hypotheses," the foundations of Newtonian mechanics seem uncritical, if not naive. Berkeley reacted against them, of course, and both Descartes and Leibniz sought to develop their natural philosophies in ways that would employ contact forces alone, of whose physical character they could be quite well assured. Yet it did not take long for Newton's strictures on how his *Principia* was to be interpreted to be forgotten, and for all his forces to be equated with physical causes in the strongest possible sense. Kant's *Metaphysical Foundations* shows the extremes to which philosophers would quickly be driven by their fascination for force concepts as explanatory factors in physical science.

It was with Herschel and Whewell, however, that causal reasoning in the mechanical mode reached its highest degree of perfection. Coupling Newton's insights with Bacon's insistence on inductive reasoning, and rejecting Comte's positivistic interpretation of the resulting product, they systematically expounded how knowledge of forces, seen now as "true causes," could lay bare all the secrets of the physical universe. If someone were to ask, "Why does the earth bulge at the equator?" or "Why do the trade winds blow in the direction they do?" or "What accounts for the precession of the equinoxes?" they could give precise answers in terms of the velocity of the earth's rotation and the attractive forces of sun and moon exerted on its resulting bulge. Herschel, in particular, documented all the advances in the study of the solar system, showing how perturbations in planetary orbits could reveal the existence of new planets, and even extending Newtonian principles into the sidereal regions of the heavens to explain binary star phenomena (pp. 112–17). Mechanical reasoning from effect to cause, to new effect again, reached its apogee in his physical astronomy, which thenceforth became the model on which all of modern science would be based.

Compared to preclassical and contemporary themes, this first theme of the classical period led to extravagant claims for truth and certitude, showing little of the methodological sophistication of those that preceded and would follow. The new beginning in the seventeenth century thus saw too sharp a break with the traditions of the Middle Ages and the Renaissance, for the methodologists of classical science could have learned much from Zabarella, Nifo, and Paul of Venice, to say nothing of their Parisian and Oxonian predecessors.[35] Bacon, Hobbes, and Descartes knew only the scholastic rudiments of this Aristotelian teaching, and Herschel and Whewell apparently knew nothing at all. Yet, as the classical period wore on, the problems of hypothetical reasoning were newly addressed, some progress in eliminating circular reasoning was made through the consilience of inductions and other proposals, and an awareness of the difficulty of reaching final results, even in the astronomical sciences, was gradually generated.

More than counterbalancing these defects, if they were such, was the great stimulus the mechanical philosophy gave to understanding the world of nature in terms of its underlying structures and mechanisms. The causal explanations of physical astronomy were all reducible to force concepts, and thus to efficient causality. Toward the latter part of the classical period, progress was made in another direction, with explanations that would pertain more to the orders of formal and material causality. These make up the next theme to be discussed, namely, the methodological employment of mechanisms and models, for these also were to contribute significantly, though in unsuspected ways and after some time delay, to the growth of scientific knowledge.

b. Mechanisms and Models

The tendency to think of natural processes mechanically dates from Greek antiquity, in the form of the atomistic explanations of Democritus, which came to be known in the Latin West through the didactic poem of Lucretius, *De rerum natura*. Some medievals, such as Nicholas of Autrecourt, offered atomistic accounts of generation and corruption as alternatives to Aristotelian analyses in terms of matter and form, but it was not until the early seventeenth century that mechanistic explanations of natural phenomena came to be consistently proposed. Descartes was the author who did the most to stimulate such mechanistic thinking, and his disciples, the Cartesians, quickly propagated his ideas throughout all of Europe. Galileo, Hobbes, and Locke, to say nothing of Newton, were also significant proponents of the mechanical philosophy, contributing to its diffusion and general acceptance in the seventeenth and eighteenth centuries.

While appealing to the imagination, these mechanistic

explanations of the early classical period soon encountered difficulty among the philosophers, of whom Locke is typical (pp. 23–27). The very minuteness of the particles of which the explanatory mechanisms were thought to consist precluded any empirical observation of them, and thus they could only be proposed as mechanical hypotheses. With the growth of modern chemistry, it is true, the particulate nature of matter was put on a more empirical base, and greater credence could be given to atomic and molecular structures, and to changes in such structures, as explanations of chemical phenomena. But still, before such developments were forthcoming, and continuing into more recent times, mechanisms were found to have explanatory value even without their being known to mirror accurately the structure of the real. This value consisted precisely in their utility for modeling hidden processes, and thus providing analogues in terms of which these processes could be understood. To explain this feature of mechanical reasoning, and for purposes of future reference, we shall here enter into a somewhat lengthy digression on models and their various kinds, to show how they have been, and continue to be, an important thematic component in the growth of man's knowledge of the universe.[36]

The growth of human knowledge as it takes place in the individual is somewhat mysterious, but it is nonetheless an incontrovertible fact. Knowledge grows in individuals because they perceive, and observe, and learn from the things around them. Generally they do this by noting the similarities and differences among these things. When a person encounters something he does not know, he attempts to understand it by conceiving it after the fashion of something he does know; thus he uses the known to advance into the realm of the unknown. One way of doing this is through the use of analogy, which is a type of proportionate knowing in which such similarities and differences are explicitly acknowledged. For example, one may attempt to explain intellectual knowing, itself difficult to comprehend, on the analogy of the sense knowledge involved in seeing. To grasp an idea is not the same as to discern a visible object, and yet there are similarities between the two processes, as witnessed by a person's using the words "I see" to signify his intellectual comprehension. Analogy resembles metaphor, a more poetic form of expression, and on this account the scientist tends to avoid it in his formal language, where he aims for precise predication in an unequivocal or univocal way. But in the process of discovery, before he comes to formulate this precise language, he sometimes does employ a type of analogy in his thought processes. He may not use this term explicitly, but he will frequently speak of a model, particularly in connection with a new theory he is proposing. It is this device, the model, that can shed light on the processes by which scientific knowledge grows.

The term "modeling," as applied to scientific discovery — and here we follow Harré's analysis while modifying his terminology — has two referents, one of which is something already known, from which the model is taken, and the other something unknown, at least initially, to which the model is applied. The known factor may be referred to as the source or origin of the model and the unknown factor may be called its application. Thus a model is taken from one thing, its origin, and used to understand another, its application.

There are many kinds of model employed in scientific reasoning; the more important of these may be indicated in terms of simple relationships that hold between the origin and the application. If the origin and application, for example, are similar in form, we may refer to this as uniform, or one-form, modeling. A simple instance of uniform modeling is that occasionally used in applied physics where an exact replica is constructed, on a smaller or larger scale, in order to study a particular phenomenon. Since an actual replica is involved, both origin and application are similar in form, and only a size or dimensional change serves to distinguish the two. In difform modeling, on the other hand, the origin and the application are different in form. Such a difference sometimes arises from the fact that the origin pertains to the subject matter of one field of study whereas the application pertains to the subject matter of another. An example, again from applied physics, is the use of electrical circuit analysis to study problems of mechanical vibration. The modeling is difform because the origin, an electrical circuit, is different in form from the application, mechanical vibratory motion.

Two subdivisions of uniform modeling should also be noted. Mention has already been made of the fact that changes of size, or dimensional changes, frequently characterize such modeling, but this need not always be the case. The type of uniform modeling in which it does occur may be labeled micromorphic, to indicate that the thing modeled is much smaller than the source from which the model is taken; when it does not occur, it may be referred to as macromorphic modeling, to indicate that there is no appreciable difference of size. An interesting case of micromorphic modeling, taken from the medieval period, is Theodoric of Freiberg's discovery of the first essentially correct theory of the rainbow.[37] Whereas most of his predecessors had regarded the rain cloud as an effective agent in the production of the rainbow, and even saw some similarity between the colors of the bow and the spectrum resulting from the sun's rays as they pass through a spherical flask of water, they all tended to think of the flask, and hence to model it, as a cloud or as a collection of raindrops. Theodoric was the first to see that a globe of water could be thought of, and hence used to model, not a small spherical cloud but a magnified raindrop. His experiments with rays of sunlight passing through the water-filled globe enabled him to duplicate in a laboratory situation, and thence to explain, the essential properties of the primary and secondary rainbows. His modeling here was uniform, since the spherical flask of water is similar in form to the raindrop, but it was also micromorphic, in the sense that there is an appreciable size difference between the two. An instance of macromorphic modeling, on the other hand, as taken from the classical period, might be the explanation of a planetary perturbation in the solar system by means of a putative or hypothetical planet not yet known to exist. Here the unknown entity is modeled after a known entity and, upon discovery, say, in the case of Neptune, is found not to be appreciably different in size from Uranus, whose planetary orbit it was perturbing.

One ought not make too much of this distinction between micromorphic and macromorphic modeling, however, as differences in size can be quite relative, depending on the observer, his methods of observation, the instruments he has available, etc., and so may have little significance for the ultimate type of scientific explanation achieved. By way of example, the modeling between planets may be referred to as macromorphic, while the actual difference in size between them could be the same as that between a flask of water and a raindrop, which has just been referred to as micromorphic. Again, what appears to be micromorphic modeling at the outset may actually prove to be macromorphic when the effects of distance on observation are taken into account. Stars, for instance, appear so small that they were first modeled as points of light; with the advance of astronomical knowledge they have been more accurately modeled as suns. Now the sun is surely the largest object in reasonable proximity to the earth, and compared to this, a point of light is as micromorphic as one could imagine. Yet, the progress of science has revealed that many of these points of light are bodies of the same order of magnitude as the sun, so the end result is macromorphic modeling. In fact, the very statement that the sun is a star of a certain type shows how scientists do tend to model one entity on another, and how the study of one type of phenomenon leads them to an understanding of others.

As in the case of uniform modeling, so in difform modeling there are various types or distinctions. The first is that between modeling which is simply difform and modeling which is multiply difform. In simply difform modeling, the model is taken from one discipline in an attempt to understand a phenomenon occurring in another, whereas in multiply difform modeling, a more complex model is constructed with elements taken from different disciplines. Studying mechanical vibration problems through electrical circuit analogues is, on the basis of this distinction, simply difform modeling. A better example, and one associated with a famous discovery in biology by a founder of classical science, is William Harvey's work on the circulation of the blood.[38] Here, rather than analyze the flow of blood in animals on the model of total absorption from a linear flow process as Galen had done, Harvey correctly understood it on the model of a circulatory flow maintained by a mechanical pump. His modeling was difform in the sense that the pump pertains to mechanics, whereas the flow of blood pertains to biology or physiology.

As opposed to simply difform modeling, multiply difform would be used when an extremely baffling or complex phenomenon is being studied and its diverse aspects require different constructs in order to be understood. An example, taken from the contemporary period, is the attempt to understand the elementary constituents of matter on the model of a wave-particle. Here the application is in the area of atomic or nuclear physics, whereas the origin has a twofold source: particles are usually studied in dynamics, whereas waves pertain to hydrodynamics or to electromagnetic theory. Another example would be the Bohr atom when it is used as a model to explain the absorption and emission spectra of various substances. Here the application is broadly in the area of chemistry, whereas the model itself is based on two disciplines: mechanics for the planetary features of the atom, and radiation theory for the way in which it absorbs and emits energy.

Another important type of difform modeling shares some characteristics with both the simply and the multiply difform, but is sufficiently different to be proposed as another category. This is where the model is drawn from one or more sources, but in the process a considerable idealization is involved, or an abstraction is made from certain characteristics that normally would be found in the source. Because the source, through idealization or abstraction, is used only partially, we may refer to this as partially difform modeling. A good example of this is the kinetic theory of gases, whose explanatory power we have seen defended by Campbell (p. 201), which models the gas molecule on a massive particle that is vanishingly small, referred to as a "mass point." Abstraction or idealization is involved in this process, and thus it may be regarded as partially difform modeling. It may also be seen alternately as simply difform, in the sense that the chemistry of gases is based on a model taken from mechanics, or as multiply difform, inasmuch as "mass" is taken from mechanics and "point" from mathematics. However, since mathematical analogues are used so extensively in the physical sciences, in the mode of Newton's mathematical physics, and since these involve idealization and abstraction to some degree, it is probably better to regard mathematically inspired models as instances of partially difform modeling. This is par-

ticularly important when they involve limit concepts or ideal-
izations such as the type indicated in the expression "ideal
gas." Such models pose special problems with regard to both
existential statements and lawlike generalizations, to which
we shall return in the next section.

It may be observed at this point that in many situations
where a novel modeling technique is employed to gain understanding of a phenomenon, a new way of looking at things
is involved and a type of Gestalt switch may take place. In
this sense Kuhn is quite correct in seeing scientific revolutions
as involving such switches and changed viewpoints. In fact,
his paradigm shifts can very frequently be seen as modeling
shifts. Feyerabend is also correct in maintaining that there is
not strict meaning invariance throughout the history of science, for under a new modeling technique the entities to
which reference is made do take on new meanings and significance. For example, to say, "A star is a minute hole in the
canopy of the heavens," or, "A star is a pinpoint of light," is
quite different from saying, "A star is a sun." Other statements that would point out similar differences, and at the
same time may serve to illustrate the importance of the modeling theme for the growth of classical science, are the following:

> A rainbow is light dispersed by a cloud.
> A rainbow is light differentially reflected and refracted
> > by spherical raindrops.

> Planets are bodies composed of a quintessence and
> > moved by deferents in eccentric and epicyclic orbits
> > around the earth.
> Planets are heavy or massive bodies moving in elliptical
> > orbits around the sun.

> The flow of blood in mammals is a linear absorption pro-
> > cess originating in the liver and going to the extrem-
> > ities.
> The flow of blood in mammals is a circulation resulting
> > from the pumping action of the heart.

> Elements are *minima naturalia*.
> Elements are the atoms of which molecules are com-
> > posed.

The Milky Way is a cloud of star-like particles.
The Milky Way is a spiral galaxy seen from its side.

All of these pairs of statements, and the list includes some classical discoveries made by the founding fathers of astronomy, optics, chemistry, and biology, do represent changed viewpoints, and yet more is involved in them than mere subjective changes on the part of the viewer. In each pair the second statement represents an advance of objective content as well, it represents a growth of knowledge. If the growth is not cumulative in the Baconian sense of progress by uniform accretion, it is cumulative in the sense that the first statement can be readily understood in terms of the second, and the second actually offers a better explanation of the whole range of phenomena the first was initially thought to account for. To justify these assertions, however, more details will have to be given, and these are best taken up in the context of contemporary themes relating to causal explanation.

3. Contemporary Themes

The foregoing exposition of modeling, like that of mechanical reasoning, has shown the extent to which causal analysis was implicit in classical science, not only in the search for efficient causes of which mechanical forces are the clearest exemplars, but also in the search for formal and material causes in the sense of inner determiners that serve to explain phenomena. While such determiners were never completely or accurately known during the classical period, they were grasped to some extent through analogy by way of the modeling techniques already described, with the wide variety of forms thereby made available to confer intelligibility on subject matters often refractory to understanding. In contemporary science this general trend has continued, although, because of difficulties encountered in quantum theory, the search for ultimate mechanical causes, understood in the efficient sense, has been largely abandoned. The themes that occupy the attention of philosophers of science center around theories and their methods of confirmation and laws or lawlike generalizations and the inductive procedures by which they can be established. These, with slight variations dictated by our interest in causality and the "growth of knowledge" problem, suggest thematic components appropriate for our analysis of the contemporary period.

Scientific knowledge grows in ways similar to other human knowledge, but more specifically it progresses along two main paths: one, the acceptance of new existential statements and the other, the recognition of the validity of new generalizations. With regard to the first, existential statements are usually answers to existential questions; these, in turn, are at least implicit in the theories, with their hypotheses and conjectures, that scientists devise to explain the phenomena they study. The use of expressions such as "atomic hypothesis" and "theoretical entity" is an indication of such implicit questioning, to which answers are normally given through the verification and falsification of existential claims. It was through this process, as we have seen, that Herschel rejected "phlogiston exists" as a valid assertion and opted instead for "oxygen exists" as a new existential statement (p. 112). The second type of knowledge-acquisition device is the new generalization, which is usually associated with scientific laws. Law statements, or lawlike generalizations, are classified in various ways and each type presents its peculiar problems. Models and causes, however, can throw new light on these as on the problems associated with theories, and thus theories and laws, from the viewpoint of their causal implications, are the two themes to which we now turn our attention.

a. Causal Theories

A fruitful way of studying the ontological referents of scientific theories is to investigate the paths by which new existential statements make their way into the language of science. Two routes, not mutually exclusive, would seem to be available: the first through instrumentation, refined techniques of observation, and experimentation, and the second through postulation and ultimately through demonstration, understanding postulation in the sense of theoretical inquiry and demonstration in the sense of conclusive proof. Theories are inevitably involved in the second route, but they are also associated with the first, since the hypotheses on which they are based usually arise in the context of new observation and experimentation.

The invention of the telescope and the microscope were not essential to the Scientific Revolution, but they did much to accelerate its progress and led immediately to the incorporation of a host of new existential statements into the literature of science. One need mention here only the variety of new objects found by Galileo in the heavens with his telescope, described so enticingly in his *Sidereus nuncius,* including myriads of stars, planets of strange shapes, and the mysterious "four Medicean stars" that produced such consternation in Renaissance Florence. The same could be said of Antony van Leeuwenhoek's work with the microscope and the revelation of scores of new microbes, microorganisms of unheard of types, that were eventually to give new stimulus to the sciences of biology and medicine. Such instruments contributed immeasurably to the growth of scientific knowledge, and this growth was for the most part made cumulative by means of micromorphic modeling. Because both instruments magnify, they put the human observer in contact with objects whose size is different from those of ordinary experience, and to understand the change in dimensionality micromorphic modeling proves most helpful. Microbes are organisms, but very much smaller than the organisms ordinarily seen by man. The Medicean stars are moons, but imperceptible to the naked eye and thus not seen as the spherical body that illumines nights on earth. Thus, the universe is populated with new entities, but they are basically the same as entities already known. And so it is uniform modeling that leads to these new existential statements.[39]

Such statements, however, frequently have only a problematic or hypothetical status, and then it becomes necessary for the scientist to verify or falsify them. For example, in the study of the solar system by telescopic means, a planet departs from its projected orbit, calculated on the basis of the influences known to be affecting its motion, and it is suspected that there might be another planet in the solar system that is perturbing its orbit. Such a planet then becomes a hypothetical entity, and criteria are established for verifying or falsifying the statement that accords it existence. In general these criteria are of two types, indicative criteria and recognitive criteria.[40] The simplest example of an indicative criterion is pointing or delimiting the spatio-temporal region in which the postulated object is to be found. Along with this goes a recognitive criterion whereby the object is identified as belonging to the expected type. Using Aristotelian terminology, one could say that indicative criteria of this type establish the *ei esti* or *an sit*, whereas recognitive criteria establish the *to hoti* or *quia*, and in some cases even the *ti estin* or *quid*. Such criteria work for verifying existential statements, but they can also serve to falsify them. Assume, for example, that an astronomer's calculations indicate a spatio-temporal region that is to be searched for the hypothetical planet, on the condition that if there is such an entity, this is where it will be found. The existential statement is falsified if the region is searched and it is found either to be empty or to be occupied by something not meeting the appropriate recognitive criteria. Through the use of such verification and falsification techniques the planets Uranus, Neptune, and Pluto were discovered and are now regarded as parts of the solar system, whereas the putative planet Vulcan, originally postulated to account for other planetary perturbations, is no longer ascribed a real existence.

The cases discussed so far involve only optical magnification, and thus are well suited to analysis in terms of micromorphic modeling. More sophisticated instruments, such as the spectroscope, permit similar uniform modeling, whereby, for example, through the comparison of spectra the sun is identified as a star of a certain type. As more complex instrumentation is utilized, however, and particularly the experimental configurations used in recent times to study the structure of matter, existential statements are encountered that are much more difficult to verify or falsify. Consider the assertion, based on the interpretation of experiments with diffraction patterns, that "There is a lattice structure in crystals." Or the statements, based on the observation of scintillations and tracks in cloud chambers, to the effect that "This is an alpha particle" or "That is a positron." The verification of such statements involves indicative criteria, but these are not simply pointing to the entity described; rather they are indirect criteria whereby one reasons from effect to cause. Similarly, the recognitive criteria are not as simple as in direct pointing, for here the very entity spoken of is quite probably different from anything encountered in previous experience. One may speak of a postulated planet as a theoretical entity, but lattice structures, alpha particles, and positrons are seemingly theoretical entities of a different sort. Yet a distinction may be made on the basis of the type of modeling involved, for the putative planet, as already explained, is based on uniform modeling, whereas these other postulated entities are based on difform modeling. And depending on the three types of difformity already indicated, it is quite possible that different indicative and recognitive criteria will be required to verify or falsify existential statements. Such statements, it may be noted, are implicit answers to the frequently asked questions concerning the ontological status of theoretical entities.

Indicative and recognitive criteria for theoretical entities, then, should be patterned on those used to verify or falsify the existence of the more ordinary types. With indicative criteria there is no special problem, since the indication can only be direct or indirect and, with regard to the indirect, one need have no scruples about employing cause and effect relationships, since these are used to indicate even ordinary types of things. So litmus paper would be inserted into a liquid to verify the presence of an acid or a base, depending on the particular effect of the substance on the paper to supply the indication. It would seem, however, that some type of spatio-temporal localization is necessary for even this indirect pointing, and thus any entity that does not fit into a space-time matrix in one way or another will fail to satisfy indicative criteria. When investigating the types of theoretical entities that enter into the structure of matter, however, such as elementary particles and genes, so long as these are viewed as parts of a whole that has determinate dimensions and exists over a knowable time span, there would seem to be no insuperable problems with spatio-temporal localization.

Recognitive criteria present a more complex problem, for the range of possibilities becomes great as soon as one speaks of entities different from those already known. It is here that some type of ontology becomes essential, and for purposes of discussion we may propose that any postulated entities should fall generally within one of three categories, namely, those of (1) substance or thing, which manifests some permanence and independence in being; (2) property or attribute, which shows dependence in being but with a characteristic way of initiating or affecting activity; and (3) motion or change, which gives indication of being a process or event of some type, either transient or ongoing. How these categories may be utilized will become apparent from a brief consideration of the various types of difform modeling. Suffice it to say, for the moment, that the most interesting cases are those concerned with classifying entities that enter into the structure of ordinary bodies, or with classifying entities that themselves constitute new subsistent types, even though they be extremely transitory and thus exhibit minimal spatio-temporal localization.

Entities based on difform modeling, whether this be simply or multiply difform, therefore present the general problem of how to incorporate novel kinds into an ontology, understanding these kinds as species or subspecies within the categories already enumerated. Obviously multiple difformity raises problems of even greater complexity than simple difformity, particularly when the multiple origin suggests contradictory characteristics. This, as we have seen, is one of the main sources of the extensive literature on the philosophy of quantum theory. Let it be suggested here that the very need to employ multiply difform modeling may already be an indication that the novel kind pertains to a different general category from those of the models that serve as its source. For example, and here Bohm's criticisms are suggestive, to think of a photon — after the fashion of a "wave-particle" — as a thing or substance because this is the way one thinks of particles of matter or water waves, may be wrongheaded; perhaps photons are better thought of in the category of property or attribute, or even in that of process or event. And when such difformly modeled entities are regarded as components of other things, then perhaps they should not be thought of as subsistent entities at all, but rather as modal transforms that result from looking at the same entity in two or more different ways. As examples of such modal transforms one might cite viewing crystals as lattice structures and colors as wavelengths of light.[41]

A special difficulty arises, however, with regard to partially difform modeling, for in this type, as already mentioned, idealization or abstraction is involved, and the question naturally arises as to how much idealization is possible without losing all plausibility of existence. Here one's ontology is again of primary significance, particularly how one goes about incorporating mathematical entities into it, since so much of the idealization and abstraction is of the mathematical sort. It is in this context that a theory of ontological depth, implicitly treated in the foregoing discussion of causal definitions of sensible qualities, can prove of assistance. Briefly, this would maintain that the quantitative aspects of things are ontologically more fundamental than their qualitative aspects, and the material or substantial aspects of things are more fundamental than their quantitative aspects, with the limit being set by a protomatter that can be thought of only as a potency for receiving forms of whatever type. Once this is accepted, then the problem of abstractness translates into something like this: Is it possible for an entity to exist and still be qualityless or even quantityless? Such questioning, as can be seen, is very apt for establishing recognitive criteria in terms of which one can consider answers to further questions such as "Do atoms exist?" and "Do wave-particles exist?" For an atom, as normally conceived, is a kind of thing, but practically speaking it is a qualityless thing, and similarly a wave-particle, if it is a thing at all, gives indication of being not only qualityless but quantityless as well, or at least of not possessing quantitative attributes in the same way as determinately localized bodies. Finally, extremely transitory entities may resist categorization either in terms of material substance or quantity-quality attributes and may have to be thought of as merely processes or events. All of these possibilities are relevant when verifying existential statements in high energy physics, but they serve also to give increased knowledge of the structure of matter. This can be of help in resolving difficulties relating to generalizations and lawlike statements, to which topics we now turn.

b. Causal Laws

There are many problems associated with scientific laws and generalizations of various types, but of key importance is the question of how any generalization is possible for one who would maintain that there can be cumulative growth in scientific knowledge. Generalizations are seemingly based on confirming instances, but a person never knows what the future may bring, and the next instance examined or the next discovery announced may nullify any generalization already made. One may say, "All sulphur is yellow," but apparently he can never be sure that the next sulphur he examines will not be purple, and thus he cannot make even this descriptive generalization with certitude. This will be recognized as the source of numerous paradoxes relating to confirmation theory and the problem of induction, which have given rise to an extensive literature within the past few decades.[42]

In answer to these puzzles, a defensible position is that valid generalizations are possible in science and that these have the character of laws of nature, but they are never easy to arrive at, and they involve an ongoing process of recategorization and refinement of understanding that is part and parcel of knowledge growth. It is impossible, moreover, to explain these changes in terms of formal logic alone, whereas they become quite intelligible to anyone who employs taxonomic principles and causal reasoning in the tradition of the *Posterior Analytics*.

These points may be made through the consideration of a few examples. Contemporary authors commonly distinguish between accidental generalizations and lawlike generalizations on the basis that the first cannot sustain counterfactual inference whereas the second can.[43] To use Nagel's example, an accidental generalization would be "All the screws in Smith's car are rusty," and this is understood to be a mere contingency such that it would not permit one to state of any screw, "If this were a screw in Smith's car, it would have to be rusty." On the other hand, the lawlike statement "All copper expands when heated" permits one to state of a particular piece of copper, "If this were heated, it would expand." On face value the second case assumes that one possesses some knowledge of the nature of copper or what causes it to expand when heated, and thus he knows what would happen even if the event did not take place. Empiricists such as Braithwaite and Nagel, however, because of their unwillingness to concede causal or necessary connections in nature, will not accept this explanation. And, is it not true that there is a finite possibility that the next piece of copper one heats will not expand? If so, how can a law be sustained in the face of disconfirming evidence?

To answer this we now inquire what one would do with a generalization such as "All birds are feathered" in similar circumstances.[44] This is obviously a taxonomic generalization, and so it is open to the possibility of a disconfirming instance. Suppose that a small birdlike creature is presented to us, and it is not feathered. What are the moves that are then open to us? To preserve the taxonomic generalization we can say simply, "This is not a bird." Such a move is equivalent to maintaining "All *true* birds are feathered," but that this is not a true bird even though it looks like a bird. And then, we may understand "not a true bird" in a variety of ways. If this is a single instance, or one of extremely rare occurrence, we may say, "This creature belongs in the category of birds, all right, but actually it is a freak," on the basis that accidents sometimes happen in natural generation. Or, alternatively, if we run into such creatures in great numbers and find that they are of regular occurrence, we divide birdlike creatures into two classes, those that are feathered and those that are not. If we follow usual scientific practice we will retain the name "bird" or "ordinary bird" for the feathered class and we will invent a new name for the nonfeathered; Harré suggests that we do this by spelling "bird" backwards and calling the new class "dribs." So we end up by preserving the generalization, "All birds are feathered," at only the slight expense of adding another generalization, "All dribs are nonfeathered." The well understood case of heavy water versus ordinary water seems to parallel precisely this procedure.[45]

A similar instance, but closer to the concerns with modeling and scientific discovery that have occupied us earlier, is the descriptive generalization, "All sulphur is yellow." [46] Now what does such a generalization normally mean? Nothing more than that this is the hue or color that sulphur manifests to us, where the "this" is what we commonly see and agree to call "yellow," assuming that none of us is blind or afflicted with the organic defect known as color blindness. Now, assume the case where sulphur is presented to someone under a red light, and he sees it not as yellow but as red. Assume also that this is a sophisticated person who knows that the specimen is sulphur and that sulphur under white light is normally yellow. He may observe the red sulphur and state, "It may look red, but it is *really* yellow." What would the word "really" mean in a context such as this? The case is somewhat analogous to that of the "true bird," for what is meant by "really" is "under normal conditions," or "in daylight," or, if the person happens to be a scientist and subscribes to the causal definition of color presented earlier in this chapter, "This substance's surface structure is such that it selectively reflects light of 5745 Angstrom units in wavelength." All three statements are equivalent, upon consideration, to the affirmation that sulphur by its very nature manifests itself as yellow under appropriate conditions. Or, enough is known about the nature of sulphur to assert with confidence how it will appear under various conditions of illumination.

Following this line of thought, we would maintain that it is somewhat simplistic to characterize a law of nature as a formal statement of the type, "All A is B," or "For any x, if x is A then x is B." Rather the correct way is that of attributing an underlying nature to a subject in the much more suppositional mode expressed in Harré's formulation, "Under conditions C, A will manifest sensible quality or characteristic B in virtue of its being of nature N." [47] This statement is based on more than formal analysis, and it attempts to take into account some of the factors behind our thinking when we maintain generalizations such as "All sulphur is yellow." We do have reasons other than mere instance confirmation that encourage us to make such generalizations, and usually these are convictions that the distinctive nature manifests itself in the internal constitution of the subject, or that something such as sulphur has a particular type of surface structure or generative mechanism that will dispose it to display, under appropriate conditions, the sensible quality ascribed to it. The term "nature" is apt for referring to these internal determiners, especially when taken in the sense of Aristotle's *phusis* or *natura*, which is an internal principle of activity or stability that is characteristic of the type. At the outset of scientific investigation it is not necessary that this principle be understood thoroughly, so long as it is seen as a determining internal source of characteristic activity or reactivity. Or, as Harré has indicated, whereas it is quite necessary for us to know what a thing can *do* in a specific way, it is not at all necessary that we grasp what nature it *has* in a specific way, but only generically.[48] So, when we accord a statement lawlike status, we treat it as ascribing an activity or a property to a subject that we believe has a determined nature, or generative mechanism or structure, without attempting to state precisely what that mechanism or structure has to be. It is true also that with the growth of scientific knowledge, we continually revise our estimates regarding that underlying structure or determiner of whatever type, and that this becomes the basis for successive qualifications in our lawlike statements, or for taxonomic recategorizations of the entities they are used to describe. In this connection, both Kuhn and Feyerabend have hit upon an element of truth in the sense that these revised views of internal structures, etc., do constitute new ways of looking at things and do result in variations of meaning, even for the objects of ordinary experience. But such changed viewpoints and variations in meaning do not nullify scientific progress; indeed, they are the very means that insure the cumulative growth of knowledge and its enduring character.

With regard to taxonomic generalizations, therefore, it may be concluded that these are initially based on descriptions that are regularly verified, and thus they are empirically established by instance confirmation, and that it is in this way that a knowledge of the descriptive natures of things is attained. As science progresses, however, exceptions are found to occur and deeper explanations sought for the new characteristics exhibited. It is in this way that descriptive definitions give way to real definitions, which attempt to describe, to the extent possible, the nature or real essence that gives rise to these characteristics. Ultimately the taxa that are used to classify things are established on the basis of internal determiners, such as structures and generative mechanisms, the modern-day equivalent of formal and material causes.[49] So it is that scientists have learned to classify the elements, and all of their manifest properties, in terms of a real essence or nature that they feel is modeled quite accurately by the Bohr atom. Again, they are now beginning to have increased knowledge of all living species in terms of generative mechanisms that they are reasonably confident are modeled by such structures as the DNA molecule, gene pools, and so forth. From this may be seen the crucial importance of modeling, since it can give some insight into the natures of the material substances studied, can provide the basis for revising taxa from time to time, and so assure the possibility of valid lawlike generalizations.

The foregoing has been concerned mainly with taxonomic generalizations, but a final word should be added now about generalizations of other types. The most significant among these are lawlike statements of concomitant variation, such as Boyle's law, $PV = k$, which describes the behavior of a gas under various conditions of pressure and volume.[50] Many scientific laws are of this type, and once such a generalization has been discovered, scientists make efforts to qualify it, as necessary, to guard it against falsification. The devices they use are somewhat different, however, from those employed in preserving taxonomic generalizations. Three may be mentioned here, namely, limitation, modification, and idealization.[51] Working experimentally within the framework of Boyle's law, a scientist may discover disconfirming instances in certain areas where the law was first thought to hold. In this case the law is retained, but the range of its application is set by limiting the values that may henceforth be substituted for its variables. This is an instance of law preservation by limitation. Alternatively, the law may be modified so as to be able to subsume the disconfirming instances as special cases. In this way, for example, Boyle's law was modified to yield Van der Waal's equation, which successfully takes care of instances that would seem to disconfirm the initial law. This is the technique of modification. A third move is to retain the law but to claim that it is not directly applicable to substances of ordinary experience, but rather describes the action of an "ideal gas," which serves to model the behavior of ordinary gases and furnishes some insight into their structure on this account. This final technique is that of idealization. It is by devices such as these that most lawlike statements in the physical sciences are continually revised and understood, while still retaining their character as true generalizations.

With this we terminate our discussion of the varieties of causal explanation in contemporary science and how these can account for the cumulative growth of scientific knowledge. Our handling of the contemporary themes associated with theories and laws diverges, of course, from the interpretations of logical positivists and empiricists, particularly in its reading of their causal implications. Yet the themes we have selected for emphasis do show a continuous development through the preclassical, the classical, and the contemporary periods, and they lend strong support to a realist philosophy of science. The underlying thesis of such a philosophy, stated plainly, is that science is concerned with a study of the real, not with the logical as such, that real entities have natures that can be understood, and that there can be progress in this understanding. Much of this progress comes about through the continued application of modeling techniques, which enable generalizations to be preserved, while being modified and interpreted with an ever-deepening understanding. And all of this is done in virtue of man's ability to understand effects through their causes, and so to explain phenomena in terms of the very determiners that make them be what they are.

CHAPTER FIVE

Causality in Contemporary Science

Among Bertrand Russell's aphorisms on causality is one where he notes the paradox that, while philosophers of every school imagine the notion of causality to embody one of the fundamental axioms of science, in any advanced science the word "cause" never occurs.[1] Some have seen in this statement a prophetic utterance to the effect that causal concepts, having figured largely in the science of former times, are destined to pass into oblivion as the specialized disciplines reach more advanced stages. One may indeed wonder whether such a Comtean prediction is being verified in the latter part of the twentieth century. Fortunately for our purposes, precisely this question has been addressed by the Hayden Colloquium on Scientific Method and Concept and the results of the investigation made available in a work entitled *Cause and Effect*.[2] In his introduction to the volume the editor states the problem concisely:

> The papers collected in this volume deal in different ways with the questions raised by Russell. In the conduct of the contemporary sciences what need, if any, is there for causal concepts? Which concepts are especially useful in which sciences? Is there an underlying conception of causality that is common in all scientific work today?

Can any formulation be made that is generally acceptable to contemporary scientists?[3]

It is obviously much easier to ask questions of this type than
it is to answer them, and yet the editor feels that the overall
results of the conference show that the "trend of contemporary science reformulates the concept of causality but does
not obviate it."[4]

More detailed findings of the colloquium may be indicated briefly from the contributions of the specialists who
participated. All were seemingly aware that scientists rarely
advert to philosophical problems explicitly, and it was even
noted that many scientists now have a "disciplined disinterest" or even a "trained incapacity" to deal with them.[5] Again,
it was generally conceded that the absence of the word
"cause" is not a conclusive indication that the concept of causality is not functioning implicitly in scientific discourse.
Nagel, who participated in the colloquium, spoke for the
group when he observed:

> It is beyond serious doubt that the term "cause" rarely if
> ever appears in the research papers or treatises currently
> published in the natural sciences, and the odds are heav-
> ily against any mention in any book on theoretical phys-
> ics. Nevertheless, though the *term* may be absent, the
> *idea* for which it stands continues to have wide currency.
> It not only crops up in everyday speech, and in investi-
> gations into human affairs by economists, social psychol-
> ogists, and historians; it is also pervasive in the accounts
> natural scientists give of their laboratory procedures, as
> well as in the interpretations offered by many theoretical
> physicists of their mathematical formalism. Descriptions
> of laboratory procedures refer to changes produced by
> the operations of various instruments, as well as by
> human agents, and are unavoidably couched in causal
> language. Similarly, attempts to understand a physical
> theory not simply as a self-contained system of formal
> operations but as statements about physical processes in-
> volve obvious causal connotations. . . . The notion of
> causality, though not necessarily the word "cause," is also
> present when scientists distinguish in various inquiries
> between spurious and genuine correlations. In short, the
> idea of cause is not as outmoded in modern science as is
> sometimes alleged.[6]

This statement was consistently confirmed in the papers of the remaining contributors. Abraham Kaplan stressed the fact that causality becomes particularly significant "when science is seen as an instrument of control over phenomena," and thus causal concepts are especially operative when it is possible to have the type of "controlled intervention" that is characteristic of experimental method.[7] As a practicing biologist, Ernst Mayr expressed a strong commitment to causal concepts, and some of his statements will occupy us later. Talcott Parsons and Robert Dahl, sociologist and political scientist respectively, saw causal thinking as generally implicit in their disciplines. Parsons emphasized in particular their value for taxonomic generalizations and for singling out "internal types of factors or causes" that enable one to advance beyond the knowledge of mere functional dependencies,[8] whereas Dahl noted that in the systematic study of politics, which owes so much to Aristotle, vestiges of all four of his types of causal explanation are still to be found.[9]

While admittedly sketchy, this summary shows how one might use the conference method, as exemplified in the Hayden Colloquium, to ascertain the status of causal concepts in contemporary science. In this method philosophers of science would not be used exclusively to assess how such concepts function, although at least one such philosopher turned out to be a significant contributor to that colloquium; rather one would go directly to scientists practicing in the various disciplines and seek answers from them, in a more sociological mode of inquiry, as to their use of causal explanation. And along the lines of Holton's "thematic analysis" this should be a valid data-gathering procedure, for it is to be expected that there will be themes operative within each discipline or community of scientists that influence the terminology they employ, as also its causal connotations. Such themes should therefore be detectable by the sociological as well as by the philosophical method of analysis.

Either method as it has been described thus far, however, focuses attention on themes that are more or less internal to the disciplines discussed, and thus results in what contemporary historians of science refer to as an "internalist" analysis.[10] There is the further possibility, suggested by the qualification "internalist," that the use or disuse of causality in science may be influenced by larger themes or movements of a social and political character, which may be referred to as "externalist" in the sense that they are external to the discipline or to the particular community of scientists engaged in its study. Such external factors could have a marked effect on terminological and conceptual emphases, and as a matter of fact they do seem to have influenced the use of causal notions in the physical sciences, particularly among German-speaking physicists between the years of 1918 and 1927. Since such factors have been the subject of a recent study and since they throw additional light on some of the statements of such scientists cited in Chapter 3, they merit at least brief consideration here.

The study referred to was made by Paul Forman and concerns the way in which German physicists and mathematicians adapted to the hostile intellectual environment of the Weimar culture, as reflected in their expressed attitudes toward causality well before the enunciation of Heisenberg's uncertainty principle in 1927.[11] Forman takes as his point of departure a statement by Max Jammer that the intellectual climate of the period was opposed to mechanical determinism and causality on grounds other than purely scientific ones, and that these contributed to the shaping of modern quantum mechanics.[12] Spelling out more specifically the nature of this intellectual climate, Forman identifies it with the Weimar intellectual movement, which, after the defeat of Germany in 1918, showed itself particularly antagonistic to science. The new ideology that came into being was a neoromantic, existentialist *Lebensphilosophie* that incorporated classical German idealism and even assimilated elements of an antirationalistic mysticism. Thus, Ernst Troeltsch called for a "revolution in science" that would repudiate its methods — which he viewed pejoratively — "of causal explanation, of natural necessity, of psychophysical, psychological, and sociological causality." [13] The educational reform brought about in the Weimar Republic under the leadership of Carl Becker and others was also indifferent to science, so much so that the "Krisis der Wissenschaft" and the "collapse of science" became popular slogans that characterized the German *Kulturkrise* generally.[14] The latter was itself epitomized in the first volume of Oswald Spengler's *The Decline of the West,* which appeared in 1918 and enjoyed an enormous popularity in postwar Germany. Spengler's main thesis was that the key to the problem of world history could be found in the opposition between the "destiny-idea" and the "causality-principle." The first he exalted as an indescribable inner certainty that is creative and leads to life, whereas the second was for him stiff, rigid, mechanical, and ultimately leads to death.[15]

Surrounded by the hostile intellectual environment that was thereby created, German physicists and mathematicians, whose academic addresses and other public utterances are analyzed by Forman in detail, apparently reshaped their ideology to fit into the general cultural patterns. They continued to stress the importance of their disciplines, but now not so much for utility and applied technology as for human life and culture, and in so doing found that they could dispense with causality and all its feared implications. Biologists such as Hans Driesch readily effected the transition to the new mode of thought, but so did mathematicians such as Richard Courant, and also mathematical physicists, including Wilhelm Wien, Richard von Mises, and Arnold Sommerfeld. Forman finds in the addresses and writings of these men and their associates a gradual capitulation to Spenglerism, more and more of an admission of "crisis" in science, and a growing acceptance of intuitionism in mathematics, the latter particularly as exemplified in the work of Hermann Weyl. And it was in this milieu, influenced largely by such external pressures, that German-speaking physicists began to find the anti-causal philosophical positions of Mach and Duhem acceptable. So one by one, to use Forman's expression, they became "converts to acausality." [16] His list includes Franz Exner, Hermann Weyl, Richard von Mises, Walter Schottky, Walter Nernst, and finally, among the "later notable conversions," Erwin Schrödinger and Hans Reichenbach.[17] Of all of these only Weyl seems to have rejected causality on internalist grounds, for he had been captivated by Husserl's phenomenology and Brouwer's intuitionism, and saw both of these as incompatible with a rigid causal determinism.[18]

Among the outstanding physicists in the early 1920s, as a consequence, only Planck and Einstein took the stand in defense of causality. Planck was particularly outspoken in his affirmation of the importance of causal reasoning, and this not only for the natural sciences but for the *Geisteswissenschaften* as well. In a lecture to the Prussian Academy on February 17, 1923, he insisted that "the assumption of a causality without exception, of a complete determinism, forms the presupposition and the precondition for scientific [*wissenschaftlich*] cognition." [19] Well aware of the issues that would be raised on the basis of the quantum theory he had fathered, Planck went on:

> But has it then — one could now certainly ask — any sense whatsoever to continue speaking of a definite causal interconnection when no one in the world is actually capable of comprehending that causal connection as such? . . . Absolutely. . . . For causality is . . . transcendental, it is entirely independent of the constitution of the inquiring intellect, indeed it would retain its significance even in the complete absence of a knowing subject. [20]

Later, in 1925, Wien rethought his position and came out also in favor of causality; he was then joined by Schrödinger, partly for personal-political reasons and partly because of his discovery of the wave equation that bears his name, which suggested a causal interpretation. [21] Yet this was "causality's last stand," [22] as Forman describes it, for in less than a year Max Born would offer his statistical interpretation of the wave equation, Heisenberg would state his uncertainty principle, and both would join Niels Bohr and Arnold Sommerfeld in the group that has come to be known as the Copenhagen School, to whose position we have previously had reference. [23]

Forman's analysis is not here presented as apodictic, for such a subject is extremely difficult to treat with complete objectivity, and by its nature almost precludes the possibility of arriving at results on which there will be universal agreement. The study does have value, however, for it calls attention to complicating factors that perhaps serve to explain the vacillations of physicist-philosophers when discussing causality during this particular period, including some whose views we have already considered. Indeed, it not only highlights the importance of contextual understanding when such issues are involved, but it serves to illustrate how causal themes can take on broad ideological, cultural, or even religious significance, with the result that their acceptance or rejection in any science may be dictated as much by extrinsic considerations as by those proper to its subject matter.[24] Yet such extrinsic factors, while admittedly influential, have not been our main interest throughout this study, for we have been dealing quite consistently with substantive issues that relate in one way or another to causality and scientific explanation. Throughout the remainder of this chapter, therefore, we shall attempt to assess further the status of causality in current science by considering a sampling of problems that seem to offer special challenges for causal analysis. First we shall be concerned with the physical sciences, particularly with problems posed by the relativity and quantum theories, and then we shall turn our attention to the life and social sciences to take up problems relating to evolution and to the causal explanation of human behavior.

1. *The Physical Sciences*

Thus far, discussion of causality in contemporary physics has centered around indeterminism and uncertainty as these are associated with quantum theory. Even before such problems had arisen, as we have seen, there was a questioning of causality on the basis of probability and statistical considerations, and when Einstein's theory of special relativity was first proposed, this too gave rise to difficulties. In fact, Spengler's indictment of causal reasoning was at least partially inspired by Einstein, whom he did not understand correctly but whose concepts and terminology he used nonetheless to impugn causality.[25] Thus we shall begin with the relativity theories, as offering a convenient introduction to the contemporary problematic.

a. Relativity Theories

The term "relativity" is applied to two physical theories elaborated by Albert Einstein, the first called "special relativity" and proposed in 1905, and the second, "general relativity," formulated in 1915.[26] Both are concerned with describing spatio-temporal aspects of the universe in such a way that the laws of physics will remain the same, or be invariant, regardless of the coordinate systems to which they have reference and in which they are found to apply. The special theory seeks to achieve this result for all frames of reference that are in uniform rectilinear motion with respect to each other, usually spoken of as inertial frames, whereas the general theory attempts to extend the result to include frames of reference that are accelerating with respect to inertial frames. The guiding inspiration behind both theories is Einstein's operational definition of simultaneity, according to which the temporal relations between spatially separated events can be determined only from the physical relationships that obtain between them. An example of such a physical relationship would be the transmission of light signals from one system to another. Reasoning along lines suggested by this operational definition, Einstein found that all measurements of length and time are relative to the frame of reference in which they are made, and also that certain physically separated events that appear to be simultaneous in one frame of reference will not be simultaneous in another.

The latter consideration gives rise to the causality paradox when causality is taken in the Humean sense of mere temporal sequence between events. Since the simultaneity of distant events, and more generally the time interval between them, will vary depending on the frame of reference from which they are observed, the possibility suggests itself that the temporal sequence of events might also be found to vary depending on the frame used for observation. If there could indeed be a time interchange of this type, then it would be possible for event A to precede event B in one frame of reference, whereas event B would precede A in another. Such a state of affairs would actually undermine causality, since an event that appears to precede, and hence to cause, another event in one frame of reference would be found to follow, and hence could not cause, the second event viewed from another frame of reference. In other words, if the temporal sequence of events is dependent upon the frame of reference from which they are viewed, then "earlier" and "later" become relative concepts and so depend upon the viewer's frame of reference. If that turns out to be the case, then causation also, as revealed by temporal sequence, cannot be invariant with respect to all inertial systems, and so causal laws cannot be invariant either and thus are not to be retained among the true laws of physics.

So stated, the causality paradox, like other paradoxes associated with relativity, can be resolved by having recourse to the equations and technical details of the special theory.[27] The resolution reveals not only that causal laws are invariant with respect to inertial frames of reference, but that the relativity theories themselves are causal theories in the accepted sense of the term. To show this, it is necessary to invoke another premise of the special theory, namely, that the velocity of light in free space is constant throughout the universe, being the same in all inertial frames of reference, and the related premise that no physical influence can be transmitted from one frame to another with a velocity exceeding that of light. When these premises are applied consistently to world events as represented in a four-dimensional space-time manifold referred to as Minkowski space, calculations show that any two events are separated by an "interval," computed from their spatio-temporal coordinates, that is itself invariant with respect to the frames of reference from which the events are observed. On the basis of signal transmission, moreover, it is found that such events can stand in two different types of relatedness, spoken of as timelike relatedness and spacelike relatedness respectively. Events are in timelike relatedness if a signal can be sent between them in such a way that the first event can influence the second, whereas they are in spacelike relatedness if no such signal is physically possible. The particular type of relatedness, like the interval between the events, can be shown to be invariant with respect to the frames of reference employed; as a consequence it is impossible to go from one frame of reference where two events stand in timelike relatedness to another frame where the same events stand in spacelike relatedness, or vice versa.

Now it is precisely this state of affairs that has important ramifications for causality. On its basis, for example, each event can be said to have a causal future, in the sense that it will be able to influence some future events, and each event can be said to have a causal past, in the sense that some past events could similarly have influenced it. At the same time, considering any particular event, there are also events that are causally unrelated to it, in the sense that it can or could neither affect them nor be affected by them. Moreover, in the case of events that are causally connected, and thus stand in timelike relatedness, calculations show that although the time lapse between the events may vary depending on the coordinate system used for measurement, any actual reversal of their temporal sequence is impossible. In the case of events, on the other hand, that are not causally connected, and thus stand in spacelike relatedness, a reversal in the temporal sequence is possible. But in the latter case, since causality is not operative, time reversal has no causal significance, and thus the possibility of its occurring in no way jeopardizes the causality principle.

The fusion of space and time in the Minkowski manifold, on the basis of the foregoing analysis, does not mean that the dimensionality of space is completely homogeneous with the dimensionality of time, since a relatedness that is timelike has completely different causal implications from one that is spacelike. Commenting on this fact, Albertson observes:

> Minkowski has said of the special theory of relativity that "in themselves space and time have been reduced to mere shadows and only a kind of union of the two is destined to survive." By referring to the mixture of space and time coordinates in the Lorentz transformation, it is clear in what sense the statement is true. But the statement should not be taken to imply that the physical difference of space and time coordinates had disappeared, for it would be difficult to imagine a greater physical difference than the invariant character of timelike and spacelike relatedness and the corresponding implications for physical causality. Far from eliminating the physical differences of space and time, Einstein's theory has opened the way to a new and deeper understanding of their interrelatedness and their involvement in the processes of the universe.[28]

Again, rather than the special theory of relativity being resistant to causal interpretation, it is solidly based on the existence of causal influences, and therefore on causation, understood at least in its minimal Humean sense. Perhaps it was for this reason that Einstein continued to affirm the need for causal explanation in modern physics when most of his colleagues had given it up. It also serves to explain why David Bohm, when defending the role of causality in quantum theory, did not find it necessary to discuss relativity. So he asserts:

> Now, while the theory of relativity brought about important modifications in the specific forms in which the causal laws are expressed in physics, it did not go outside the previously existing theoretical scheme, in which the values of suitable parameters at a given instant of time would in principle determine the future behavior of the universe for all time. We shall, therefore, not discuss the theory of relativity in this book, in which we are interested primarily in the question of causality, because this theory raised no question that went to the root of the problem of causality.[29]

In the last citation Bohm does not distinguish explicitly between the special and the general theories of relativity, and his remarks seemingly apply to both. The general theory is more complex, however, and lends itself to a variety of causal interpretations, not merely in the sense of efficient causality, whether in a Humean or a stronger understanding, but in formal, material, and final senses as well. The latter circumstance arises from the fact that the general theory of relativity has been largely a theory of gravitation, and as such reopens questions regarding the causes of falling motion that go back, past Newton, to the early Greeks. Yet the technical formulations on which these interpretations are based are quite formidable, and in what follows we must limit ourselves merely to general statements of what the precise mathematical theory entails.

The special theory of relativity proposes to state the laws of physics so that they will remain invariant for all frames of reference in uniform relative motion. Such frames are defined as inertial with respect to distant galaxies, for in them any particle upon which no forces are acting should move at uniform speed in a straight line in accordance with Newton's first law. In the general theory of relativity Einstein attempted to generalize the special or restricted theory in such a way that the laws of physics would become invariant in all spatio-temporal coordinate systems, and not merely in those of inertial frames. Carrying out the calculations necessary to achieve this result, he found that the "interval" between any two events in the four-dimensional space-time manifold, to which we have previously referred, would have to be written in the form of a tensor equation. This interval could then be made invariant by describing it in a space developed by G. F. B. Riemann and thus known to mathematicians as Riemannian. Einstein also noted that gravity, so far as can be detected experimentally, produces the same acceleration on all bodies on which it acts, regardless of their size; stated otherwise, in a uniform and constant gravitational field all bodies subjected only to gravitational forces accelerate at the same rate. Since this is the case, by properly choosing accelerating frames of reference one can eliminate the effects of these gravitational forces. As a consequence, in such accelerating frames all bodies of whatever size, when subjected only to gravity, will be seen as moving at uniform speed in straight lines, just as they appear in inertial frames when gravitational forces are not present. In Riemannian space such straight lines are referred to as geodesics. In "flat" Minkowskian space, these geodesics would appear as curved lines, but in the "curved space" of Riemannian geometry they are indeed "straight," in the sense that they fulfill the definition of being the shortest distance between two points.

Written in its general form, the expression for the interval in Riemannian space is mathematically quite complicated, requiring the use of a metric tensor that takes account of the distribution of all matter from which gravitational forces may arise. Now, in the physical universe as we know it, the gravitational forces that so arise are generally not uniform, and therefore it is not possible to define coordinate systems in which all such forces everywhere disappear. Yet it is possible, on a small scale, to select certain regions of the universe where these forces will effectively be found to disappear. Moreover, in regions that are far removed from any gravity-producing matter, a similar situation will obtain. In such cases the metric tensor takes a simple form, and the regions in which it applies are referred to as "locally flat" in the sense that the flat geometry of special relativity is there found to apply.

What is most interesting is that the general theory of relativity, developed along the lines just indicated, leads to a quite different interpretation of gravity and its causal implications than does the Newtonian theory. To show this Arthur Stanley Eddington has proposed a simple model or analogy that brings out the differences between the two.[30] It is a two-dimensional analogue, easy to visualize, and well suited for our purposes. Thus we shall reproduce it here, even retaining, in so doing, the parabolic form of Eddington's original account:

> A race of flat-fish once lived in an ocean in which there were only two dimensions. It was noticed that in general fishes swam in straight lines, unless there was something obviously interfering with their free courses. This seemed a very natural behaviour. But there was a certain region where all the fish seemed to be bewitched; some passed through the region but changed the direction of their swim, others swam round and round indefinitely. One fish invented a theory of vortices, and said that there were whirlpools in that region which carried everything round in curves. By-and-by a far better theory was proposed; it was said that the fishes were all attracted towards a particularly large fish — a sun-fish — which was lying asleep in the middle of the region; and that was what caused the deviation of their paths.[31]

Eddington's allusion here, of course, is to Descartes's theory of vortices, to which he opposes Newton's theory of gravitational attraction, both of which have already been discussed in our first volume.[32] He goes on, referring to Newtonian theory:

> The theory might not have sounded particularly plausible at first; but it was confirmed with marvelous exactitude by all kinds of experimental tests. All fish were

found to possess this attractive power in proportion to their sizes; the law of attraction was extremely simple, and yet it was found to explain all the motions with an accuracy never approached before in any scientific investigations. Some fish grumbled that they did not see how there could be such an influence at a distance; but it was generally agreed that the influence was communicated through the ocean and might be better understood when more was known about the nature of water. Accordingly, nearly every fish who wished to explain the attraction started by proposing some kind of mechanism for transmitting it through the water.[33]

The mentality expressed toward the end of this citation could be that of Herschel and Whewell, although it more probably applies to nineteenth-century ether theorists such as Lorentz and Larmor, whereas the "grumblers" would have to include Leibniz and Berkeley, to say nothing of Comte and Mach, and might even allude to Newton himself, with his personal reservations about "action at a distance." [34] But Eddington here is obviously telescoping a considerable amount of history so as to set the stage for Einstein's entrance on the scene:

But there was one fish who thought of quite another plan. He was impressed by the fact that whether the fish were big or little they always took the same course, although it would naturally take a bigger force to deflect the bigger fish. He therefore concentrated attention on the courses rather than on the forces. And then he arrived at a striking explanation of the whole thing. There was a mound in the world round about where the sun-fish lay. Flat-fish could not appreciate it directly because they were two-dimensional; but whenever a fish went swimming over the slopes of the mound, although he did his best to swim straight on, he got turned round a bit. . . . This was the secret of the mysterious attraction, or bending of the paths, which was experienced in the region.[35]

Here Eddington, having introduced a third spatial dimension in his analogue to explain two-dimensional phenomena, goes on to advise us that an additional dimension in space-time will similarly be necessary to explain what we encounter as

three-dimensional phenomena. Although the resulting analogy "is not perfect," he hopes that it will serve to illustrate
"how a curvature of the world we live in may give an illusion
of attractive force, and indeed can only be discovered
through some such effect."[36]

Note, in the phrase just cited, that Eddington has spoken
of "an illusion of attractive force" as an "effect" which pre-
sumably is caused by "a curvature of the world" in which we
live. This curvature, in turn, is commonly ascribed to the
presence of matter, or of mass-energy, in the universe. Thus,
what Herschel saw in the Newtonian world system as explainable in terms of efficient causality becomes in the Einsteinian world view explainable in terms of formal and material causality, understanding "formal" in the sense of the
mathematical formalism required to describe such curvature
and "material" in the sense of the matter or substrate needed
to bring it about. As one author has put it:

> The curvature of space-time is due to its energy and
> mass content. The remarkable success of this theory [of
> general relativity] derived from its automatic explana-
> tion of two features of gravitation: why is the inertial
> mass equal to the gravitational mass? and why is gravita-
> tion a universal property acting on everything in the uni-
> verse? The answer is that the two masses are equal be-
> cause they are one and the same, since they appear in
> the theory uniquely as the cause of the curvature of
> space-time. Gravitation is a universal manifestation be-
> cause it is the property of space-time, and hence every-
> thing that is in space-time (which is, literally, every
> thing) must experience it.[37]

The radical explanatory principle here, of course, is matter,
though expressed in terms of its metrical manifestations as
mass-energy, and thus the explanation that the theory of general relativity affords is ultimately in terms of material causality. Such an interpretation, it may be pointed out, need not
rule out the possibility of alternate or complementary interpretations in terms of efficient causes. In the case of special
relativity, as already indicated, the formalism is interpretable
in a Minkowskian sense, which parallels that through formal-
material causality, and yet this interpretation is consonant

with an alternate one through the propagation of physical influences made in terms of efficient causation.

More frequently remarked than these types of causality, however, are the teleological implications of the general theory, taking "teleological" in the Leibnizian maximum-minimum sense of final causality. Along similar lines, the fact that gravitational motion can be accurately described by a geodesic in space-time suggests an analogy with Aristotle's explanation of such motion in terms of natural place. Place, for Aristotle, was a physical concept, and thus could be thought of as a type of physical space different from the homologous space of pure geometry. Motion to place, furthermore, would consist in a body's finding its proper location in a physical environment, which location would itself be determined by the character of the material constituents of the universe in its local region.[38] In an Aristotelian context, therefore, the geodesic of general relativity bears some similarities to the trajectory a falling object should follow as it seeks its natural place. This has been remarked by Jammer in his *Concepts of Space*, where he writes:

> It is perhaps not wholly unjustified to suggest a comparison between the notion of physical space in Aristotle's cosmology and the notion of Einstein's "spherical space" as expounded in early relativistic cosmology. In both theories a question of what is "outside" finite space is nonsensical. Furthermore, the idea of "geodesic lines" determined by the geometry of space, and their importance for the description of material particles or light rays, suggests a certain analogy to the notion of "natural places" and the paths leading to them. The difference is, of course, that in Einstein's theory the geometry of space itself is a function of the mass-energy distribution in accord with the famous field equations, and is not Euclidean but Riemannian.[39]

For the Aristotelian, moreover, the attraction of "natural place" would not pertain to the order of efficient causality but rather to that of final causality.[40] In the classical period, as we have seen, such an explanation through the final cause was associated with the name of Leibniz, although others accepted it also, and even Newton's system remained open to a comparable teleological interpretation. Edmond Halley, in fact, was among those to point out that the final cause of gravity, meaning by this the center of gravity of the local region, could be quite clearly known, even though its efficient cause might not be.[41] And, following Aquinas's method of demonstrating *ex suppositione finis*, when such a final cause is more readily known or reveals itself to experimental analysis, it can serve as an empirical base for discovering the other, more recondite causes of the motion of the falling body.

Before leaving the relativity theories, a few remarks should be made on their relevance to the problems of the "growth of scientific knowledge" and "meaning invariance" mentioned in the last chapter. The revolution instituted by Einstein is second only to the Copernican-Newtonian revolution, and its very emphasis on the term "relativity" seems to reinforce the idea that all spatio-temporal knowledge will be relative to the observer's frame and thus revisable when seen from a different viewpoint. More specifically, it would appear that, since Einstein's theories have shown that there are no privileged frames of reference in the universe, and in particular that the Newtonian concept of "absolute space" is no longer defensible, one cannot even be certain of the earth's rotation on its axis or of its movement around the sun. If that is the case, then Ptolemy had as much claim to truth as Copernicus, Galileo was thoroughly misguided in his battles with Bellarmine and the Inquisition, and the causal reasoning in which Herschel engaged, wherein he conceded to Newton's law of gravitation "a degree of certainty . . . which attaches to no other creation of the human mind," [42] was completely fallacious.[43]

While some have seen such a radical relativism implied in the theories of relativity, most physicists take a more sober view of the epistemological impact of Einstein's theories. The basic difficulty arises from the application of formal developments in pure mathematics to theories of the physical universe, which not only brings with it the problems of mathematical idealization and abstraction mentioned in the previous chapter, but also leaves the ontological reference of any explanation that is achieved quite obscure. Unfortunately, philosophers of science have not devoted as much attention to physical geometries, considered from a nonformal point of view, as they have to other topics in their discipline. Just as one might remark the lack of sophistication among classical methodologists when discussing circularity and proof vis-à-vis the comparable analyses of the Paduan Aristotelians, so one might observe the relative lack of attention given to the relations between mathematics and physics in recent times as contrasted to the strenuous debates over these topics centuries ago at Oxford, Paris, and Padua.[44] It goes without saying that one who equates physical reasoning with mathematical reasoning, for example, might tend toward complete relativism when considering the earth's movement with respect to distant galaxies, because *mathematically* it makes no difference whether the earth is moving, or the fixed stars, or even both. Again, a mathematical realist who hypostasizes the notion of absolute space or who sees a space-time construct as the ultimate reality may tend to make extravagant ontological claims on the basis of his theorizing.[45]

Within the boundaries set by these extreme positions, however, most scientists agree that the relativity theories and their experimental confirmations have not falsified our knowledge of the earth's rotation and its movement in the solar system. Sir Edmund Whittaker, for instance, argues that the Copernican axes are inertial whereas the Ptolemaic are not, and that the earth is quite clearly rotating with respect to the local inertial axes.[46] The claims of some that Einstein, with his general theory, has successfully implemented Mach's program of eliminating Newtonian absolute space from cosmology, has similarly been attacked by others as inaccurate and misleading.[47] Adolf Grünbaum, for example, cites Einstein's own testimony that the supplanting of the concept of absolute space is "a process which is probably by no means as yet completed." [48] Grünbaum's own criticism of the Machian enterprise reads as follows:

Mach has urged against Newton that both translational and rotational inertia are intrinsically dependent on the large-scale distribution and relative motion of matter. Assuming the indefinite extensibility of terrestrial axes to form an unlimited Euclidean rigid system, S_e, the rotational motion of the stars seems to be clearly defined with respect to S_e. Unfortunately, however, the general theory of relativity was not entitled to make use of S_e: the linear velocity of rotating mass points increases with the distance from the axis of rotation, and hence the existence of a system S_e of unrestricted size would allow *local* velocities greater than that of light, in contravention of the requirement of the local validity of the special theory of relativity. But to deny, as the general theory therefore must, that S_e can extend even as far as the planet Neptune is to assert that the Machian concept of the *relative* motion of the earth and the stars is no more meaningful physically than the Newtonian bugaboo of the *absolute* rotation of a solitary earth in a space which is structured independently of any matter that it might contain accidentally and indifferently! Accordingly, the earth must be held to rotate *not* relative to the stars but with respect to the local "star-compass" formed at the earth by stellar light rays whose paths are determined by the local *metrical* field.[49]

In a different but related criticism, Marshall Spector allows the identification of absolute space with the ether concept,[50] and then goes on to maintain not only that special relativity has not made the ether concept "meaningless" but also "that within the context of the general theory of relativity the concept of an ether has returned in a new guise." [51]

Such statements are not proposed as definitive solutions to problems in recent field theory, but they do serve to indicate how one can still argue validly for the earth's rotation and orbital movement after the Einsteinian revolution, without having to reopen the question of the validity of the Ptolemaic hypotheses. They serve to illustrate how the contemporary astronomer has a more sophisticated knowledge of the earth's movements and the frames of reference to which they must be referred than Newton could have had, just as the present-day geologist has more accurate data relating to the earth's oblate spheroidal shape. It is in this sense that A. Rupert Hall is essentially correct in seeing, despite the many changes of viewpoint, a progressive growth of man's knowledge concerning the universe through the nineteenth and early twentieth centuries. Writing of science's progress since 1800, he asserts that

the later discoveries have always embraced the earlier:
Newton was not proved wrong by Einstein, nor Lavoisier
by Rutherford. The formulation of a scientific proposition
may be modified, and limitations to its application recognized, without affecting its propriety in the context to
which it was originally found appropriate.[52]

Hall then goes on to recall the sage observation of J. R. Op-
penheimer to the effect that "the old knowledge, as the very
means of coming upon the new, must in its old realm be left
intact; only when we have left the realm can it be trans-
cended." [53]

These last citations suggest a final observation on the
problem of meaning invariance in relativity theories. One of
Kuhn's main contentions with respect to the Einsteinian revolution is that it has introduced significant conceptual changes
into science, particularly into the meaning of terms such as
mass and energy, and thus "illustrates with particular clarity
the scientific revolution as a displacement of the conceptual
network through which scientists view the world." [54] Now
this supposed result of the theories of relativity is examined
by Spector with considerable care, taking the mass-energy relation as a case in point, and shown not to have the extreme
consequences intimated by Kuhn. While admitting that relativistic theory has led to the discovery of a new form of energy, i.e., "rest energy" or "mass energy," Spector believes
that

> this fact is insufficient for concluding that the *concept* of
> energy is therefore different, unless one is willing to
> maintain that each new form of energy really involves a
> change in the meaning of the term "energy." But it
> sounds equally plausible, if not more so, to speak of the
> *discovery* of new *forms* of energy, where the *meaning* of
> the term "energy" does not change (but is laid down
> once and for all through the concept of work and the
> general conservation law, for example).[55]

On the basis of these and similar arguments Spector holds
that there are no solid grounds "for the claim that the term
'energy' has a different meaning in relativistic dynamics than
it has in classical dynamics." [56] Needless to say, his conclusion, no less than Grünbaum's, is quite compatible with the

views we have already advanced in favor of a cumulative growth of scientific knowledge through processes of taxonomic generalization, discovery, revision through new generalizations, etc., leading all the time to a more refined knowledge of the universe and its structure.

b. Quantum Theories

Our discussion in Chapter 3 has already dealt with the problems of determinism and predictability and the main revisions in the concept of causality occasioned by the rise of the quantum theories.[57] Most of these revisions had to do with efficient causality and its understanding in either a Humean or a Laplacean sense, although there was also some consideration of "inner determiners" that was suggestive of other types of causality. In this section we propose to complement this treatment by turning attention to other causal problems associated with quantum theory, only touched on in the previous chapter, that relate more to the ontological implications of microphysics. Here difficulties are encountered that are somewhat similar to those mentioned in connection with the general theory of relativity, but the models in terms of which they are analyzed are somewhat simpler, and questions relating to indicative and recognitive criteria, the introduction of new types of entities into an ontology, etc., can be made more pointed. The cumulative growth of scientific knowledge remains a basic concern, but the focus of attention will now be on high-energy physics and the taxonomic and existential questions raised by recent progress in this field. One may question, for example, whether the great proliferation of elementary particles is merely a multiplication of theoretical constructs required to subsume the data of nuclear physics under the axioms and rules of some formal system, or whether these particles, all of which can be said to have been "detected" experimentally in one way or another, can be regarded as having extramental existence.[58] Answers will be proposed to such questions, and to the extent that they express realist commitments, they may help to show where causal reasoning is implicitly used, the types of causality it involves, and how it is ultimately productive of new knowledge in this area of contemporary physics.

Recent discussions of the underlying problem, i.e., that of the ontological status of theoretical entities, are for the most part arguments over what has already been mentioned as the observational-theoretical dichotomy. Facts and empirical laws are expected to be stated in observational terms, whereas theories are differentiated from facts and empirical laws by their use of terms that are not observational and, by way of opposition, are referred to as theoretical. This distinction seems plausible enough on the face of it, and yet it has been contested in recent literature in the philosophy of science.[59] Those who hold that it is impossible to draw a sharp line of demarcation between observational and theoretical terms are concerned over such expressions as "electron" and "meson." While willing to concede that these designate unobservable entities, they do not on this account regard such entities as being less existent than things that are observable. So Grover Maxwell contends "that electrons, photons, and even electromagnetic fields are just as real, and exist in the same full-blooded sense, as chairs, tables, or sense impressions." [60] Among his arguments in support of this contention is one directed against those who hold that physical instruments, such as the microscope, do not see physical objects but only shadows or images. Maxwell uses this argument to show the difficulties implicit in any distinction between observing directly and observing through an instrument. In his view there is a spectrum of possibilities starting with looking at a thing directly, then looking at it through a window pane, then through glasses, through binoculars, through a low-powered microscope, through a high-powered microscope, through an electron microscope, etc. Just as one should not say that what is seen through spectacles is a "little bit less real" or "exists to a slightly less extent" than something seen with unaided vision, so the same should not be said with respect to something seen through an electron microscope when compared to what is directly observable.[61] Another of Maxwell's arguments develops this line of reasoning further by incorporating commonly-accepted views of the structure of matter. It is generally held that there is a virtually continuous transition from very small molecules, such as that of hydrogen, through medium-sized ones, to extremely large ones. Extremely large

molecules are "directly observable," whereas very small molecules "have the same perplexing properties as subatomic
particles." [62] Considerations such as this lead to perplexing
questions:

> Are we to say that a large protein molecule (e.g., a virus)
> which can be "seen" only with an electron microscope is
> a little less real or exists to somewhat less an extent than
> does a molecule of a polymer which can be seen with an
> optical microscope? And does a hydrogen molecule par-
> take of only an infinitesimal portion of existence or
> reality? [63]

To answer such questions properly, Maxwell holds, one must
effectively rule out any dividing line between observational
and theoretical entities when this is invoked in discussions of
the reality of elementary particles.

Maxwell, on this accounting, would have no scruples
about incorporating new existential statements into the language of high-energy physics. His stated basis for doing so,
however — and here we revert to the terminology of the previous chapter — is an indicative criterion alone. The "theoretical entities" of which he speaks are apparently localized
within a spatio-temporal domain, and they are simply *there*
to be "seen" by anyone who possesses the appropriate instruments for their detection. Yet there is no explicit mention of
any recognitive criteria in terms of which such new entities
are to be described, and one can only wonder how they may
be recognized, how properties and attributes are to be predicated of them, whether such attributes are to include "wave-
particle" and other strange, if not contradictory, clusters of
properties, and so on.

The posing of these further problems supports our earlier contention that recognitive criteria also play an important role in the verification of existential statements, and that
these must be considered along with indicative criteria when
assessing ontological claims in high-energy physics. Here difficulties are also encountered, however, and these may be
brought into focus by considering the explanatory role that
theoretical entities generally, and more particularly the so-
called elementary particles, are expected to play in contem-

porary science. In this connection, Norwood Russell Hanson, elaborating on a theme proposed by Heisenberg and others, has laid great stress on the principle that no explanation can presuppose the very thing it attempts to explain.[64] He exemplifies the principle as follows:

> One cannot explain why any one thing is red by saying that all red things contain red particles; nor could one explain why any single thing moves by noting that all moving things contain moving particles. In general, though each member of a class of events may be explained by other members, the totality of the class cannot be explained by any members of the class. The totality of red things cannot be explained by anything which is red; the totality of movement cannot be explained by anything which moves. Finally, all the picturable properties of objects, the totality of them, cannot be explained by reference to anything which itself possesses any of these properties.[65]

Pursuit of this line of reasoning leads Hanson to the conclusion that subatomic entities must lack certain properties if they are being invoked to explain these, and on this basis that "electrons could not be other than in principle unpicturable." [66] Indicative criteria, seemingly for Hanson as for Maxwell, do not present a serious obstacle, since one may have an indication of the existence of subatomic entities by their tracks in cloud chambers or other effects, but recognitive criteria are another matter entirely. These lead us into the strange world of the unpicturable, and they do so precisely because of the radical explanatory role accorded to such entities: "the impossibility of visualizing ultimate matter is an essential feature of atomic explanation." [67] Yet Hanson does not see this as a reason why one should deny existence to entities such as the neutrino.[68] In fact, the recognitive criteria he would use to admit entities into his own ontology allow for whole clusters of properties that are radically different from anything encountered in ordinary experience. Hanson justifies these criteria as follows:

> In general, if A, B and C can be explained only by assuming some other phenomenon to have properties a, b and c, then this is the best possible reason for taking this

other phenomenon to possess *a, b* and *c.* In macrophysics, such an hypothesis is tested by looking at the "other phenomenon" to see if it has *a, b* and *c.* With elementary particles, however, we cannot simply look. . . . The cluster of properties, *a, b* and *c,* may constitute an unpicturable conceptual entity to begin with. As new properties, *d, e* and *f,* are "worked into" our idea of the particle, the unpicturability can become profound. This does not matter: there will never be any atomic particles we will fail to recognize just because we fail to form an identification picture of them in advance. The main point about fundamental particles is that they show themselves to have just those properties which they must have if they are to explain the larger scale phenomena requiring explanation.[69]

Although Hanson does not describe the nonclassical properties that may be represented by *a, b,* . . . *f,* the taxonomic generalizations worked out by Murray Gell-Mann and others in their attempts to classify strongly interacting particles suggest a few possibilities. In his theory of the "eightfold way," Gell-Mann describes all of the known high-energy particles in terms of six properties that are thought to be conserved in strong interactions.[70] These are: atomic mass, electric charge, hypercharge, isotopic spin, spin angular momentum, and parity. If Hanson's reasoning is to be taken literally, properties such as hypercharge and isotopic spin are then just as real as the attributes of bodies encountered in ordinary experience, and thus mesons and baryons, despite their radical unpicturability, are to be accorded the same ontological status as such bodies. And, if this is the case, then the observational-theoretical dichotomy effectively has no meaning when one passes to the realm of elementary particles. For Hanson the distinction is not really applicable in that realm, because by the very terms of what such particles attempt to explain they must be in principle unpicturable, unvisualizable, and a fortiori, unobservable. Yet they are real, and they exist, in the same sense as things that are observable.

Such a strong ontological claim, of course, allows for a very rapid "growth of scientific knowledge," but it also conjures up visions of a world populated with strange entities and, for the historian of science, memories of eccentrics and epicycles, phlogiston, and other ghostlike "theoretical entities" of the past. A more temperate claim for realism would therefore seem to be desirable, and one such is suggested by Stephen Toulmin's treatment of the existence of submicroscopic entities.[71] Atoms and molecules apparently present little difficulty for Toulmin, since he holds that by 1905 it was "definitively shown by Einstein that the phenomenon of Brownian motion could be regarded as a demonstration that atoms and molecules really existed." [72] But for smaller entities, like the electron, he feels it desirable to distinguish various senses of the term "exists" before attempting an answer. For example, to inquire whether an extinct species exists may be different from inquiring whether a person or a country is real and so exists, or is merely imaginary and so has no extramental existence. Toulmin proposes that the question, "Do electrons exist?" is less like these inquiries than it is like the query, "Do contours exist?" The answer he would prefer is that, just as contours are cartographical devices that have geographical counterparts, so submicroscopic entities are something like "cartographical fictions" that also have extramental counterparts.[73] They do not exist in precisely the manner in which we conceive them, but they represent something that does exist and so enable the scientist to propose explanations that are not mere fabrications of his own mind, but do have some counterpart in extramental reality. This view obviously has more modest implications for the "growth of knowledge" process, since it allows the scientist to entertain candidates for existence without being committed ontologically in every statement he makes. It also permits him to discard or revise elements in his conceptualizations as he gains more and more knowledge of the reality he is attempting to explain.

With the statement of this position, as will be recognized, we have rejoined the subject of modeling discussed at some length in the previous chapter. From a realist point of view, one may therefore say that the constructs of theoretical physicists are attempts to model the microstructure of reality, which cannot be attained directly but is more and more approximated in their successive conceptualizations. In such a setting, of course, one is tempted to go further and pose the more metaphysical question as to whether or not there are any "ultimate entities" in which such processes of inquiry will have to terminate, and if so, what type of model would best serve to characterize such ultimates. Harré has devoted some consideration to this problem, and because of the obvious limitations of any corpuscularian ultimates, has proposed that these entities be modeled as forces, somewhat along lines suggested in Boscovich's *A Theory of Natural Philosophy*.[74] The type of reasoning Harré pursues in his analysis, although he does not identify its causal typology as such, puts heavy emphasis on efficient causality. This is undoubtedly because of the centrality of the notion of power in Harré's philosophy, and his consequent identification of "the real essence of a thing" with "whatever is responsible for its causal powers." [75] Hence, when describing the "primary qualities" that characterize his ultimate entities, he sees these as "the effects of powers." [76] The force concept, for him as for Boscovich, is not as fundamental as that of power, and yet it is suggestive as an analogy or model. For this reason, when exposing "the true nature of primary qualities," Harré proposes "to use the metaphor of 'force,' understanding it as a fictional explanatory notion for the unanalysable and unexplicable power to attract or repel." [77]

From previous discussions of the force concept and the difficulties it has engendered throughout science's history, one may question the suitability of Harré's choice of modeling technique, without negating, in the process, his basic insight into the ontology of scientific explanation. Another possibility that suggests itself, in fact, is to see contemporary theories of microphysical explanation as proceeding not so much along lines of efficient causality as along those of material causality, in ways not unlike those we have just used to interpret the general theory of relativity. To outline this modeling alternative to Harré's force analogue, it will be necessary to elaborate briefly on the theory of ontological depth which we have explained in greater detail elsewhere.[78] This theory maintains that reality itself is structured in terms of different degrees of being, and can be justified most simply in terms of the logic of explanation.

The existence of a type of ontological hierarchy even among sensible qualities should be apparent to anyone who regards molecules, atoms, and electrons as explanatory factors that render intelligible the definitions of sound, heat, and color sketched in the previous chapter. Such definitions, moreover, permit one to hold that sound, heat, and color are real, and that molecules, atoms, and electrons are real, without maintaining that the former class has the same ontological status as the latter. In a sense, the latter class is more fundamental, since the entities included within it can exist independently of sound, heat, and color, whereas these sensible qualities cannot exist independently of molecules, atoms, and electrons. And, because they are more fundamental, these particles can be used to explain sound, heat, and color.

This explanatory function, as has already been pointed out, precludes one from applying these conventional attributes to molecular, atomic, and subatomic particles. Since this is so, one may well wonder how any attributes or clusters of properties are to be assigned to entities at the level of the strongly interacting elementary particles. In their attempts at taxonomy, as we have seen, high-energy physicists get around this problem by eschewing the use of sensible qualities and other conventional attributes, and by substituting attributes determined by quantitative procedures which are expressible in terms of measurable parameters such as atomic mass, hypercharge, and isotopic spin. This device, from a metaphysical viewpoint, is quite suggestive in that it points to another layer of ontological depth below that of molecules, atoms, and electrons. It serves to indicate that sensible qualities such as sound, heat, and color are rooted in quantity, or in quantifiable aspects of matter, either of which is real at a deeper level than sensible quality.[79]

The question will ultimately be asked, however, whether or not there is anything real that underlies even this quantitative level. If quantity is prerequisite to, and in a certain respect serves to explain, the presence of sensible quality, is there something ontologically prior to quantity that is prerequisite to, and serves to explain, such realities as mass, length, and the various electromagnetic attributes? No less a quantum physicist than Werner Heisenberg raises this question and answers it in the affirmative. He regards such a prior ontological subject as necessary, and identifies it, surprisingly enough, with the primary matter (*hulē*) or pure potentiality that Aristotle posited as underlying his four elements.[80] So Heisenberg writes:

> Let us discuss the question: what is an elementary particle? We say, for instance, simply "a neutron," but we can give no well defined picture of what we mean by the word. We can use several pictures and describe it now as a particle, now as a wave or as a wave packet. But we know that none of these descriptions is accurate. Certainly the neutron has no color, no smell, no taste. In this respect it resembles the atom of Greek philosophy. But even the other qualities are taken from the elementary particle, at least to some extent; the concepts of geometry and kinematics, like shape or motion in space, cannot be applied to it consistently. If one wants to give an accurate description of the elementary particle — and here the emphasis is on the word accurate — the only thing which can be written down as description is a probability function. But then one sees that not even the quality of being, if being may be called a quality, belongs to what is described. It is a possibility for being, or a tendency for being.[81]

Explaining in another place the meaning of the probability function, which is actually the psi-function of quantum mechanics, Heisenberg states:

> Probability in mathematics or in statistical mechanics means a statement about our degree of knowledge of the actual situation. . . . The probability wave of Bohr, Kramers and Slater, however, meant more than that; it meant a tendency for something. It was a quantitative version of the old concept of *potentia* in Aristotelian philosophy. It introduced something standing in the middle between the idea of the event and the actual event, a strange kind of physical reality just in the middle between possibility and reality.[82]

Rephrasing Heisenberg's solution, one could say that the explanation in the microrealm of massive, kinetic, and electromagnetic phenomena, all of which may be regarded as real, requires some underlying substrate or ultimate matter or protomatter that itself is real but only in a potential way.[83] This ultimate level of ontological depth is, of course, unpicturable, unvisualizable, and unobservable. One might almost say that it is unintelligible, if by this is meant that it is in itself unintelligible and only intelligible in terms of the various forms or determinations it can be made to assume. Similarly, it is not actually existent in itself, and in this sense is not fully real, as are tables and chairs and other determinate objects.

Again, the forms or determinations that this protomatter can be made to assume are what we know as elementary particles, and thus the latter are a second-level manifestation of the basic elementarity that is protomatter itself. These elementary particles may be said to be composed of protomatter, and, in a looser sense, may even be said to be composed of each other, since they arise from one another in the strong interactions studied in high-energy physics. Yet they may also be regarded as elements, since they enter into the composition of other bodies.[84] In addition, they are not featureless, as is protomatter, but have certain attributes that can be modeled and through which they can be analogously known. Moreover, the clusters of properties through which they are modeled, such as mass number, hypercharge, and isotopic spin, have themselves a constructional aspect, if only because of the rather extreme conditions under which they are observed in high-energy experiments. They are really measured in such experiments, however, and the realist's concern is not so much one of denying an extramental counterpart to the measurement as it is that of ascertaining how much of what is being modeled is owed to the protomatter and how much is imposed on it by the very conditions of the experiment.[85] Moreover, because of the very transient durations of most of these elementary particles, it is not necessary to ascribe to them the same actual and stable existence that is associated with the objects of ordinary experience.[86] Rather than being modeled as subsistent entities, perhaps they are better thought of as the transient states that protomatter assumes. While being real, therefore, they are not so much things in themselves as they are transient indications of the potentiality of the substrate, which is capable of assuming various forms depending upon the determining conditions to which it is subjected.[87]

This, then, is an alternative way of modeling the "ultimate entities" studied by the physicist along lines of material causality. Such a type of ultimate explanation, as has been noted in connection with the relativity theories, is not incompatible with analyses along lines of efficient causality such as that proposed by Harré. The first would stress the passivity of the substrate, whereas the second would emphasize its capacity for activity or reactivity in ways that are expressed by the terms "force," "field," and "energy." [88] Both lines of causal analysis, moreover, allow for a progressive growth of knowledge with regard to the potentialities or powers of the substrate, as more and better models are proposed by theorists, without requiring a strong ontological commitment, such as that intimated by Maxwell and Hanson, for the reality and existence of any particular "particle."

Before leaving this subject, we should resume a line of reasoning initiated in the previous chapter and append a promised corollary relating to indeterminacy and the Copenhagen interpretation of the Heisenberg uncertainty principle. As should be apparent from our exposition in Chapter 3, contemporary philosophers of science are quite divided on this subject. While practically all are agreed that the uncertainty relations express subjective uncertainties, i.e., that they refer to man's imperfect knowledge of the cosmos, a substantial number of eminent thinkers hold — and in this they are opposed by other eminent thinkers — that the uncertainties are also objective in the sense that they characterize matter or reality and not merely man's knowledge of such reality. Among those holding for an objective indeterminism, some maintain that the indeterminacy is reducible, others that it is irreducible. Those who hold that the indeterminacy is reducible, along lines suggested by Bohm, maintain that it arises from some type of lower-level motion or subquantum state that is yet to be identified.[89] Those who hold that it is irreducible, and these constitute the majority (led by Bohr and his Copenhagen School), usually give a positivist or an empiricist explanation as to why this is so, maintaining that there is something in the nature of things that makes it impossible to draw a sharp dividing line between subject and object, or that the indeterminacy results from a perturbation produced by measuring instruments that is impossible to remove.[90] Again, some wish to give a more realist explanation for the irreducibility of the indeterminacy, tracing it to the operation of absolute chance at the subatomic level; Born and Reichenbach both seem to have favored this view in arguing for probability as a more ultimate category of explanation than causality in microphysics.[91] Soviet philosophers have proposed yet another type of realist explanation consistent with their dialectical materialism, seeing the indeterminacy as arising from dialectical contradictions that are inherent in matter itself.[92]

To all of these, another variation may now be added that interprets the Heisenberg principle realistically, but avoids a commitment either to absolute chance or to the reified contradictions of dialectical materialism, and at the same time is not forced into an unorthodox interpretation of quantum theory such as Bohm's. Heisenberg himself, moreover, while commonly enumerated among those advocating the Copenhagen interpretation on the basis of his early statements, has been proposing just this type of Aristotelian realism in his more recent writings.[93] His ontological position seems to be equivalent to this: the indeterminacies of quantum theory are irreducible in a real way, not merely in a logical way, in that they represent the indetermination of some protomatter that is the basic substrate of the material universe. Because of its potential, yet determinable, character, this is the root principle of indeterminacy. It represents the lowest level of reality attainable by man in his search for the elements of which the universe is composed.

2. The Life and Social Sciences

Investigators in the life sciences, of whom Harvey and Bernard were typical in the past, have been more open to causal reasoning than have physical scientists, and have not limited their understanding to causation or efficient causality alone but have continued to employ all four types. This is perhaps owing to the complexity of their subject matter, as also to the fact that the living organism, apart from its material components and vital agencies, exhibits forms and structures that appear to function for some purpose or end. Contemporary biologists, like their predecessors, are generally appreciative of the richness of explanatory modes thereby afforded them, and resist efforts to reduce their discipline to physics, or its methods of explanation to those employed uniquely in the physical sciences. In combating such reductionism, Paul Weiss, for example, has stressed elements of organic unity and structure found in the realm of the living that lack counterparts in the inorganic world.[94] Ernst Mayr, working from another direction and concerned with the broader problems of a philosophy of biology, laments the fact that most treatises that advertise themselves as philosophies of science are really not that at all, but are rather restricted treatments of problems that pertain to the physical sciences alone. The insular attitudes that they engender, he maintains, can have harmful consequences not only for biology but for the sciences of man as well:

> Philosophy of science is more than a philosophy of physical science. When it comes to philosophical questions that specifically relate to man, his well-being and his future, it is the science of biology that will be most suitable as the starting point for all analysis, rather than the physical sciences.[95]

Mayr notes particularly the outstanding contributions made by biologists toward an understanding of the ancient philosophical concepts of species, of taxonomic classification, and of causality, to say nothing of the way in which all three of these are related to the concept of teleology.[96]

a. Evolution

Mayr's treatment of causality is especially helpful as a background for the discussion of evolution, the field wherein contemporary biologists have made the greatest advances in causal explanation. He maintains that causality is made up of three elements: the explanation of past events, the prediction of future events, and the interpretation of teleological, i.e., goal-directed, phenomena.[97] On the subject of explanation Mayr holds that biological explanation is more complex than that found in the physical sciences, since "explanations of all but the simplest biological phenomena usually consists of sets of causes." [98] To explain such "sets," he lists various categories of cause and notes that some of these, which he terms "proximate causes," are employed more by functional biologists, whereas others, which he terms "ultimate causes," are more the concern of evolutionary biologists.[99] As a way of illustrating some of these varieties and how they serve as explanatory factors for the biologist, Mayr inquires into the cause of bird migration and, more specifically, seeks the answer to the question, "Why did the warbler at my summer place in New Hampshire start his southward migration on the night of August 25?" He replies in terms of four different causes:

> 1. *An ecological cause.* The warbler, being an insect eater, must migrate, because it would starve to death during the winter in New Hampshire.
> 2. *A genetic cause.* The warbler has acquired a genetic constitution in the course of the evolutionary history of his species which induces it to respond appropriately to the proper stimuli from the environment. On the other hand, the screech owl, nesting right next to it, lacks this constitution and does not respond to these stimuli. As a result, it is sedentary.
> 3. *An intrinsic physiological cause.* The warbler flew south because its migration is tied in with photoperiodism. It responds to the decrease in day length and is ready to migrate as soon as the hours of daylight have dropped below a certain hour.
> 4. *An extrinsic physiological cause.* Finally, the warbler migrated on August 25 because a cold air mass, with northerly winds, passed over our area on that day. The sudden drop in temperature and the associated weather conditions affected the bird, already in a general physiological readiness for migration, so that it actually took off.[100]

Of the four, the last two are proximate causes, whereas the first two are ultimate in the sense that "these are causes that have a history and that have been incorporated into the system through many thousands of generations of natural selection." [101]

Mayr then contrasts these notions of causality with some of the formal definitions given by philosophers of science, and finds that the latter, while capable of describing "causal relations quite adequately in certain branches of biology, particularly those that deal with chemical and physical unit phenomena," are of "little operational value in those branches of biology that deal with complex systems." [102] Because of this circumstance, and in view of the almost unlimited structural and dynamic complexity of organisms, Mayr feels that there is little or no chance of predictability in biological systems. The resulting indeterminacy, however, does not entail a rejection of causality but rather the elimination of predictability as "a necessary component" of it.[103] And if the future is almost impossible to predict, especially the course that evolution will follow, this does not invalidate causal explanation generally, for, as Mayr puts it, "I doubt that there is a scientist who would question the ultimate causality of all biological phenomena, that is, that a causal explanation can be given for past biological events." [104]

On the subject of teleology Mayr notes the association of this term with Aristotle's "final cause," which may be defined as "the cause responsible for the orderly reaching of a preconceived ultimate goal." [105] All goal-seeking phenomena can be classified as teleological, he notes, and yet other phenomena whose goal-seeking nature is questionable have also been described by that term. Throughout the history of biology, moreover, an incompatibility has consistently been apparent between mechanistic interpretations of natural processes and the seemingly purposive sequence of events in organic growth, in reproduction, and in animal behavior. "It is only in our lifetime," he observes, "that explanations have been advanced which deal adequately with this paradox." [106] Such explanations, of course, are causal explanations, and they derive from advances made in the science of genetics.

On the basis of these explanations Mayr feels that it is now possible to give a firm and unambiguous answer to the question of how purpose and purposiveness are present in nature. He writes:

> An individual who — to use the language of the
> computer — has been "programmed," can act purpose-
> fully. Historical processes, however, *cannot* act purpose-
> fully. A bird that starts its migration, an insect that se-
> lects its host plant, an animal that avoids a predator, a
> male that displays to a female, all act purposefully be-
> cause they have been programmed to do so.[107]

Apart from its application to such programmed, goal-directed
behavior, Mayr recognizes that the term "teleological" has
also been used in a very different sense to designate the finality involved in evolutionary adaptive processes, which are in
themselves historical.[108] Artistotle used the expression "final
cause" as applicable to these adaptive processes, which have
been remarked by later authors such as Bernard as evidences
of "design" or "plan" in nature.[109] Yet the two meanings of teleology are quite different in Mayr's estimation, and they
should be distinguished one from the other: developmental
processes that are controlled by a genetically coded program
are not the same as evolutionary adaptations, which are more
properly viewed as genetic improvements controlled by natural selection. The former has more recently been referred to
as "teleonomic" and the latter, "teleological," a terminological
usage that Mayr sanctions with some reservations.[110] The
last-named type of final causality, dependent as it is upon
natural selection, is not purposive and can in no way be pre-
dicted; the former or teleonomic type, on the other hand, is
purposive in that it controls the development or behavior of
an individual.[111] And, obviously, "there is no conflict between
causality and teleonomy," [112] because programmed development is determined, and thus caused, by the genetic coding
of the DNA molecules contained within the organism itself;
similar statements, of course, cannot be made with regard to
teleology in the sense of vitalistic or finalistic theories.
Finally, commenting on Nagel's discussion of teleological systems and the ways in which nonteleological explanations may
be substituted for teleological ones, Mayr observes that all of
Nagel's examples are "actually illustrations of teleonomy." [113]

    A fuller examination of the ways in which teleological
explanations function in evolutionary biology that goes beyond Mayr's account has been made by Francisco Ayala,

drawing on the writings of his mentor, Theodosius Dobzhansky, as well as on Mayr's analyses.[114] Ayala goes deeper into
the problem of evolutionary adaptation to show how even
this is a causal process, while being teleological in a sense
different from "teleonomic." His purpose throughout is to
show "that teleological explanations are appropriate and indispensable in biology, and that they are fully compatible
with causal accounts, although they cannot be reduced to
non-teleological explanations without loss of explanatory
content." [115]

To establish his point, Ayala proposes a threefold classification of teleological phenomena, which may be summarized as follows:

> 1. Phenomena wherein the end-state or goal is con-
> sciously anticipated by the agent. This is purposeful
> activity, as deliberative human activity and probably
> also that of a deer running away from a mountain lion or
> a bird building its nest.
> 2. Phenomena connected with self-regulating or teleo-
> nomic systems, where a mechanism exists that enables the
> system to reach and maintain a specific property in spite
> of environmental fluctuations. Servo-mechanisms, al-
> though built by man, are teleological in this sense, but so
> are the homeostatic reactions of organisms, whether hom-
> eostasis be taken developmentally or physiologically ac-
> cording to present-day biological usage.
> 3. Phenomena associated with structures anatomically
> and physiologically designed to perform a certain func-
> tion. In this sense the hand of man is made for grasping
> and his eye for vision, though even tools and machines
> may be said to be teleological in this way.[116]

It is Ayala's contention that natural selection and the manner
in which it functions in the adaptation of living organisms to
their environments and to their ways of life can account for all
three types of teleological phenomena listed above.[117] Thus,
in his view, natural selection can itself be regarded as teleological. Yet there are other ways in which the term "teleological" is used that would not apply to natural selection. To
make these points, therefore, Ayala first distinguishes "two
levels of teleology in organisms":

There usually exists a specific and proximate end for every feature of an animal or plant. The existence of the feature is explained in terms of the function or end-state it serves. But there is also an ultimate goal to which all features contribute or have contributed in the past — reproductive success. The ultimate end to which all other functions and ends contribute is increased reproductive efficiency. In this sense the ultimate source of explanation in biology is the principle of natural selection.[118]

Utilizing these two levels of teleology within the organism, Ayala proposes that one may understand natural selection to be a teleological process in two ways: (1) natural selection is a mechanistic end-directed process that results in increased reproductive efficiency, and so reproductive fitness can be said to be the end-result or goal of natural selection; and (2) natural selection produces and maintains end-directed organs and processes, when the function or end-state served by the organ or process contributes to the reproductive fitness of the organisms.[119] On the other hand, natural selection is not teleological in a third sense, namely, that the overall process of evolution does not proceed toward certain specific goals, preconceived or not. Thus natural selection "does not tend in any way toward the production of specific kinds of organisms or toward organisms having certain specific properties."[120]

The foregoing tripartite classification of teleological systems is based on the nature of the relationship existing between an object or process and its end-state or goal. Ayala proposes another classification also, this alternative being based on the agent giving origin to the teleological mechanism. Thus he observes that "the end-directedness of living organisms and their features may be said to be 'internal' teleology, while that of man-made tools and servo-mechanisms may be called 'external' teleology."[121] Applying this distinction, Ayala then states:

Internal teleological systems are accounted for by natural selection, which is a strictly mechanistic process. External teleological mechanisms are products of the human mind, or more generally, are the result of purposeful activity consciously intending specified ends.[122]

Just as living organisms, in this terminology, exhibit only internal teleology, so also does the overall process of evolution, and thus it is not teleological in the external sense. From this Ayala is led to the further conclusions that the evolutionary process can be explained without recourse to a Creator, that there is no evidence for any vital force or immanent energy directing this process, and that the fossil record itself is evidence that counts against any necessitating force, external or immanent, being involved in the process.[123]

As part of his detailed examination of the relations between teleology and causality, Ayala discusses perceptively Aristotle's fourfold use of *aitia*, the nuances of his meaning of "final cause," and the ways in which this has been largely misunderstood in the intervening centuries.[124] A still more detailed examination of evolutionary biology from the viewpoint of Aristotelian methodology, however, is contained in another recent study, and this too merits a brief consideration. The author, John Deely, traces the historical development of biological science, using the concept of biological species and problems concerned with their origin as his point of departure.[125] Analyzing texts from Julian Huxley and C. H. Waddington, and substantiating his results with citations from Mayr, Simpson, Dobzhansky, Ayala, and others, Deely argues that the history of evolutionary biology exhibits four stages, each of which is characterized by attempts to answer successively the four Aristotelian questions, and that the last stage, seeking causal reasons, yields explanations in terms of all four of the *aitia* or explanatory factors. Rather than propose a Comtean model for scientific progress, Deely would thus substitute the following:

> The extent to which the science [in this case, evolutionary biology] at a given time conducts its inquiry into causes along all four of the possible lines will . . . be an index of its degree of maturity. It would be possible to draw an analogy between the predominantly fact-finding phase of the science (*an sit*) and its "infancy"; between the phase occupied especially with classifications and definitions (*quid sit*) and the "childhood" of the science; between the brief phase where the distinctive difficulties to be explained come into focus (*quale sit*) and the "ado-

316   Causality in Contemporary Science

lescence" of the science; and between the phase where the science organizes research along the lines of the difficulties in search of their proper explanations (*propter quid sit*) and the "adulthood" of the science.[126]

Deely's application of this model to the development of evolutionary biology would see the *ei esti* or *an sit* stage as essentially descriptive when biologists set out to describe as fully and accurately as possible the variety of organisms and the phenomena they exhibit.[127] The *ti estin or quid sit* stage, as he sees it, was developed in two phases, "first on the supposition of the absolute fixity of forms, and then, when classification ceased to be possible on this basis, on the supposition of the fluidity of forms." [128] Once the phylogenetic character of taxonomic divisions was recognized, materials could be rearranged accordingly, and biologists could address themselves to questions of fact, *to hoti* or *quia*, or *quale sit*. And finally, when the facts had been ascertained, they could go about their search for the reasons for the facts in answer to the question *to dioti* or *propter quid*.[129]

When seeking such reasons for the differences between biological populations, according to Huxley's account, biologists employed constitutive, differential, integrative, and analytic methods of approach.[130] In so doing, as Deely sees it, they were "in fact organizing evolutionary explanations according to the formal pattern of Aristotle's four causes." [131] Yet this is even more readily seen, he goes on, in Waddington's analysis of the entire process of evolution "as the intersection of four main sub-processes." [132] Deely interprets these subprocesses as four basic systems in interaction, each of which may be regarded as an explanatory factor (or *aitia*) that serves to illuminate the others in the sense of the axiom, *causae sunt ad invicem causae*.[133] These factors may be summarized as follows:

1. *Epigenetic factor:* the tendency of an interbreeding population to reproduce itself in a stable manner and increase in numbers ("formal causality," i.e., the maintenance of type).
2. *Genetic factor:* the tendency to variation resulting from constant small random mutations in the genetic code ("material causality," i.e., a variety of differing indi-

viduals within a species capable of transmitting their differences).

3. *Selective factor:* natural selection by the environment which eliminates those variants which are less effective in reproducing their kind ("efficient causality," i.e., the agent determining in which direction species-change will take place).

4. *Exploitative factor:* the flexibility of living things by which they are able to occupy new niches in the changing environment ("final causality," i.e., a feed-back mechanism which guides the selective process toward a *new* type which can exploit new environmental possibilities).[134]

Seen in this way, of course, the evolutionary process would itself be susceptible to causal definition as outlined in the previous chapter, and this definition could be approximated in terms of all four causes. Deely makes the important point, moreover, that the model used for definition and explanation in this Aristotelian mode is quite different from the models suggested by Plato (or Pythagoras) and Democritus in their characteristic modes of explanation. Both of the latter relied on reductive models in the sense that they attempted to explain biological phenomena by reducing them to a mathematical and to a mechanical model respectively. The Aristotelian explanatory process, on the other hand, is not reductive but factorial; rather than attempt to reduce biological phenomena to mathematical or to mechanical terms, or to some combination of the two à la Newton, it sees these phenomena as explicable in terms of four correlated factors or aspects, viz., composition and organization as correlates of structure, and agencies and products as correlates of function. The Aristotelian model, of course, is more complex, but, as Deely argues, it does fuller justice to all the facts without negating any advances made in mathematical biology, molecular biology, and all the other branches of the life sciences.[135]

Whether one agrees with Deely's analysis or not, and even making allowances for the differences of interpretation by Nagel, Mayr, Ayala, and others, one can only be struck by the outstanding contribution made by genetics to the understanding of evolutionary processes, particularly in terms of

DNA-RNA molecular groups, genes, chromosomes, and so on. And what is most remarkable about this development is that the causal explanations it supplies are made, not in terms of efficient or final causality, but rather in terms of material and formal causality.[136] As has been noted in the previous section of this chapter, an analogous tendency is detectable in the physical sciences, particularly in the interpretation of relativity and quantum theories. The advantage of a factorial type of analysis, as opposed to a strictly reductive one, is that explanations in terms of any particular type of causality need not preclude (and indeed must be supplemented by) those in terms of other causes. But the fact would seem to remain that the most striking advances in contemporary sciences, both physical and biological, have been made through a study of material and formal causes, and that in recent times a knowledge of matter, and its underlying structure, has been the most potent factor in supplying scientific explanations for natural processes.

b. Human Behavior

The social sciences have not been the subject of discussion in this book and no attempt is made here to explain their use of causal reasoning. A few final observations would seem to be in order, however, by way of a corrective to the ways in which the methodology of the physical sciences has influenced, perhaps harmfully, the development of the social sciences. Any study of man and his behavior, as Mayr has observed, would seem to be more amenable to treatment in terms of the techniques of the life sciences than those of the physical sciences. At the same time, no subject appears more suited to causal analysis than human behavior, since it is within himself that man is most aware of the agency that produces acts and the purpose or intentionality that lies behind them. Yet it is an unfortunate fact that social scientists, in their efforts to be "empirical" and thus as like the "hard sciences" as possible, have tended to undervalue their privileged source of insights. Even Hubert Blalock, who has produced some splendid analyses of causal reasoning in the social sciences, has shown the effect of these pressures. In the introduction to his *Causal Inferences in Nonexperimental Re-*

search, for example, he is almost apologetic when discussing the ontological status of causality, conceding too readily that the real world is far too complex for causal analysis, and offering such complexity as his main justification for resorting to "causal models." [137] This is not to imply, of course, that either he or other methodologists of the social scientists have fallen completely into the formalistic patterns of explanation that have dominated the treatments of such topics by philosophers of the physical sciences. In his recent anthology, Leonard Krimerman in fact takes strong exception to most of the latters' established theses.[138] The positions he urges his readers to accept then are the following:

1. That there are cogent objections and plausible alternatives to the covering-law analysis of scientific explanation. . .
2. That the methods of natural and social science are fundamentally dissimilar. . .
3. That *verstehen* (interpretative understanding) is indispensable for acquiring knowledge in the social sciences. . .
4. That where human actions are performed intentionally it is impossible to explain them by reference to empirical covering laws. . .
5. That mental concepts such as *believing, desiring, dreaming, imagining,* cannot be equated with or reduced to physical concepts and, in some cases at least, they are incompatible with operational definitions and measurement techniques. . .
6. That "social laws" or uniformities, e.g., that Catholics have lower suicide rates than Protestants, that every revolution produces counter-revolutionary activity, that men increase their consumption as their income increases but not to the same extent as the increase in their income, are either disguised analytic truths (true by virtue of what their terms mean) or arise from the avoidable activities, motives, and beliefs of individual agents. . .
7. That since social scientists cannot avoid being committed to value-judgments of a distinctive sort, objectivity must take a different form in the social as opposed to the natural sciences.[139]

Under criticism such as this, once the Humean analysis of causation has been abandoned as inadequate in the natural

sciences and, a fortiori, completely misguided in any accounting of human behavior, the way is opened for the reinstatement of all the "anthropomorphic" insights that make man intelligible to himself. And if the physical and biological
sciences have made the greatest progress in recent times
through the study of matter's substructure, and in this sense
have shed new light on material and formal causality, it is
perhaps to be expected that the sciences of man, examining
anew the concepts of action and purpose, may shed equal
light on efficient and final causality.

Richard Taylor's *Action and Purpose* is a significant beginning in the latter direction, for it attempts to do, in the
context of the agency and finality involved in human behavior, something similar to what we have been doing for the
natural sciences throughout these two volumes.[140] As Taylor,
in wording that is somewhat suggestive of Thomas Reid, observes when treating human purposefulness:

> There is . . . nothing particularly problematical to com-
> mon sense in the idea that people sometimes have rea-
> sons for what they do, that they sometimes act with a
> view to achieving certain ends, that it is sometimes up to
> them how they go about realizing those ends, and so on.
> Such ways of speaking fit perfectly into the framework of
> everyday conceptions we continually apply to our deal-
> ings with men, conceptions we seldom reflect upon be-
> cause they seem perfectly obvious. The study of philoso-
> phy and science, however, accustoms us to a rather
> different framework of concepts, one which we have
> learned to apply most usefully to the behavior of inani-
> mate things. Accordingly, when men begin to philoso-
> phize about human behavior, they feel virtually com-
> pelled to interpret it within that very framework. Now in
> case human behavior should not fit into that framework,
> enormous and indeed insoluble problems must inevitably
> result.[141]

Taylor then cites the confusion that arises from attempting to
analyze the purposefulness of human behavior on the model
of feedback devices found in inanimate objects, the problem
of "free will" and the attempts it has engendered to reduce
the free actions of men to operations that are not free at all,
and the tendency to misconstrue the reasons men give for

their actions, or to interpret them in terms of hidden wants, needs, and desires that are completely outside the order of rationality.

Similarly, in discussing efficient causality, and here again in terms reminiscent of Reid, Taylor writes:

> Men sometimes cause certain things to happen, both in their own bodies and, by this means, in their environment. In thus causing certain things to happen, typically as means to the attainment or prevention of certain other things, they are active beings, or agents. This kind of causation — causation by agents — is so different from the kind of causal sequence found in events that it is unfortunate, and the source of much error, that we use the same word for both. Causation by agents remains, however, the fundamental idea of causation that all men possess. This is significant because it obliges us to view men as being sometimes the initiating and originating sources not only of their own behavior, but of all those events, sometimes events of the greatest magnitude, which are the causal consequences of such agency.[142]

Many of our contemporaries, he remarks, would find the foregoing statement incomprehensible, for nothing appears more mysterious to them than the agency by which they move their own limbs. Yet there is a paradox here, and Taylor goes on to point out that motor activity

> is mysterious or incomprehensible *only* in the sense that it is not what a man having any familiarity with physical science or the general history of speculative thought would be led to expect. In another sense it is strange indeed to speak of some perfectly familiar thing — something so familiar as the simple act of moving one's limb — as being in any sense mysterious. If we find something in our daily experience, and if we also find that we cannot, without being led to absurdities, represent it as a special case of something else that is already familiar and well understood, there is surely no point in calling it mysterious other than to indicate that it is *not* a special case of something else that is well understood. In other words, there must be a sense in which the commonplace cannot be so strange, however badly it might fit into the philosophy and science we have learned.[143]

The limitations of any philosophy of science based exclusively on Hume, as should be apparent by now, are serious when dealing with inanimate objects, and they become insuperable when applied to the study of man. On the other hand, a philosophy of science that rejects an event ontology and encourages causal inquiry in terms of things and their attributes, including powers and potentialities, offers promise for dealing with the whole range of experience from the inanimate to the human. Harré and Secord, employing such a philosophy, have recently turned their attention to problems associated with the explanation of social behavior, and thus have made a start in this direction.[144] Rather than propose a mechanistic model of man in terms of stimulus-response that focuses on external stimulation alone and neglects any connection between cause and effect, these authors propose an "anthropomorphic model" that would treat the individual, surprisingly, as a person with his own powers and potentialities. Again, rather than conceive social behavior on the model of group responses caused by stimuli, they would treat such behavior as the actions of human agents living in society that are mediated by meanings and hence by reasons. Their proposal, it goes without saying, calls for a complete rethinking of the philosophy behind social psychology and other disciplines dealing with human behavior, but the foundation they propose is substantial and it offers promise for fruitful development. Its underlying inspiration, as one might suspect from acquaintance with Harré's other works, is that the ultimate task of the scientist is to seek "causal explanation — the rational explanation of non-random patterns, through the discovery of the mechanisms that generate such patterns." [145] These mechanisms are obviously grounded in human nature, but they are never easy to discover, and are best known analogously through a variety of modeling techniques. In the end, however, it is causal explanation, and this in terms of the agencies and purposes of distinctively human behavior — and hence in terms of efficient and final causes — that is proposed as the ultimate to which the social scientist can attain. Thus causality, far from being rejected in these disciplines, emerges once again as the key factor that renders their explanations truly scientific.[146]

Epilogue

In the preface to the first volume I indicated that a principal concern of this work is the problem of truth in science. I there affirmed the inadequacy of the hypothetico-deductive method, as presented in logical positivist philosophies of science, to guarantee the truth of the statements, e.g., that the earth is round and spinning on its axis, that the blood circulates, that molecules and atoms exist, and so forth. Such inadequacy, I noted, has been brought to more general attention by Kuhn's attack on the "cumulative growth of knowledge" thesis, which has resulted in sharp divisions between logically minded and historically minded scholars, neither of whom seems able to justify any acquisition of truth in science. I intimated that my two-volume examination of causality and scientific explanation, and more specifically of causal explanation, could contribute much to the solution of that problem.

This examination is now concluded, and the reader will have noted that, while practically every aspect of causality and explanation has been discussed at length, there has been no explicit treatment of truth itself. The omission has been deliberate on my part. Truth, as I see it, is a property of knowledge, and concern with truth, as such, is a reflective concern that is usually not part of the scientist's mentality. Those who are unconvinced that there is such a thing as knowledge, or who are unable to see how new knowledge can be acquired, are in no position to address themselves to the problem of truth. And if this is so with truth, it is even more so with the problem of certitude. Those who do not know, or who despair of ever being able to come to know, will never be in a position to know *that* they know and hence to be certain of their knowledge. Rather than force a premature reflective consideration of such difficult matters, therefore, I have preferred to concentrate on first-level problems that relate to the existence of scientific knowledge itself.

There has been no systematic justification, on this account, of the truth of the statements that the earth is round and spinning on its axis, that the blood circulates, and that molecules and atoms exist. But evidence has been presented throughout the two volumes to show how men, for the past several centuries, have pondered the problems implicit in these statements and sought proofs that would lead to their establishment and common acceptance. The probative force of their arguments has, in fact, produced what we now know as scientific knowing, or science itself. The new truths that they discovered in the process sometimes led to the relinquishing of erroneous opinions, but they did not necessarily falsify "old truths," and particularly not the knowledge on which their very acquisition was based. To discover that "the earth is an oblate spheroid" is not to disprove that "the earth is round," just as to show that it rotates relative to a local "star-compass" is not to disprove its rotation with respect to Cartesian coordinates at the center of the solar system. Again, to discover that the blood circulates does not falsify the fact that it flows, or to maintain that atoms or electrons or anti-xi-minuses exist is not to question the existence of molecules. These and similar conclusions, moreover, as I have attempted to show, are based on causal reasoning, generally proceeding from effect to cause, and in many cases laying bare the ontological factors that determine things to be the way in which we have come to know them.

It may be objected that the examples on which I have concentrated do, in fact, make the point about truth, but they are really trivial examples for scientists of the present day who are working at the frontiers of knowledge. In a sense, this is correct. But one of the advantages of doing philosophy of science from the perspective of history is that these very examples, now so commonly accepted as truths that they can be regarded as trivial, at an earlier time were questions being posed by inquirers then working at the frontiers of their knowledge. Whether the blood circulates or not was by no means a trivial question for Harvey and his contemporaries, nor was the question whether the earth is an oblate or a prolate spheroid trivial to the English and French scientists who organized expeditions to verify Newton's and Cassini's alternative explanations of its shape. As to the question of the earth's rotation, that would seem to have been what the Scientific Revolution was all about, and it is difficult to see how that revolution can be regarded as in any way trivial.

Throughout my exposition I have called attention repeatedly to the *Posterior Analytics* and to the relevance of its canons for the solution of problems in classical and contemporary science. This may be criticized as a benighted return to Aristotle or to medieval scholasticism, although it is not my intention to urge any such regression. Anyone who seriously studies the methodology of classical science, however, cannot fail but be impressed with how deeply its roots are anchored in the Middle Ages. Unfortunately, and I would be the first to admit it, the medievals saw the *Posterior Analytics* uniquely as a method of guaranteeing certitude in science, and were generally unaware of the lengthy process of inquiry that the discovery of causes inevitably entails. This explains the excessive emphasis placed on certainty by the scholastics, an emphasis that was taken over by many thinkers in the classical period and converted almost into a mystical ideal. Empiricism and mathematicism competed with each other as guarantors of the new certitudes that would henceforth displace the discredited peripatetic philosophy. But both the medieval and the classical emphases were misguided, as the development of contemporary science has shown. Truth is difficult enough to attain; certainty is an idol before which only the pure mathematician is now willing to torture himself. But this does not mean that the search for causes is to be abandoned, or that one can take refuge in the world of logical or mathematical forms whenever the physical universe proves refractory to his understanding.

It is this latter tactic that, in my view, has vitiated much of the work done by the philosophy of science "establishment" in American universities. Generally, philosophers of science have spoken of truth, but by this they meant "truth value," something that could be assimilated into a propositional calculus and that could decide all debatable issues on purely formal grounds. Coupled with this concern with logic has been an exclusive interest in empiricist epistemology and its implied ontology of events, neither of which permits any insight into the natures of things or their causal interconnectedness. Within the limitations imposed by their resulting commitments, contemporary philosophers of science have dealt skillfully with a sub-set of problems concerned with efficient causality understood in the weak Humean sense of causation. But their efforts, in my opinion, have not gone far enough, for there are other alternatives, evident not only in the proposals of the philosophers and methodologists of classical science but also in the procedures actually employed by scientists themselves. I have therefore urged an expansion of causal thinking far beyond the narrow domain of Humean causation, to include what contemporary thinkers have spoken of as "powers," "inner determiners," and other real "explanatory factors" that can account for the phenomena being studied by today's scientists. Semantics, for me, has not been a problem: I am willing to substitute "factorial analysis" for "causal analysis," or to use any other terminology that will focus attention on the manifold of ontological antecedents that can truly explain natural phenomena.

Finally, I do not pretend to have solved the many technical philosophical problems that relate to causal analysis. This two-volume work, as I see it, is not so much definitive as it is programmatic. My hope is that I have provided a setting in which the question of causal explanation can be reopened, wherein philosophers of science can examine these problems anew in the light of the rich tradition that is rightfully a part of their heritage. In recent years, unfortunately, the philosophy of science has developed in isolation from the main body of substantive philosophy. It is time that it be reunited to the tradition from which science itself sprang, wherein the answers to its many pressing problems still remain to be found.

Notes

CHAPTER ONE

1. Cf. Gerd Buchdahl, *Metaphysics and the Philosophy of Science: The Classical Origins: Descartes to Kant*, Cambridge, Mass.: The M.I.T. Press, 1969, pp. v–vi.

2. Discourse on Method is, in fact, a poor translation for the first words of the title of this famous work, which reads in full: Discours de la méthode pour bien conduire sa raison, et chercher la vérité dans les sciences. Plus la Dioptrique, les Météores et la Géometrie, qui sont des essais de cette méthode.

3. Paul J. Olscamp, in the introductory essay to his translation of *Discourse on Method, Optics, Geometry, and Meteorology*, The Library of Liberal Arts, New York: Bobbs-Merrill, 1965, p. ix.

4. I. Bernard Cohen, ed., *Isaac Newton's Papers and Letters on Natural Philosophy and Related Documents*, Cambridge, Mass.: Harvard University Press, 1958, p. 457.

5. *Ibid.*, p. 458.

6. Étienne Gilson, *Études sur le rôle de la pensée médiévale dans la formation du système cartésien*, Paris: J. Vrin, 1930; see also R. I. Markus, "Method and Metaphysics: The Origins of Some Cartesian Presuppositions in the Philosophy of the Renaissance," *Dominican Studies* 2 (1949), 356–384; for details of Descartes's life, see J. R. Vrooman, *René Descartes, A Biography*, New York: Putnam, 1970. For an introduction to his thought, see S. V. Keeling, *Descartes*, 2d ed., Oxford: Oxford University Press, 1968. For his contributions to science, see the article on him by A. C. Crombie, M. S. Mahoney, and T. M. Brown, *Dictionary of Scientific Biography*, ed. Charles Gillispie, New York: Charles Scribner's Sons, 1970– , Vol. 4, pp. 51–65.

7. March 11, 1640. *Oeuvres de Descartes*, ed. C. Adam and

P. Tannery, 12 vols., Paris: 1897–1913, Vol. 3, p. 39. The "essays" referred to were written in 1637.

8. L. M. Régis, "Analyse et synthèse dans l'oeuvre de saint Thomas," *Studia Mediaevalia in honorem A. R. P. Martin*, Bruges: St. Catherine Press, 1948, pp. 303–330.

9. *Oeuvres*, Vol. 11, p. 47.

10. For Descartes's influence on Newton, see Koyré, *Newtonian Studies*, Cambridge, Mass.: Harvard University Press, 1965, pp. 53–200, and I. B. Cohen, "Quantum in se est: Newton, Kepler, Galileo, Descartes and Lucretius," *Proceedings of the American Catholic Philosophical Association* 38 (1964), 36–46. The laws of motion are not identical in the two, however, as is shown by Alan Gabbey, "Force and Inertia in Seventeenth-Century Dynamics," *Studies in History and Philosophy of Science* 2 (1971), 1–67, esp. pp. 20–31 and 56–67.

11. Letter to Morin, July 13, 1638, *Oeuvres*, Vol. 2, p. 198.

12. From the French version of the *Principia philosophiae*, *Oeuvres*, Vol. 11, pt. 2, p. 310.

13. October 11, 1638, *Oeuvres*, Vol. 2, p. 380.

14. N. K. Smith, *Studies in the Cartesian Philosophy*, London, 1914; reprint ed., New York: Russell and Russell, Inc., 1962, pp. 71–73, 137–180.

15. J. F. Scott, *The Scientific Work of René Descartes (1596–1650)*, London: Taylor & Francis, Ltd., 1952, pp. 22–23, 167–181, and *passim*.

16. J. P. Mahaffy, *Descartes*, Philadelphia: J. B. Lippincott & Co., 1881, pp. 163–164.

17. N. K. Smith, ed., *Descartes: Philosophical Writings*, New York: Modern Library, 1958, p. 6. Note that the French *expériences* may be translated either as experiences or experiments, depending on the context.

18. *Ibid.*

19. *Lettres de M. R. Descartes*, 3 vols., Paris: 1657–67, Vol. 3, p. 190. Cited by Scott, *Scientific Work* . . . , p. 68.

20. In the *Meteorology*, 8th discourse, trans. Olscamp, p. 342.

21. Sixth Pt., trans. Olscamp, p. 51.

22. *Ibid.*, p. 52.

23. *Ibid.*

24. *Ibid.*

25. For a reconstruction of Descartes's actual use of these terms, see Buchdahl, *Metaphysics* . . . , pp. 126–147; for a more negative critique from the viewpoint of Thomism, see Régis, "Analyse et synthèse . . . ," p. 330.

26. Olscamp, Introduction, p. xiv.

27. *Meditations*, Reply to Objections II, in *The Philosophical Works of Descartes*, trans. E. S. Haldane and G. R. T. Ross, 2 vols., Cambridge: At the University Press, 1911; corrected ed., 1931; reprint ed., 1970; Vol. 2, p. 48.

28. *Ibid.*, pp. 48–49, italics added.

29. See Olscamp, Introduction, p. xvi.

30. *Ibid.*

31. *Ibid.*, pp. xv–xvii.

32. Apart from Olscamp, the following shed light on Descartes's methodology: Gerd Buchdahl, "The Relevance of Descartes' Philosophy for Modern Philosophy of Science," *British Journal for the History of Science* 1 (1963), 227–249; J. M. Morris, "Descartes and Probable Knowledge," *Journal for the History of Philosophy* 8 (1970), 303–312; and Élie Denissoff, *Descartes, premier théoricien de la physique mathématique: Trois essais sur le Discours de la méthode.* Bibliothèque philosophique de Louvain, Vol. 22, Louvain: Publications Universitaires, 1970.

33. R. M. Blake, "The Role of Experience in Descartes' Theory of Method," in *Theories of Scientific Method: The Renaissance Through the Nineteenth Century*, ed. E. H. Madden, Seattle: University of Washington Press, 1960, pp. 75–103, esp. pp. 78–79; for a concrete illustration, see A. I. Sabra, *Theories of Light from Descartes to Newton*, New York: American Elsevier Co., 1967, pp. 17–45.

34. Blake, *ibid.*, pp. 89–91.

35. *Ibid.*, p. 92.

36. First Discourse, trans. Olscamp, p. 263.

37. *Ibid.*, p. 264.

38. *Ibid.*

39. February 22, 1638, *Oeuvres*, Vol. 1, pp. 563–564; cited by Blake, p. 93.

40. Pt. VI, trans. Haldane and Ross, Vol. 1, pp. 128–129.

41. *Ibid.*, p. 129.

42. July 13, 1638, *Oeuvres*, Vol. 2, p. 198; cited by Blake, p. 94.

43. *Ibid.*, p. 199; Blake, pp. 94–95.

44. *Ibid.*

45. *Ibid.*; again see Sabra, *Theories of Light* . . . , pp. 17–24.

46. *Principia philosophiae*, pt. 3, n. 43, *Oeuvres*, Vol. 8, p. 99; cf. pt. 4, n. 205, *ibid.*, p. 328.

47. Scott, *Scientific Work* . . . , pp. 76–77, 175–178, 183–184, 188–192; also Mahaffy, *Descartes*, pp. 156–164, esp. 161–164.

48. See Descartes's letter to Morin, July 13, 1638, *Oeuvres*, Vol. 2, p. 200; cited by Blake, pp. 95–96.

49. *Meditations*, Reply to Objections V, trans. Haldane and Ross, Vol. 2, p. 217, pp. 159–160; on Descartes's teaching on causality generally, see Keeling, *Descartes*, pp. 112–120, 127–128, and 267–270.

50. Heimo Dolch, *Kausalität im Verständnis des Theologen und der Begründer neuzeitlicher Physik*, Freiburg-im-Breisgau: Verlag Herder, 1954, pp. 93–113.

51. Letter to Mersenne, May 27, 1630, *Oeuvres*, Vol. 1, pp. 151–152.

52. *Principles of Philosophy*, pt. 1, no. 24, trans. Haldane and Ross, Vol. 1, p. 229; this statement, of course, is suggestive of the occasionalism advocated by Malebranche.

53. *Ibid.*, no. 20, p. 227.

54. *Ibid.*, no. 21, p. 227.

55. *Meditations*, Reply to Objections VI, trans. Haldane and Ross, Vol. 2, p. 251.

56. Pt. 2, no. 25, trans. Haldane and Ross, Vol. 1, p. 266.

57. *Ibid.*; this is Aristotle's teaching in Bk. 3 of the *Physics*.

58. Pt. 2, no. 36, in *Descartes: Philosophical Writings*, ed. and trans. E. Anscombe and P. T. Geach, London: Nelson & Sons, Ltd., 1954, p. 215.

59. *Ibid.*, pp. 215–216.

60. *Ibid.*, no. 37, p. 216.

61. *Ibid.*, no. 39, p. 217.

62. Pt. 3, n. 48, *Oeuvres*, Vol. 8, p. 103.

63. See Dolch, *Kausalität* . . . , pp. 106–113, esp. p. 111.

64. *Principles of Philosophy*, pt. 1, no. 28, trans. Haldane and Ross, p. 230.

65. *Ibid.*, pp. 230–231.

66. For a summary account, see the article by Samuel I. Mintz, *Dictionary of Scientific Biography*, vol. 6, pp. 444–451.

67. See Hobbes's "Epistle Dedicatory" to his *Elements of Philosophy*, in the *English Works*, 11 vols., London: John Bohn, 1839, Vol. 1, pp. viii–ix.

68. On Hobbes's knowledge of Aristotle and the Schoolmen, especially Suarez, see Frithiof Brandt, *Thomas Hobbes' Mechanical Conception of Nature*, Copenhagen: Levin & Munksgaard, 1928, pp. 55–57, 62–73.

69. E. H. Madden, "Thomas Hobbes and the Rationalist Ideal," in *Theories of Scientific Method* . . . , p. 110.

70. *English Works*, Vol. 1, p. 3.

71. *Ibid.*, pp. 65–66.

72. *Ibid.*, p. 66.

73. *Ibid.*, p. 67; these Greek expressions are the equivalents of the Latin *an sit* and *quid sit*, which played such a large role in medieval scientific methodology.

74. *Ibid.*, pp. 67–68.

75. *Leviathan*, in *English Works*, Vol. 3, pp. 23–24.

76. *Elements of Philosophy*, in *English Works*, Vol. 1, p. 69.

77. *Ibid.*, p. 68.

78. *Ibid*, p. 79.

79. *Ibid*.

80. *Ibid.*, p. 88.

81. *Ibid.*, pp. 88–89.

82. Brandt, *Thomas Hobbes' Mechanical Conception* . . . , p. 371.

83. *Leviathan,* in *English Works,* Vol. 3, p. 6.
84. See Madden, "Thomas Hobbes and the Rationalist Ideal," p. 109.
85. *Ibid.,* p. 112.
86. Chap. 9, *English Works,* Vol. 1, pp. 120–127.
87. *Ibid.,* p. 121.
88. *Ibid.*
89. *Ibid.,* p. 122.
90. *Ibid.,* p. 123.
91. *Ibid.,* chap. 10, pp. 131–132.
92. Brandt, *Thomas Hobbes' Mechanical Conception . . . ,* p. 274.
93. *Ibid.*
94. For an exhaustive analysis of this aspect of Hobbes's thought, see Arrigo Pacchi, *Convenzione e Ipotesi nella formazione della filosofia naturale di Thomas Hobbes,* Florence: La Nuova Italia Editrice, 1965.
95. Brandt, *Thomas Hobbes' Mechanical Conception . . . ,* pp. 195–201.
96. In the *Leviathan,* pt. 4, chap. 46, Hobbes inveighs against the Schoolmen's teaching on gravity, and yet his own discussion of the cause of gravity marks no substantial advance over those he criticizes; see pt. 4 of his *Elements,* in *English Works,* Vol. 1, pp. 387–532, esp. chap. 30, "On Gravity," pp. 508–532.
97. For general information on Locke, see M. V. C. Jeffreys, *John Locke: Prophet of Common Sense,* London: Methuen & Co., Ltd., 1967; D. J. O'Connor, *John Locke,* London: Penguin Books, 1952; reprint ed., New York: Dover Publications, 1967; R. I. Aaron, *John Locke,* 2d ed., Oxford: Clarendon Press, 1955; and Gerd Buchdahl, *The Image of Newton and Locke in the Age of Reason,* London: Sheed & Ward, 1961.
98. For background, see P. J. White, "Materialism and the Concept of Motion in Locke's Theory of Sense-Idea Causation," *Studies in History and Philosophy of Science* 2 (1971), 97–134.
99. Buchdahl, *Metaphysics and the Philosophy of Science,* pp. 193, 212, 229.
100. *Ibid.,* p. 181.
101. *An Essay Concerning Human Understanding,* ed. A. C. Fraser, Great Books Ed., Chicago: Encyclopaedia Britannica, 1952, Vol. 35, Bk. 2, chap. 21, n. 2, p. 178; for a summary analysis, see D. J. O'Connor, *John Locke,* pp. 88–94.
102. *Essay, ibid.,* n. 4, p. 179.
103. *Ibid.,* chap. 22, n. 11, p. 203.
104. R. M. Yost, Jr., "Locke's Rejection of Hypotheses About Sub-Microscopic Events," *Journal of the History of Ideas* 12 (1951), 111–130.
105. *Essay,* Bk. 2, chap. 23, n. 22, p. 209.
106. *Ibid.,* n. 23, p. 209.
107. *Ibid.,* p. 210.

108. *Ibid.*, nn. 23–28, pp. 209–211.

109. *Ibid.*, chap. 25, n. 11, p. 217.

110. *Ibid.*, chap. 26, n. 2, p. 217.

111. *Ibid.*, chap. 21, n. 1; see Buchdahl, *Metaphysics* . . . , pp. 261–265.

112. M. J. Osler, "John Locke and the Changing Ideal of Scientific Knowledge," *Journal of the History of Ideas* 31 (1970), 3–16.

113. *Essay,* Bk. 4, chap. 3, n. 12, p. 316.

114. *Ibid.*, n. 16, p. 317.

115. *Ibid.*, n. 26, p. 321.

116. *Ibid.*

117. *Ibid.*, n. 29, pp. 322–323.

118. *Ibid.*, n. 28, p. 322.

119. *Ibid.*, chap. 6, n. 4, pp. 331–332.

120. *Ibid.*, n. 16, p. 336.

121. *Ibid.*, n. 11, p. 335.

122. *Ibid.*, chap. 12, n. 9, p. 360.

123. *Ibid.*

124. *Ibid.*, pp. 360–361.

125. *Ibid.*, n. 10, p. 361.

126. *Ibid.*, nn. 12–13, p. 362.

127. *Ibid.*, n. 13, p. 362; for a full discussion of Locke's teaching on hypotheses, see L. L. Laudan, "The Nature and Sources of Locke's Views on Hypotheses," *Journal of the History of Ideas* 38 (1967), 211–223.

128. *Ibid.*, n. 14, p. 362.

129. *Ibid.*, chap. 16, n. 12, p. 371.

130. J. H. Humber and E. H. Madden, "Natural Necessity," *The New Scholasticism* 47 (1973), 214–227.

131. Buchdahl, *Metaphysics* . . . , p. 216, 217 fn. 1.

132. *Ibid.*, p. 233.

133. *Ibid.*, p. 259.

134. For a brief treatment of Berkeley's life and works, see the article on him by Gerd Buchdahl in the *Dictionary of Scientific Biography,* Vol. 2, pp. 16–18; for a study of his philosophy of science, see chap. 5 of Buchdahl's *Metaphysics* . . . , pp. 275–324, esp. pp. 285–290 and 307–317.

135. *The Works of George Berkeley, Bishop of Cloyne,* ed. A. A. Luce and T. E. Jessop, 9 vols., Edinburgh: Thomas Nelson & Sons, Ltd., 1948–57, Vol. 4, n. 2, p. 31.

136. *Ibid.*, n. 4, p. 32.

137. *Ibid.*

138. *Ibid.*, n. 5, p. 32.

139. *Ibid.*, n. 6, p. 32.

140. *Ibid.*, n. 7, p. 32.

141. *Ibid.*, n. 17, p. 35.

142. *Ibid.*, n. 28, p. 38.

143. See n. 52, *supra*.
144. *De motu*, n. 34, *Works*, Vol. 4, p. 40.
145. *Ibid*., n. 35, p. 40.
146. *Ibid*., n. 41, p. 42.
147. *Ibid*., n. 47, p. 44.
148. *Ibid*., n. 67, p. 50.
149. *Ibid*.
150. *Ibid*., n. 72, p. 52.
151. *Ibid*., n. 71, p. 51.
152. *Ibid*.
153. For a brief analysis, see Gabriel Moked, "A Note on Berkeley's Corpuscularian Theories in *Siris*," *Studies in History and Philosophy of Science* 2 (1971), 257–271.
154. *Works*, Vol. 5, *Siris*, n. 220, p. 106.
155. *Ibid*., nn. 227–228, p. 109.
156. *Ibid*., n. 231, p. 111.
157. *Ibid*.
158. *Ibid*., n. 234, p. 112.
159. *Ibid*., n. 237, p. 114.
160. *Ibid*., n. 245, p. 117.
161. *Ibid*., n. 247, p. 118.
162. *Ibid*., n. 250, p. 119.
163. *Ibid*., n. 266, p. 125.
164. *Ibid*., n. 285, p. 133.
165. *Ibid*., n. 293, p. 136.
166. See Buchdahl, *Dictionary of Scientific Biography*, Vol. 2, p. 17.
167. Great Books Ed., Chicago: Encyclopaedia Britannica, 1952, Vol. 35, n. 107, p. 434.
168. *De motu*, n. 69, *Works*, Vol. 4, p. 51.
169. *Ibid*., n. 36, p. 41.
170. Buchdahl, *Metaphysics* . . . , p. 315.
171. For biographical details see John Passmore's article in the *Dictionary of Scientific Biography*, Vol. 6, pp. 555–560; on Hume's thought, see N. K. Smith, *The Philosophy of David Hume*, A Critical Study of Its Origins and Central Doctrines, London: Macmillan, 1941; and J. A. Passmore, *Hume's Intentions*, Cambridge: At the University Press, 1952; also chap. 6 of Buchdahl's *Metaphysics* . . . , pp. 325–387.
172. Great Books Ed. (L. A. Selby-Bigge), Chicago: Encyclopaedia Britannica, 1952, Vol. 35, sect. 7, pt. 2, n. 58, p. 476.
173. *Ibid*., sect. 11, nn. 105–106, pp. 498–499; n. 113, p. 502.
174. *Ibid*., sect. 7, pt. 2, n. 59, p. 476.
175. *Ibid*.
176. *Ibid*. For a critical analysis, see Leonard Greenberg, "Necessity in Hume's Causal Theory," *Review of Metaphysics* 8 (1955), 612–623.

177. Bk. 1, pt. 3, sect. 3, Everyman's Library Ed., New York: E. P. Dutton & Co., 1911, 2 vols., Vol. 1, p. 81.

178. *Ibid.*, p. 82.

179. *Ibid.*, p. 84.

180. *Ibid.*, Vol. 2, p. 319.

181. For a critical discussion, see A. D. Lindsay's Introduction to the Everyman's Library Ed., Vol. 1, pp. vii–xxvii; also A. C. Ewing, *Kant's Treatment of Causality*, London: Routledge and Kegan Paul, 1924; reprint ed., Archon Books, 1969, pp. 6–15; and Jerrold Aronson, "The Legacy of Hume's Analysis of Causation," *Studies in History and Philosophy of Science* 2 (1971), 135–156.

182. See C. J. Ducasse, "Causality: Critique of Hume's Analysis," in *Nature, Mind, and Death*, La Salle, Ill.: Open Court Publishing Co., 1951, pp. 91–100; also "David Hume on Causation," in *Theories of Scientific Method . . .* , ed. E. H. Madden, pp. 144–152.

183. J. W. Lenz, "Hume's Defense of Causal Inference," *Journal of the History of Ideas* 19 (1958), 559–567.

184. *Treatise*, Bk. 1, pt. 4, sect. 3, Vol. 1, p. 183.

185. *Ibid.*, pt. 3, sect. 2, p. 78.

186. *Ibid.*, sect. 8, p. 107.

187. See Buchdahl, *Metaphysics . . .* , pp. 345–348.

188. *Treatise*, sect. 8, p. 107.

189. *Enquiry*, sect 4, pt. 2, n. 29, p. 461.

190. *Ibid.*, pt. 1, n. 26, p. 460.

191. *Ibid*.

192. *Treatise*, pt. 3, sect. 12, p. 140.

193. *Ibid.*, p. 133.

194. *Ibid.*, p. 131; cf. Locke, *Essay*, Bk. 4, chap. 3, n. 25, p. 321.

195. *Treatise*, sect. 15, Vol. 1, p. 170.

196. Buchdahl, *Metaphysics . . .* , pp. 343–345; see also E. H. Madden, "Hume and the Fiery Furnace," *Philosophy of Science* 38 (1971), 64–78.

197. Buchdahl, *Metaphysics . . .* , pp. 378, 361–364.

198. C. T. Ruddick, "Hume on Scientific Law," *Philosophy of Science* 16 (1949), 89–93.

199. For details of Reid's life and teaching, see the article on him by S. A. Grave in *The Encyclopedia of Philosophy*, ed. Paul Edwards, 8 vols., New York: Macmillan and Free Press, Vol. 7, pp. 118–121.

200. L. L. Laudan, "Thomas Reid and the Newtonian Turn of British Methodological Thought," *The Methodological Heritage of Newton*, ed. R. E. Butts and J. W. Davis, Toronto: University of Toronto Press, 1970, pp. 103–131, esp. p. 106; see also Laudan's "The *Vis viva* Controversy, a Post-Mortem," *Isis* 59 (1968), 131–143; the last four pages of this article contain, in an Appendix, a part of Reid's "Essay on Quantity."

201. Laudan, "Thomas Reid . . . ," p. 107.

202. *Ibid.*, pp. 109–119; for more details, see G. N. Cantor, "Henry Brougham and the Scottish Methodological Tradition," *Studies in History and Philosophy of Science* 2 (1971), 69–89.

203. *Ibid.*, pp. 120–121.

204. *Ibid.*, p. 122, citing Reid's *An Inquiry into the Human Mind;* see *The Works of Thomas Reid, D.D.*, now fully collected, with selections from his unpublished letters, by Sir William Hamilton, 2 vols., Edinburgh & London: Longmans, 1863, Vol. I, p. 97.

205. *Works*, Vol. I, p. 705.

206. Letters to Dr. James Gregory, *Works*, Vol. I, p. 75.

207. *Ibid.*

208. *Ibid.*, pp. 75–76.

209. *Essays on the Active Powers of the Human Mind*, Essay IV, chap. 9, *Works*, Vol. I, p. 627.

210. *Ibid.*

211. Letters to James Gregory, June 14, 1785, *Works*, Vol. I, p. 65.

212. [n.d.] *Works*, Vol. I, p. 77.

213. Letters to Gregory, June 14, 1785, Vol. I, p. 65.

214. [n.d.] *Works*, Vol. I, p. 78.

215. *Ibid.*, p. 81.

216. *Ibid.*, p. 75. Passages such as this have suggested comparisons between Reid and Kant; see, for example, William Hamilton's note to Reid's *Works*, Vol. I, p. 628.

217. Letters to Gregory, June 14, 1785, *Works*, Vol. I, p. 66. Admission of this usage is made by Reid elsewhere, as for example: "I likewise admit laws of nature may be called (as they commonly are called) physical causes — in a sense indeed somewhat different from the former — because laws of nature effect nothing, but as far as they are put to execution either by some agent or by some physical cause; they being, however, our *ne plus ultra* in natural philosophy, which professes to show us the causes of natural things, and being both in ancient and modern times called *causes*, they have by prescription acquired a right to that name." — Letter of July 31, 1789, *ibid.*, p. 73.

218. Letter to Gregory in March, 1786, *Works*, Vol. I, p. 67.

219. *Active Powers* . . . , in *Works*, Vol. I, pp. 627–628.

220. Letter to Gregory, July 30, 1789, *ibid.*, p. 74.

221. *Works*, Vol. I, p. 66.

222. *Active Powers* . . . , in *Works*, Vol. I, p. 628; for Reid's evaluation of Leibniz and his controversy with Newton, see *ibid.*, p. 626; for his appreciation of Malebranche, see Letters to Gregory, *ibid.*, p. 80; on Bacon and again on Newton, *ibid.*, p. 76.

223. *Active Powers* . . . , p. 627.

224. *Ibid.*

225. *Ibid.*

226. *Ibid.*

227. Leibniz refers to Berkeley only once in his writings, and this in not flattering fashion. See *Gottfried Wilhelm Leibniz: Philosophical Papers and Letters*, A Selection Translated and Edited, with an Introduction by Leroy E. Loemker, 2 vols., Chicago: University of Chicago Press, 1956, Vol. 2, pp. 993, 1200–1201.

228. R. S. Westfall, *Force in Newton's Physics*, The Science of Dynamics in the Seventeenth Century, New York: American Elsevier Co., 1971, p. 284.

229. See Loemker's Introduction to *Philosophical Papers and Letters*, pp. 1–101.

230. For general expositions, see Nicholas Rescher, *The Philosophy of Leibniz*, Englewood Cliffs, N.J.: Prentice-Hall, Inc., 1967; Gottfried Martin, *Leibniz: Logic and Metaphysics*, trans. K. J. Northcott and P. G. Lucas, Manchester: Manchester University Press, 1964; J. T. Merz, *Leibniz*, London: William Blackwood & Sons, 1914; also Buchdahl, *Metaphysics . . .* , chap. 7, pp. 388–469.

231. *Philosophical Papers and Letters*, Vol. 1, pp. 265–270.

232. *Ibid.*, pp. 266–267.

233. *Ibid.*, p. 269.

234. *Ibid.*

235. *Ibid.*, Vol. 2, p. 719.

236. *Ibid.*, p. 720.

237. *Ibid.*, p. 712.

238. *Ibid.*, p. 713.

239. *Ibid.*, p. 714.

240. *Ibid.*

241. *Ibid.*

242. *Ibid.*, p. 717; for a full exposition of Leibniz's dynamical thought, see Westfall, *Force in Newton's Physics*, pp. 283–322; also Carolyn Iltis, "Leibniz and the *Vis Viva* Controversy," *Isis* 62 (1971), 21–35.

243. *Ibid.*, p. 714.

244. *Ibid.*, pp. 810–811.

245. *Ibid.*, p. 722.

246. *Ibid.*, p. 606.

247. *Ibid.*, p. 721.

248. *Ibid.*, p. 722.

249. *Ibid.*, p. 813.

250. "Ein einziges Prinzip der Optik, Katoptrik und Dioptrik," 1682, in *Leibniz: Schöpferische Vernunft*, trans. and ed. W. v. Engelhardt, Marburg, 1951; cited by Buchdahl, *Metaphysics . . .* , p. 430.

251. Westfall, *Force . . .* , p. 316.

252. *Philosophical Papers and Letters*, Vol. 2, p. 778.

253. *Ibid.*, p. 779.

254. *Ibid.*, pp. 779–780.

255. *Ibid.*, p. 781.

256. *Ibid.*, p. 780.

257. *The Leibniz-Clarke Correspondence,* together with extracts from Newton's *Principia* and *Opticks,* edited with introduction and notes by H. G. Alexander, New York: Philosophical Library, 1956, pp. 11–12.

258. *Ibid.*, p. 29.

259. *Ibid.*, p. 30.

260. *Ibid.*, p. 43.

261. *Ibid.*, p. 94.

262. Alexandre Koyré, *From the Closed World to the Infinite Universe,* Baltimore: Johns Hopkins Press, 1957, pp. 235–272; René Dugas, *Mechanics in the Seventeenth Century,* trans. F. Jacquot, New York: Central Book Co., 1958, pp. 552–561; and F. E. L. Priestley, "The Clarke-Leibniz Controversy," *The Methodological Heritage of Newton,* ed. R. E. Butts and J. W. Davis, Toronto: Toronto University Press, 1970, pp. 34–56.

263. See, for example, Mario Bunge, *Causality:* The Place of the Causal Principle in Modern Science, Cambridge, Mass.: Harvard University Press, 1959, p. 229.

264. Buchdahl, *Metaphysics . . .* , pp. 457–463.

265. *Philosophical Papers and Letters,* Vol. 1, p. 415.

266. Ewing, *Kant's Treatment of Causality,* p. 21; see also Gottfried Martin, *Kant's Metaphysics and Theory of Science,* trans. P. G. Lucas, Manchester: Manchester University Press, 1955.

267. Buchdahl, *Metaphysics . . .* , p. 471; chap. 8 of this work, pp. 470–681, is devoted to a systematic analysis of Kant's philosophy of science.

268. See Hansgeorg Hoppe, *Kants Theorie der Physik,* Eine Untersuchung über das Opus postumum von Kant, Frankfurt-am-Main: Vittorio Klostermann, 1969.

269. John Handyside, trans., *Kant's Inaugural Dissertation and Early Writings on Space,* Chicago: Open Court Publishing Co., 1929; this contains selections from "Thoughts on the True Estimation of Living Forces."

270. Handyside, trans., p. 3, n. 1.

271. *Ibid.*, p. 3.

272. *Ibid.*

273. *Ibid.*, p. 4; the reference is to Leibniz's *Specimen dynamicum.*

274. *Ibid.*, p. 5.

275. *Ibid.*, p. 8.

276. *Ibid.*, p. 9.

277. *Ibid.*, p. 11.

278. *Ibid.*, p. 14.

279. *Ibid.*, pp. 14–15.

280. See Martin, *Kant's Metaphysics . . .* , esp. pp. 1–16.

281. *Kant's Cosmogony,* As in His Essay on the Retardation of the Rotation of the Earth and His Natural History and Theory

of the Heavens, trans. W. Hastie, rev. and ed. with Introduction and Appendix by Willy Ley, New York: Greenwood Publishing Co., 1968, pp. vii–xvi.

282. *Ibid.*, p. x.

283. *Immanuel Kant's Critique of Pure Reason*, trans. N. K. Smith, London: Macmillan & Co., 1929; reprint ed., New York: St. Martin's Press, 1965, Axi, p. 9.

284. *Ibid.*, p. 9, fn. a.

285. *Ibid.*, p. 9.

286. *Ibid.*, Bvii, p. 17.

287. *Ibid.*, Bxvi–xvii, p. 22.

288. *Ibid.*, Bxvi, p. 22.

289. *Ibid.*, Bxviii, p. 23.

290. *Ibid.*, Bxx, p. 24.

291. *Ibid.*, A26, B42, p. 71.

292. *Ibid.*, A35, B52, p. 78.

293. *Ibid.*, A79, B105, p. 113.

294. *Ibid.*, B161, p. 171.

295. *Ibid.*, B168–169, p. 175.

296. *Ibid.*, B166, p. 174.

297. *Ibid.*, A132, B171, p. 177.

298. *Ibid.*, B232, p. 218.

299. *Ibid.*, A297, B353, p. 299.

300. See Ewing, *Kant's Treatment of Causality*, pp. 72–103.

301. *Critique of Pure Reason*, trans. Smith, pp. 220–221.

302. *Ibid.*, A193, B238, p. 221.

303. *Ibid.*, p. 222.

304. *Ibid.*, A201–202, B246–247, pp. 226–227.

305. *Kant's Treatment of Causality*, p. 236.

306. See L. M. Régis, *Epistemology*, trans. I. C. Byrne, New York: Macmillan & Co., 1959, pp. 47–61.

307. E. B. Bax, trans., *Kant's Prolegomena and Metaphysical Foundations of Natural Science*, London: George Bell & Son, 1883. See also Peter Plaass, *Kants Theorie der Naturwissenschaft, Eine Untersuchung zur Vorrede von Kants 'Metaphysische Anfangsgründen der Naturwissenschaft,'* Göttingen: Vandenhoeck & Ruprecht, 1965.

308. Bax, trans., p. 139.

309. *Ibid.*, pp. 144–145.

310. *Ibid.*, p. 147.

311. *Ibid.*, p. 169.

312. *Ibid.*, p. 170.

313. *Ibid.*, p. 172.

314. *Ibid.*, p. 176.

315. *Ibid.*, p. 182.

316. *Ibid.*, p. 185.

317. *Ibid.*, p. 199.

318. *Ibid.*, p. 211.

319. *Ibid.*, p. 213.
320. *Ibid.*
321. *Ibid.*, p. 220.
322. *Ibid.*, p. 223.
323. *Ibid.*, p. 222.
324. *Ibid.*, p. 230.
325. See J. J. Kockelmans, *Philosophy of Science: The Historical Background*, New York: The Free Press, 1968, p. 12.
326. *Ibid.*, p. 15.
327. *Critique of Pure Reason*, trans. Smith, B165, p. 173; see Buchdahl, *Metaphysics . . .* , pp. 651–652.
328. Buchdahl, *Metaphysics . . .* , pp. 530–532; also his "Causality, Causal Laws and Scientific Theory in the Philosophy of Kant," *British Journal for the Philosophy of Science* 16 (1965), 187–208.

CHAPTER TWO

1. The detailed history of this development has yet to be written, but a good bibliographical survey is provided in Laurens L. Laudan, "Theories of Scientific Method from Plato to Mach: A Bibliographical Review," *History of Science* 7 (1968), 1–63.

2. Auguste Comte uses the expression "la philosophie des sciences" with some frequency throughout his *Cours de philosophie positive,* see *infra;* André-Marie Ampère and William Whewell also used it in titles of major works, *Essai sur la philosophie des sciences* (1834) and *Philosophy of the Inductive Sciences* (1840), respectively.

3. Apart from specific sources treated below, ample selections from the first three of these writers are given in Joseph J. Kockelmans, ed., *Philosophy of Science: The Historical Background*, New York: The Free Press, 1968, pp. 28–103; and three essays are devoted to them in Edward H. Madden, ed., *Theories of Scientific Method:* The Renaissance Through the Nineteenth Century, Seattle: University of Washington Press, 1960, pp. 153–232.

4. Bacon never even endorsed the Copernican "hypothesis," attacking both Ptolemy and Copernicus for producing mere calculations and predictions instead of true philosophy; see M. B. Hesse's article on Bacon in the *Dictionary of Scientific Biography,* Vol. 2, pp. 373–377; as also F. H. Anderson, *The Philosophy of Francis Bacon*, Chicago: University of Chicago Press, 1948, pp. 136–138, 292.

5. For fuller details, see F. H. Anderson, *Francis Bacon, His Career and His Thought*, Los Angeles: University of Southern California Press, 1962; Benjamin Farrington, *The Philosophy of Francis Bacon*, An Essay on Its Development from 1603 to 1609 with New Translations of Fundamental Texts, Liverpool: Liverpool University Press, 1964; Paolo Rossi, *Francis Bacon: From Magic to*

Science, trans. Sacha Rabinovitch, Chicago: University of Chicago Press, 1968; and Walter Frost, *Bacon und die Naturphilosophie,* Munich: Verlag Ernst Reinhardt, 1927.

6. All of our citations will be taken from *The Works of Francis Bacon,* ed. James Spedding, Robert L. Ellis, and Douglas D. Heath, 15 vols., New York: Hurd and Houghton, 1869; the earlier volumes contain the Latin text of writings on method and natural philosophy, the English translations for which are given mainly in Vol. 8.

7. Robert E. Larsen, "The Aristotelianism of Bacon's *Novum Organum," Journal of the History of Ideas* 23 (1962), 435–450.

8. *Novum organum,* Bk. 1, 26; *Works,* Vol. 8, p. 73.

9. Plan of the *Great Instauration; ibid.,* p. 41.

10. *Ibid.,* pp. 41–42.

11. See H. G. Van Leeuwen, *The Problem of Certainty in English Thought 1630–1690,* The Hague: Matinus Nijhoff, 1963, pp. 1–12.

12. Plan of the *Great Instauration,* p. 42.

13. *Ibid.*

14. *Novum organum,* Bk. 1, 70, p. 100.

15. *Ibid.*

16. *Ibid.*

17. *Ibid.*

18. Bk. 1, 99, p. 135.

19. *Ibid.,* pp. 135–136.

20. Bk. 2, 11–20, pp. 179–218; for a clear summary of Bacon's exposition, see M. B. Hesse, *Dictionary of Scientific Biography,* Vol. 2, pp. 374–375.

21. Bk. 2, 20, p. 211; see also the fuller definition on p. 217.

22. Bk. 2, 21–52, pp. 218–350.

23. Bk. 2, 36, p. 253; the English translation inaptly renders *instantiae crucis* as "instances of the fingerpost," and thus we use the Latin expression.

24. *Ibid.,* pp. 253–254.

25. *Ibid.,* p. 254.

26. *Ibid.,* pp. 254–264.

27. Bk. 1, 92, p. 144.

28. A. I. Sabra, *Theories of Light . . . ,* p. 179; Sabra has a good discussion of Baconian induction in relation to the optical studies of Descartes and Huygens, pp. 30–37, 173–184.

29. This statement is consistent with Sabra's analysis; some argue, however, for a hypothetical element in Bacon's thought, e.g., C. J. Ducasse, "Francis Bacon's Philosophy of Science," *Theories of Scientific Method,* ed. E. H. Madden, pp. 50–74, esp. pp. 71–74, and M. B. Hesse in her article on Bacon in the *Dictionary of Scientific Biography.*

30. Bk. 1, 124, p. 156.

31. *Ibid.*

32. Bk. 2, 2, p. 168.

33. See *De augmentis scientiarum*, Bk. 2, chap. 4, *Works*, Vol. 8, p. 482, for Bacon's concessions to "ancient" terminology.

34. *Ibid.*, pp. 484–485.

35. Bk. 2, 1, p. 167.

36. Bk. 2, 9, pp. 177–178.

37. Bk. 2, 17, p. 205.

38. *Ibid.*, p. 206.

39. Bk. 3, chap. 5, p. 512.

40. See R. L. Ellis, "General Preface to Bacon's Philosophical Works," Vol. 1, p. 111; also his note to this passage in the Latin text, Vol. 2, p. 298, fn. 1.

41. Ellis, "General Preface," Vol. 1, pp. 71–78; also F. H. Anderson, *The Philosophy of Francis Bacon*, pp. 156–164 and 190–216, esp. 208–213.

42. Some go so far as to discredit altogether, on this basis, Bacon's role in the Scientific Revolution; see Alexandre Koyré, *Études galiléennes*, 3 vols., Paris: Hermann, 1939, Vol. 1, p. 6, fn. 4.

43. It has been said that such men had to "read between the lines" to see this method in Bacon's writings, but this need not detract entirely from his influence. As Ducasse has justly observed, ". . . Bacon's greatness may perhaps most truly be said to lie in having written lines between which so much that was true and vital was later so plainly to be read." — "Francis Bacon's Philosophy of Science," p. 70.

44. Thomas Sprat, *The History of the Royal Society*, ed. with notes by J. I. Cope and H. W. Jones, St. Louis and London: 1958, pp. 34–35; cited by H. G. Van Leeuwen, *The Problem of Certainty . . .* , p. 1.

45. For a sketch of this influence, with bibliography, see Lilo K. Luxembourg, *Francis Bacon and Denis Diderot, Philosophers of Science*, Copenhagen: Munksgaard, 1967.

46. For a brief summary of Comte's life and teachings, with bibliography, see the article on him by L. L. Laudan in the *Dictionary of Scientific Biography*, Vol. 3, pp. 375–380.

47. Auguste Comte, *Cours de philosophie positive*, 6 vols., Paris: Bachelier, Libraire pour les mathématiques, 1830–1842, Vol. 1, pp. 8, 34, 39, 58, 62, 63, etc. Since there is no complete English edition of Comte's writings, all citations will be from this first French edition and the translation provided will be my own.

48. George Sarton, "Auguste Comte, Historian of Science. With a Short Digression on Clotilde de Vaux and Harriet Taylor," *Osiris* 10 (1952), 345, n. 14.

49. *Ibid.*, p. 347, n. 18, whence Huxley's epigram, "Comte's positivism is Catholicism minus Christianity."

50. *Ibid.*, pp. 328–357; this calendar is the major source of Sarton's information.

51. See Auguste Comte, *A General View of Positivism*, trans. J. H. Bridges [1865], with an Introduction by Frederic Harrison [1908], New York: E. P. Dutton & Co., n.d.

52. *Cours*, Vol. 1, pp. 3–4.

53. *Ibid.*, p. 4.

54. *Ibid.*, pp. 4–5.

55. *Ibid.*, p. 5.

56. L. L. Laudan, "Towards a Reassessment of Comte's 'Méthode Positive,'" *Philosophy of Science* 38 (1971), p. 39, fn. 14; this article as a whole, pp. 35–53, gives an accurate appraisal of Comte's methodology in relation to later work in the philosophy of science.

57. *Cours*, Vol. 1, pp. 8–9.

58. *Ibid.*, pp. 14–15. Note here that Comte is implicitly acknowledging the existence of causes, while disclaiming any interest in their investigation.

59. *Ibid.*, p. 15.

60. *Ibid.*, pp. 15–16.

61. *Ibid.*, pp. 62–63.

62. *Cours*, Vol. 2, p. 28.

63. *Ibid.*, pp. 401–402.

64. *Cours*, Vol. 3, pp. 10–11.

65. *Cours*, Vol. 6, p. 718.

66. In his *System of Positive Polity*, 4 vols., trans. Bridges et al., London: 1875–77, Vol. 1, p. 431; cited by Laudan, "Towards a Reassessment . . . ," p. 46.

67. *Ibid.*, p. 419; cited by Laudan, p. 42.

68. *Cours*, Vol. 2, p. 433.

69. *Ibid.*, p. 434.

70. *Ibid.*

71. *Ibid.*

72. *Ibid.*, pp. 434–435.

73. *Ibid.*, p. 435; for a fuller discussion of these aspects of Comte's methodology, see Laudan, "Towards a Reassessment . . . ," esp. pp. 46–52.

74. The basis for Comte's selectivity, according to Laudan, was the properties attributed to entities in the different hypotheses; thus the properties ascribed to atoms in the atomic hypothesis were well defined and coherent, whereas a property such as imponderability ascribed to an optical ether was both inconceivable and unverifiable; *Dictionary of Scientific Biography*, Vol. 3, p. 377.

75. *Cours*, Vol. 2, p. 243.

76. *Ibid.*

77. *Ibid.*, pp. 246–247. Notice the slip here into Aristotelian terminology, with explanation proceeding from the "more known" to the "less known," although with a relativism that is linked to the explainer's previous training.

78. *Ibid.*, p. 247.

79. *Ibid.*, p. 248.
80. *Ibid.*, p. 249.
81. *Ibid.*, p. 258.
82. *Ibid.*, pp. 258–259.
83. Laudan, *Dictionary of Scientific Biography*, p. 379.
84. See R. E. Schofield, *Mechanism and Materialism*, British Natural Philosophy in An Age of Reason, Princeton, N.J.: Princeton University Press, 1970, for a full account of this development.
85. William Minto, *Logic, Inductive and Deductive*, New York: Charles Scribner's Sons, 1904, p. 257; cited by C. J. Ducasse, "John F. W. Herschel's Methods of Experimental Inquiry," *Theories of Scientific Method*, ed. E. H. Madden, p. 153; for biographical details concerning Herschel, see the article by David S. Evans, *Dictionary of Scientific Biography*, Vol. 6, pp. 323–328.
86. See M. A. Hoskin, *William Herschel: Pioneer of Sidereal Astronomy*, London: Sheed & Ward, 1959; idem, *William Herschel and the Construction of the Heavens*, London: Oldbourne Press, 1963.
87. W. F. Cannon, "John Herschel and the Idea of Science," *Journal of the History of Ideas* 22 (1961), 215.
88. London: Longman et al., 1830; reprinted in Sources of Science, No. 17, New York: Johnson Reprint Corporation, 1966.
89. London: Longman et al., 1833.
90. References below are to the 11th ed., London: Longmans, Green & Co., 1871.
91. Cannon, "John Herschel . . . ," pp. 238, 219.
92. *Preliminary Discourse*, pp. 104–113, 72.
93. M. F. Partridge, "Introduction" to the Johnson reprint of the *Preliminary Discourse*, p. xvii.
94. Ducasse, "John F. W. Herschel's Methods . . . ," pp. 154, 156, 180–182; Cannon, "John Herschel . . . ," pp. 220–222.
95. Partridge, "Introduction," pp. xviii–xix.
96. *Preliminary Discourse*, p. 7.
97. Cannon, "John Herschel . . . ," pp. 222, 225, 231.
98. *Preliminary Discourse*, p. 75, title to pt. II.
99. *Ibid.*, p. 18.
100. *Ibid.*, p. 75.
101. *Ibid.*, pp. 75–76.
102. *Ibid.*, p. 76.
103. *Ibid.*, p. 221.
104. *Ibid.*, p. 19.
105. *Ibid.*
106. *Ibid.*, p. 22.
107. *Ibid.*, p. 144.
108. *Ibid.*
109. *Ibid.*, p. 92.
110. *Ibid.*, pp. 50, 59, 329.
111. *Ibid.*, pp. 239, 242.

112. *Ibid.*, p. 86.

113. *Ibid.*, pp. 87–88.

114. *Ibid.*, p. 149.

115. *Treatise*, pp. 232–233; *Outlines*, pp. 290–291. Herschel does not here cite Hume's work, however, but rather Brown's "Cause and Effect," 3d ed., Edinburgh: 1818, p. 47, which he refers to in a footnote as "a work of great acuteness and subtlety of reasoning on some points, but in which the whole train of argument is vitiated by one enormous oversight; the omission, namely, of a *distinct and immediate personal consciousness of causation* in his enumeration of that *sequence of events*, by which the volition of the mind is made to terminate in the motion of material objects. I mean the consciousness of *effort*, accompanied with *intention thereby* to accomplish an end, as a thing entirely distinct from mere *desire* or *volition* on the one hand, and from mere spasmodic contraction of muscles on the other."

116. *Treatise*, p. 233.

117. *Preliminary Discourse*, pp. 197–198.

118. *Ibid.*, p. 35.

119. *Ibid.*, pp. 35–36; note the use of Reid's example of night and day, cited *supra*, p. 50.

120. *Ibid.*, pp. 36–37.

121. *Ibid.*, p. 100.

122. *Ibid.*, p. 102; on the notion of "general facts," see Partridge, "Introduction," pp. xxv–xxvi.

123. See Cannon, "John Herschel . . . ," pp. 221–222; cf. Ducasse, "John F. W. Herschel's Methods . . . ," pp. 164–170.

124. *Preliminary Discourse*, p. 132.

125. *Ibid.*, p. 151.

126. *Ibid.*, p. 158.

127. *Ibid.*, p. 144, title to chap. IV.

128. *Ibid.*, p. 190, title to chap. VII.

129. *Ibid.*, p. 190.

130. *Ibid.*, p. 191.

131. *Ibid.*

132. *Ibid.*, p. 193.

133. Quoting Horace, *Epistles*, Bk. 1, 1, 32: "It is possible to advance a certain distance even if one cannot go farther."

134. *Ibid.*, p. 196.

135. *Ibid.*, pp. 196–197.

136. *Ibid.*, p. 198.

137. *Ibid.*, p. 204.

138. *Ibid.*, pp. 181–189.

139. *Ibid.*, p. 206.

140. *Ibid.*, p. 207.

141. *Ibid.*, p. 229.

142. *Ibid.*, p. 228.

143. *Ibid.*, pp. 229–230.

144. *Ibid.*, p. 230.
145. *Ibid.*, p. 151.
146. *Ibid.*, pp. 151–152.
147. *Ibid.*, p. 152.
148. *Ibid.*, pp. 152–159; all ten observations are cited and commented upon by Ducasse, "John F. W. Herschel's Methods . . . ," pp. 175–176.
149. *Ibid.*, p. 152.
150. *Ibid.*, p. 153.
151. *Ibid.*, p. 154.
152. *Ibid.*, p. 155.
153. *Ibid.*, p. 156.
154. *Ibid.*, pp. 157–158.
155. *Ibid.*, pp. 158–159.
156. *Ibid.*, p. 159.
157. See Ducasse, "John F. W. Herschel's Methods . . . ," pp. 180–181; also Partridge, "Introduction," pp. xlii–xliv, 1.
158. *Preliminary Discourse*, pp. 88–92.
159. *Ibid.*, p. 89.
160. *Ibid.*
161. *Ibid.*, p. 90.
162. *Ibid.*, p. 91.
163. *Ibid.*, pp. 159–164; see J. S. Mill, *A System of Logic*, 8th ed., London: Longmans [1872], new impression, 1959, pp. 271–276. For an empiricist critique of Herschel's example, see Partridge, "Introduction," pp. xl–xlii.
164. *Ibid.*, p. 159.
165. *Ibid.*, p. 163.
166. *Ibid.*, p. 159.
167. *Ibid.*, p. 160.
168. *Ibid.*, pp. 160–162.
169. *Ibid.*, p. 162.
170. *Ibid.*, pp. 162–163; again, see Partridge's critique, "Introduction," p. xli.
171. *Ibid.*, pp. 249–264.
172. *Ibid.*, pp. 310–323.
173. *Ibid.*, p. 310.
174. *Ibid.*, p. 301.
175. *Ibid.*
176. *Ibid.*
177. *Outlines*, 11th ed., p. vii; the prefaces to the first, fifth, and tenth editions are reprinted in the eleventh edition.
178. *Ibid.*, p. viii.
179. *Ibid.*, p. x.
180. *Ibid.*; it was his own father, of course, who had discovered Uranus, as Herschel notes on p. 333; he discusses Neptune's discovery on pp. 335 and 540.
181. *Ibid.*, pp. xiv–xv.

182. *Ibid.*, p. xviii.
183. *Ibid.*, p. 3.
184. *Ibid.*, p. 4.
185. *Ibid.*
186. *Ibid.*
187. *Ibid.*, p. 9.
188. *Ibid.*, p. 10.
189. *Ibid.*
190. *Ibid.*, p. 12.
191. *Ibid.*
192. *Ibid.*, p. 13.
193. *Ibid.*, p. 15.
194. See Vol. I, pp. 80–86.
195. *Outlines*, pp. 17, 37–38.
196. *Ibid.*, p. 130.
197. *Ibid.*, p. 54.
198. *Ibid.*
199. *Ibid.*, p. 55.
200. *Ibid.*, p. 140.
201. *Ibid.*, pp. 144–145; for a fascinating account of the difficulties encountered in obtaining measurements of this ellipticity, see T. B. Jones, *The Figure of the Earth*, Lawrence, Kans.: Coronado Press, 1967. The British attempted to verify Newton's theory that the earth was flattened at the poles, while the French organized one expedition after another to prove J. D. Cassini's theory that the earth was actually elongated along its axis of rotation.
202. *Ibid.*, p. 149.
203. *Ibid.*, p. 150.
204. See *supra*, p. 19.
205. *Outlines*, p. 156.
206. *Ibid.*
207. *Ibid.*, p. 161.
208. These contributions are summarized by Cannon, "John Herschel . . . ," pp. 226–229.
209. As witnessed by the articles now appearing in the literature and by recent reprints of his works; on the latter, see R. Harré and J. D. North, "William Whewell and the History and Philosophy of Science," Essay Review, *British Journal for the History of Science* 4 (1969), 399–402. Harré gives enthusiastic endorsement to Whewell's philosophy of science: "Its greatest merit, from which its other virtues spring, is that Whewell really knew science and had a profound understanding of its history. His philosophy gives us a realistic epistemology, metaphysics and logic, in the sharpest possible contrast to the philosophy of science of J. S. Mill, his contemporary rival, whose ideas are manufactured in a vacuum, and are immensely difficult to relate to any actual scientific investigation." (p. 399) P. B. Medawar also commends Whewell as a methodologist, and this from the viewpoint of the practicing scientist,

stressing his superiority over nonscientists such as Bacon and Mill; he likewise calls attention to Whewell's contributions to scientific terminology in coining such terms as "scientist" and "physicist" among others — see *Induction and Intuition in Scientific Thought*, Jayne Lectures for 1968, Philadelphia: American Philosophical Society, 1969, p. 10; also pp. vii, 25, 45, 48–50, 53–54. For a brief introduction to Whewell's thought, see A. W. Heathcote, "William Whewell's Philosophy of Science," *British Journal for the Philosophy of Science* 4 (1954), 302–314.

210. For details, see John Herivel, "Introduction" to the reprint edition of *The Philosophy of the Inductive Sciences*, New York: Johnson Reprint Corp., 1967, pp. ix–xiv; also R. E. Butts, "Introduction" to *William Whewell's Theory of Scientific Method*, Pittsburgh: University of Pittsburgh Press, 1968, p. 3. In preparing this section we have used the following editions of Whewell's works: *History of the Inductive Sciences, From the Earliest to the Present Time*, 2d ed., 3 vols., London: John W. Parker, 1847; *The Philosophy of the Inductive Sciences, Founded Upon Their History*. 2d ed., 2 vols., London: John W. Parker, 1847; reprint ed., New York: Johnson Reprint Corp., 1967; *Novum Organum Renovatum*, Being the second part of the Philosophy of the Inductive Sciences, 3d ed., with large additions, London: John W. Parker & Son, 1858; and *On the Philosophy of Discovery, Chapters Historical and Critical*, Including the completion of the third edition of the Philosophy of the Inductive Sciences, London: John W. Parker & Son, 1860.

211. See Heathcote, "William Whewell's . . . ," p. 302.

212. The latter aspect is sometimes overlooked in accounts of Whewell's philosophy, but attention is redirected to it by L. L. Laudan, "William Whewell on the Consilience of Inductions," *The Monist* 55 (1971), 372.

213. See C. J. Ducasse, "William Whewell's Philosophy of Scientific Discovery," *Theories of Scientific Method*, ed. E. H. Madden, pp. 188–195; also H. T. Walsh, "Whewell on Necessity," *Philosophy of Science* 29 (1962), 139–145.

214. *Philosophy of the Inductive Sciences*, Vol. 1, p. 36; generally in what follows we cite the 2d edition (1847) as most widely available, since there is little variation of thought throughout the successive editions.

215. *Ibid.*, pp. 76, 250–251; Vol. 2, pp. 20–26; cf. Heathcote, "William Whewell's . . . ," p. 305.

216. Heathcote, "William Whewell's . . . ," p. 304.

217. *Philosophy of the Inductive Sciences*, Vol. 2, pp. 95–106.

218. *Ibid.*, pp. 219–220.

219. *Ibid.*, p. 220.

220. *Ibid.*, p. 323.

221. *Philosophy of Discovery*, p. 181.

222. "Comte and Positivism," *Macmillan's Magazine* 13 (1866), 353–362.

223. *Philosophy of the Inductive Sciences*, Vol. 2, p. 103; in a footnote the quotation is referenced to "Comte, *Philosophie Positive*."

224. "Whewell on the Inductive Sciences," *Essays from the Edinburgh and Quarterly Reviews, with Addresses and Other Pieces*, London: Longman et al., 1857, p. 246.

225. *Philosophy of the Inductive Sciences*, Vol. 2, p. 104.

226. *Ibid.*, p. 105.

227. "Comte and Positivism," p. 355.

228. *Philosophy of the Inductive Sciences*, Vol. 2, p. 329.

229. *Ibid.*, pp. 322–324.

230. *Ibid.*, p. 324.

231. *Ibid.*, p. 329.

232. *Ibid.*, pp. 451–452, 278–295; for additional analyses, see R. E. Butts, "Whewell on Newton's Rules of Philosophizing," *The Methodological Heritage of Newton*, ed. R. E. Butts and J. W. Davis, pp. 132–149; L. L. Laudan, "William Whewell . . . ," pp. 378–381; and C. J. Ducasse, "William Whewell's . . . ," pp. 186–187, 207–211.

233. *Philosophy of the Inductive Sciences*, Vol. 2, pp. 451–452.

234. *Ibid.*, p. 451.

235. But see *supra*, pp. 69–70 and 73–75, on the difficulty of arriving at any consistent interpretation of Kant's teaching on cause and force.

236. *Philosophy of the Inductive Sciences*, Vol. 2, p. 452. The inspiration here would seem to be Reid or Herschel rather than Hume; see *supra*, pp. 44–51 and 101–102.

237. *Ibid.*, p. 452.

238. *Ibid.*, p. 453.

239. *Ibid.*

240. *Ibid.*, p. 454.

241. *Ibid.*

242. *Ibid.*, pp. 277–295.

243. *Ibid.*, p. 286.

244. *Ibid.*, pp. 286, 65–68.

245. *Ibid.*, p. 286.

246. *Ibid.*, pp. 65–66.

247. *Ibid.*, p. 99.

248. *Ibid.*

249. *Ibid.*, p. 98.

250. *Ibid.*, Vol. 1, pp. 618–636.

251. *Ibid.*, Vol. 2, p. 117.

252. *Novum Organum Renovatum*, facing p. 140; the tables are missing from the Johnson Reprint edition of *Philosophy of the Inductive Sciences*.

253. *Philosophy of the Inductive Sciences*, Vol. 2, p. 177.

254. *Ibid.*, p. 78; cf. *History of the Inductive Sciences*, Vol. 2, pp. 160–194. It is in connection with this example that Herschel calls attention, as we have already noted, to Whewell's teaching on consilience; see *supra*, p. 114.

255. *Philosophy of the Inductive Sciences*, Vol. 2, p. 79.

256. *Ibid.*, p. 93.

257. *Ibid.*, pp. 93–94.

258. *Ibid.*, p. 94.

259. G. H. Lewes regarded Whewell as a Kantian, and H. L. Mansel criticized him for not being Kantian enough; Whewell discusses the views of both in *Philosophy of Discovery*, pp. 332–346.

260. "William Whewell's . . . ," p. 184, citing *Philosophy of Discovery*, p. 334.

261. *Philosophy of the Inductive Sciences*, Vol. 1, pp. 700–708; Vol. 2, pp. 435–440.

262. *Ibid.*, Vol. 2, pp. 477–478.

263. *Ibid.*, p. 478.

264. "Whewell on the Inductive Sciences," pp. 181–182, 239.

265. *Ibid.*, p. 151.

266. *Ibid.*

267. *Ibid.*, p. 250.

268. *Ibid.*

269. Vol. 2, pp. 669–679.

270. *Ibid.*, p. 675.

271. *Ibid.*

272. *Ibid.*

273. See Silvestro Marcucci, "William Whewell: Kantianism or Platonism," *Physis* 12 (1970), 69–72; also E. W. Strong, "William Whewell and John Stuart Mill: Their Controversy About Scientific Knowledge," *Journal of the History of Ideas* 16 (1955), 222.

274. Cf. Butts, "Whewell on Newton's Rules . . . ," pp. 147–148.

275. Heathcote, "William Whewell's . . . ," p. 302.

276. Whewell, *Philosophy of Discovery*, pp. 264–265; Strong, "William Whewell and John Stuart Mill," pp. 210, 230; Harré and North, "William Whewell . . . ," p. 399.

277. For a brief biography, see J. B. Schneewind's article on Mill in the *Encyclopedia of Philosophy*, Vol. 5, pp. 314–323; also Ernest Nagel's "Introduction" to *John Stuart Mill's Philosophy of Scientific Method*, New York: Hafner Publishing Co., 1950, pp. xv–xlviii.

278. Nagel, "Introduction," p. xxvii.

279. The following editions of these works will be cited in what follows: *A System of Logic*, Ratiocinative and Inductive. Being a connected view of the principles of evidence and the methods of scientific investigation, 8th ed., London: Longmans [1872]; new impression, 1959; *An Examination of Sir William*

Hamilton's Philosophy, and of the principal questions discussed in his writings, 2 vols. Boston: William V. Spencer, 1865.

280. Schneewind, "Mill," pp. 314–315.
281. *System of Logic,* Bk. 3, chap. 1, n. 1, p. 185.
282. Nagel, "Introduction," p. xlii.
283. *System,* Bk. 3, chap. 1, n. 2, p. 186.
284. *Ibid.,* n. 1, p. 185.
285. *Ibid.,* chap. 3, n. 1, p. 200.
286. *Ibid.,* p. 201.
287. *Ibid.,* p. 203.
288. *Ibid.,* chap. 4, n. 1, p. 206.
289. *Ibid.,* chap. 5, n. 1, p. 211.
290. *Ibid.*
291. *Ibid.,* p. 212.
292. *Ibid.*
293. *Ibid.,* n. 2, p. 213.
294. See *supra,* pp. 48–49.
295. *System,* Bk. 3, chap. 5, n. 2, p. 213.
296. *Ibid.*
297. *Ibid.*
298. *Ibid.,* chap. 8, p. 253.
299. *Ibid.,* p. 255.
300. *Ibid.,* n. 2, p. 256.
301. *Ibid.,* n. 4, p. 259.
302. *Ibid.,* n. 5, p. 260.
303. *Ibid.,* n. 6, p. 263.
304. *Ibid.,* chap. 7, n. 4, p. 251.
305. *Ibid.,* chap. 5, n. 3, p. 215.
306. *Ibid.*
307. *Examination,* Vol. 2, p. 34.
308. *Ibid.*
309. *Ibid.*
310. *Ibid.,* p. 33.
311. *Ibid.,* p. 34.
312. *Ibid.,* p. 33.
313. *System,* Bk. 3, chap. 14, n. 4, p. 322.
314. *Ibid.*
315. *Ibid.*
316. *Ibid.*
317. *Ibid.*
318. *Ibid.*
319. *Ibid.*
320. *Ibid.,* p. 325; how such an influence could be verified at the phenomenal level is unfortunately never explained by Mill.
321. *Ibid.*
322. *Ibid.*
323. *Ibid.*
324. *Ibid.,* pp. 325–326.

325. *Ibid.*, p. 326; as an example of a hypothesis that has enabled us to arrive "at conclusions not hypothetical" Mill cites Gilbert's teaching "that the earth is a natural magnet." He also mentions approvingly Darwin's hypothesis of "natural selection," and even concedes it the status of a *vera causa* of the origin of species—*ibid.*, n. 5, p. 327 and lengthy footnote on pp. 327–328.

326. *Ibid.*, chap. 16, n. 1, p. 338.

327. *Ibid.*

328. *Ibid.*, chap. 12, n. 6, p. 310.

329. *Ibid.*, pp. 310–311.

330. *Ibid.*, p. 311.

331. *Auguste Comte and Positivism*, London: N. Trübner & Co., 1865; reprint ed., Ann Arbor: University of Michigan Press, 1961, p. 15.

332. *Ibid.*, p. 57.

333. *Ibid.*, pp. 57–59.

334. See *System of Logic*, Bk. 2, chap. 5, n. 6, pp. 156–164.

335. *Ibid.*, Bk. 3, chap. 1–2, pp. 185–200.

336. *Ibid.*, chap. 2, n. 4, p. 193.

337. *Ibid.*, chap. 14, n. 6, p. 329.

338. See Gerd Buchdahl, "Inductivist *versus* Deductivist Approaches in the Philosophy of Science as Illustrated by Some Controversies Between Whewell and Mill," *The Monist* 55 (1971), 343–367; Laudan, "William Whewell . . . ," pp. 368–391; Strong, "William Whewell . . . ," pp. 209–231; and H. T. Walsh, "Whewell and Mill on Induction," *Philosophy of Science* 29 (1962), 279–284; idem, "Whewell on Necessity," pp. 139–145.

339. See W. C. Kneale, *Probability and Induction*, Oxford: Clarendon Press [1949], reprint ed., 1952, from corrected sheets of the first edition, pp. 57–59; also E. H. Madden, *The Structure of Scientific Thought*, An Introduction to Philosophy of Science, Boston: Houghton Mifflin Co., 1960, pp. 288–289.

340. *Auguste Comte and Positivism*, p. 53: "The philosophy of a science thus comes to mean the science itself, considered not as to its results, the truths which it ascertains, but as to the process by which the mind attains them, the marks by which it recognizes them, and the co-ordinating and methodizing of them with a view to the greatest clearness of conception and the fullest and readiest availability for use: in one word, the logic of the science."

341. See *supra*, pp. 40–44. Mill, like Hume, even professes that a universal law of nature may be inferred from a "single instance" or experiment, although he is no better at explaining how this can be done in terms of his theory of induction than was his Scottish predecessor; see *System of Logic*, Bk. 3, chap. 3, n. 3, pp. 205–206.

342. C. J. Ducasse, "John Stuart Mill's System of Logic," *Theories of Scientific Method*, ed. E. H. Madden, pp. 218–232, esp. pp. 223–230.

343. See, for example, Medawar, *Induction and Intuition* . . . , pp. 2, 10, and 45.

344. C. C. Gillispie, *The Edge of Objectivity*, An Essay in the History of Scientific Ideas, Princeton, N.J.: Princeton University Press, 1960, pp. 58, 260.

345. For an excellent summary of Bernard's life, thought, and contributions to science, see the article on him by M. D. Grmek in the *Dictionary of Scientific Biography*, Vol. 2, pp. 24–34.

346. The following editions are cited in what follows: *An Introduction to the Study of Experimental Medicine*, trans. H. C. Greene, with an Introduction by L. J. Henderson, New York: Henry Schuman, Inc. [1927], 1949; *Cahier Rouge*, English trans. H. H. Hoff and L. and R. Guillemin in F. Grande and M. B. Visscher, eds., *Claude Bernard and Experimental Medicine*, Cambridge, Mass.: Schenkman Publishing Co., 1967.

347. *Introduction* . . . , p. 221; *Cahier*, p. 59.

348. *Introduction* . . . , p. 27.

349. *Ibid.*, p. 28.

350. *Ibid.*

351. *Ibid.*, p. 80.

352. *Ibid.*

353. *Ibid.*; also p. 82.

354. *Ibid.*, p. 80.

355. *Ibid.*

356. *Ibid.*, p. 34.

357. *Cahier*, p. 37.

358. *Ibid.*, pp. 35–36.

359. *Introduction* . . . , p. 41.

360. *Ibid.*

361. *Ibid.*, p. 45.

362. *Ibid.*, p. 46.

363. *Ibid.*, p. 47.

364. *Ibid.*, p. 151.

365. *Ibid.*, p. 225.

366. *Ibid.*, p. 53.

367. *Ibid.*

368. *Ibid.*

369. *Ibid.*

370. *Ibid.*

371. *Ibid.*, pp. 69, 219; cf. *Cahier*, p. 56.

372. *Ibid.*, p. 54.

373. *Ibid.*

374. *Ibid.*, p. 55.

375. *Ibid.*, pp. 55–56; cf. the text cited from *Cahier*, p. 37, on page 144 *supra*.

376. *Ibid.*, p. 57.

377. *Ibid.*, p. 65.

378. *Ibid.*, pp. 65–66.

379. *Ibid.*, p. 83.

380. *Ibid.*, pp. 83–84.

381. *Ibid.*, p. 84.

382. *Ibid.*, p. 66.

383. *Cahier*, p. 30; in another reference to Newton, Bernard pens the somewhat enigmatic note: "One ought not to stop at final causes; scientifically this explains nothing, because efficient causes are required. Newton has said, and rightly, that this search is not scientific." — *ibid.*, p. 44.

384. *Ibid.*, p. 30.

385. *Introduction* . . . , p. 66; "mineral force" here seems to have the same meaning as "affinity," which for Bernard also has the character of an occult force, *ibid.*, pp. 80–81.

386. *Ibid.*, p. 67.

387. *Ibid.*; possibly the last sentence of this citation derives from the teaching of Maupertuis, who offered a similar interpretation of Newtonian doctrine — see Max Jammer, *Concepts of Force*, A Study in the Foundations of Dynamics, Cambridge, Mass.: Harvard University Press, 1957; rev. ed., New York: Harper Torchbook, 1962, pp. 208–210; Comte's influence is, of course, also detectable; see *supra*, pp. 93–96.

388. *Ibid.*

389. *Ibid.*, p. 78, pp. 66–67.

390. *Cahier*, p. 53.

391. *Ibid.*, pp. 54, 47.

392. *Ibid.*, p. 84.

393. *Introduction* . . . , p. 89.

394. *Cahier*, pp. 24–25.

395. *Ibid.*, p. 25. Such advocacy of teleology on the part of biologists was not, of course, extraordinary, and this even following the introduction of the theory of natural selection to explain evolutionary phenomena. For an interesting advocacy of teleology in the context of a general methodology based on causality, by a cofounder of the theory of natural selection, see Roger Smith, "Alfred Russel Wallace: Philosophy of Nature and Man," *British Journal for the History of Science* 6 (1972), 177–199, esp. 186–191.

396. *Introduction* . . . , p. 221.

397. *Ibid.*, pp. 28, 42, 49–51, 145, 220.

398. *Ibid.*, p. 49. Possibly because of such derogatory remarks, and in view of the fact the *Introduction* was used as one of the official philosophy textbooks in the *lycées* of France, the Dominican philosopher and theologian A. G. Sertillanges wrote a series of critical notes to accompany Bernard's text, which are printed in some of the French editions of the work, e.g., *Introduction à l'étude de la médecine expérimentale*, avec les notes critiques par le R. P. Sertillanges, Paris: Imprimerie F. Levé, 1900; Sertillanges generally gives an Aristotelian interpretation of Bernard's teaching on causality, *ibid.*, pp. 16–22, 38–39, 46–48, 55–59, 65–68, and 72–75.

399. *Introduction* . . . , p. 221.

400. *Ibid.*

401. *Ibid.*, p. 224.

402. *Ibid.* By "the cause or the source of things" Bernard means God, of whose existence he had a strong consciousness and certainty, but which he admitted derived from his faith and not from scientific proof; see *Cahier,* p. 68.

403. *Introduction* . . . , p. 222.

404. See R. Harré, *Matter and Method,* London: Macmillan & Co. Ltd., 1964, pp. 13–15, 20.

CHAPTER THREE

1. *Turning Points in Physics,* with an Introduction by A. C. Crombie, Amsterdam: North-Holland Publishing Co., 1959, pp. 84–154.

2. *Ibid.*, p. 93.

3. *Ibid.*, p. 127.

4. *Ibid.*, p. 113.

5. Including Waismann himself, who admitted that "all our knowledge concerning the inner structure of atoms is ultimately derived from experiments in which atoms emit energy or collide with one another," and that "in any such experiment causality is already presupposed . . . ," *ibid.*, p. 119.

6. For a brief sketch of Jevons's thought, a bibliography, and a representative excerpt from his *The Principles of Science: A Treatise on Logic and Scientific Method,* 2d ed., London: 1877, see Kockelmans, *Philosophy of Science* . . . , pp. 133–146; see also E. H. Madden, "W. S. Jevons on Induction and Probability," *Theories of Scientific Method,* pp. 233–247.

7. Madden, "W. S. Jevons . . . ," p. 233.

8. *Elementary Lessons in Logic: Deductive and Inductive,* With copious questions and examples, and a vocabulary of technical terms, new ed., London & New York: Macmillan, 1898, p. vii. Jevons here also acknowledges his debt to Herschel and Whewell.

9. *The Principles of Science,* 2d ed., reprint ed., New York: Dover Publications, 1958, p. 222; cf. Madden, "W. S. Jevons . . . ," p. 236.

10. *Principles of Science,* p. 222. Despite a general acquaintance with Aristotelianism, Jevons apparently was unaware of the lengthy discussions of this difficulty in Aristotle's commentators, and of the technique of demonstrating *ex suppositione finis* that was developed to circumvent it; see Vol. I, esp. pp. 75–80.

11. *Ibid.*, p. 226.

12. *Ibid.*

13. *Elementary Lessons* . . . , p. 333.

14. *Principles of Science,* p. 222.

15. *Ibid.*, pp. 224–226.

16. *Ibid.*, p. 221.

17. Madden is also critical of the lack of consistency in Jevons's teaching on causality; cf. "W. S. Jevons . . . ," pp. 236–237.

18. Even before Stallo, the British chemist Benjamin C. Brodie, Jr., had proposed a phenomenalist philosophy of chemistry, but his views were not sufficiently influential for him to be regarded as the beginning of a movement. On Brodie, see the article by D. C. Goodman in the *Dictionary of Scientific Biography*, Vol. 2, pp. 484–486; for biographical details and a bibliography of Stallo, see Kockelmans, *Philosophy of Science* . . . , pp. 147–150.

19. See L. D. Easton, *Hegel's First American Followers: The Ohio Hegelians:* John B. Stallo, Peter Kaufmann, Moncure Conway, and August Willich, with key writings, Athens: Ohio University Press, 1966.

20. See Kockelmans's introductory essay, pp. 148–149.

21. *The Concepts and Theories of Modern Physics*, excerpt in Kockelmans, p. 164.

22. For details of Mach's philosophy of science, see Bernhard Hell, *Ernst Machs Philosophie:* eine erkenntniskritische Studie über Wirklichkeit und Wert, Stuttgart: Fr. Fommanns Verlag (E. Hauff), 1907; also J. Bradley, *Mach's Philosophy of Science*, London: Athlone Press, 1971.

23. *The Science of Mechanics*. A Critical and Historical Account of Its Development, trans. T. J. McCormack, new Introduction by Karl Menger, 6th ed., with revisions through the 9th German ed., La Salle: The Open Court Publishing Co., 1960, p. xxii; also Menger's Introduction, p. xiv.

24. Menger's Introduction, pp. vi–xii.

25. *Science of Mechanics*, p. 579.

26. *Ibid*. Noteworthy in this citation is Mach's use of the examples "colors, tones, pressures, spaces, [and] times," which may be regarded not merely as sense data but also as the real attributes of existing bodies. Because of this interpetative ambivalence, Mach is sometimes seen not as a phenomenalist but as a physicalist, i.e., as a reductionist who regards his reduction as being made not to sense data alone, but to the ordinary properties of physical things.

27. *Ibid.*; Mach's thought, in this respect, is similar to that of Richard Avenarius, as Mach acknowledges in his Preface, p. xxiii.

28. *Science of Mechanics*, p. 580.

29. *Ibid.*, p. 581.

30. *Ibid.*

31. *Ibid.*, p. 582, n.; Mach's example of functional dependence, it may be observed, would be regarded in the Aristotelian tradition as itself causal, but based on formal rather than efficient causality. On this understanding, Mach's accounting for causality is not purely psychological in the Humean sense, but allows for some type of extramental interdependence of events, itself represented (albeit only formally) by a mathematical function.

32. *Ibid.*, p. 325.
33. *Ibid.*, p. 266.
34. *Ibid.*
35. *Ibid.*, pp. 303–304.
36. *Ibid.*, p. 304.
37. The interpretation Mach suggests, of course, is that terms such as "produce" and "induce" are to be understood in the same way that a change in an independent variable produces or induces a change in the dependent variable; this understanding offers the obvious advantage that the relationship can be construed inversely, i.e., the dependent variable can be regarded as independent, and vice versa. The causality implied here, as mentioned in note 31 above, is formal rather than efficient; from an Aristotelian viewpoint, the use of a formal cause pertaining to the mathematical order as a surrogate for an efficient cause pertaining to the physical order enables one to safeguard some degree of causal relationship while being less specific about the details of the physical agency involved. Perhaps it is in this way that Mach makes an advance over Newton, for Mach permits a broader range of interpetation of force concepts by conceding them only a "conventional" status, whereas Newton is committed to granting them ontological status outright, even while professing to treat them only mathematically and remaining agnostic with regard to their physical causes and seats. That some elements of convention are involved even in Newton's formalization of mechanics, e.g., in deciding what types or states of motion require causal explanation and what forces can therefore be said to exist, has been well argued by Brian Ellis, "The Origin and Nature of Newton's Laws of Motion," in *Beyond the Edge of Certainty*, ed. R. G. Colodny, Englewood Cliffs, N.J.: Prentice-Hall, 1965, pp. 29–68.
38. For details on Poincaré, see the article by Peter Alexander in the *Encyclopedia of Philosophy*, pp. 360–363; also Kockelmans, *Philosophy of Science* . . . , pp. 263–280; Poincaré's main essays are contained in an edition entitled *The Foundations of Science:* Science and Hypothesis, The Value of Science, Science and Method . . . , trans. G. B. Halsted, with an Introduction by Josiah Royce, New York: The Science Press, 1921, which will be cited in what follows.
39. A full analysis of this distinction, and of the role of conventions in both types of science, will be found in Louis Rougier, *La Philosophie géométrique de Henri Poincaré*, Paris: F. Alcan, 1920.
40. *Science of Mechanics*, p. 283.
41. *Ibid.*, pp. 283–284.
42. *Ibid.*, p. 283; see *supra*, pp. 112–117.
43. *Foundations of Science*, p. 111.
44. *Ibid.*, p. 353.
45. *Ibid.*

46. *Ibid.*, Poincaré's emphasis.

47. *Ibid.*, pp. 353–354.

48. *Ibid.*, p. 354, Poincaré's emphasis.

49. *Ibid.*

50. *Ibid.*

51. On Duhem, see the fine article by D. G. Miller in the *Dictionary of Scientific Biography*, Vol. 4, pp. 225–233; also Kockelmans, *Philosophy of Science . . .* , pp. 295–313.

52. *The Aim and Structure of Physical Theory*, trans. P. P. Wiener, with a Foreword by Louis de Broglie, Princeton: University Press, 1954; see also Armand Lowinger, *The Methodology of Pierre Duhem*, New York: Columbia University Press, 1941.

53. *Aim and Structure . . .* , pp. 7–8.

54. *Ibid.*, pp. 9–14.

55. *Ibid.*, p. 19.

56. *Ibid.*

57. *Ibid.*, pp. 20–21.

58. *Ibid.*, p. 178.

59. Cf. *ibid.*, p. 277.

60. *Ibid.*, pp. 26–27.

61. *Ibid.*, pp. 274–275.

62. Especially on Jacques Maritain, Yves Simon, and a series of professors at the University of Louvain; for an analysis, see my "Toward a Definition of the Philosophy of Science," *Mélanges à la mémoire de Charles De Koninck*, Quebec: Les Presses de l'Université Laval, 1968, pp. 465–485. Among non-Catholics, Philip Wiener is noteworthy for his endorsement of Duhem's views.

63. For details, see John Passmore's "Logical Positivism," *Encyclopedia of Philosophy*, Vol. 5, pp. 52–57; in the United States many of these philosophers were associated with the Unified Science Movement, and their more important papers are contained in *Foundations of the Unity of Science*, ed. Otto Neurath et al., 2 vols., Chicago: University of Chicago Press, 1970.

64. "On the Notion of Cause," *Mysticism and Logic*, New York: W. W. Norton & Co., 1929, cited by Philipp Frank, *Philosophy of Science*, The Link Between Science and Philosophy, Englewood Cliffs, N.J.: Prentice-Hall, 1957, p. 260.

65. For fuller details, see Erik Götlind, *Bertrand Russell's Theories of Causation*, Uppsala: Almqvist & Wiksells Boktryckeri A.B., 1952; and Elizabeth R. Eames, *Bertrand Russell's Theory of Knowledge*, New York: George Braziller, 1969.

66. Götlind, pp. 11–20; the main works in which Russell exposes his views on causality are *Mysticism and Logic*, first published in 1910 as *Philosophical Essays*, and *Our Knowledge of the External World*, London: 1914; reprint ed., New York: W. W. Norton & Co., 1929.

67. For substantiation of this, see Schlick's last work, *Philoso-

phy of Nature, trans. A. von Zeppelin, New York: Philosophical Library, 1949, pp. 48–52; on Schlick himself, see the article by Béla Juhos in the *Encyclopedia of Philosophy*, Vol. 7, pp. 319–324.

68. *Philosophy of Nature*, pp. 2–3.

69. *Ibid.*, p. 55; fuller details of Schlick's teaching on causality are contained in his *Gesammelte Aufsätze, 1926–1936*, Vienna: Gerold, 1938; reprint ed., Hildesheim: G. Olms, 1969. The article entitled "Die Kausalität in der gegenwärtigen Physik," pp. 41–82, appears in English in *Physical Reality*, ed. Stephen Toulmin, New York: Harper Torchbook, 1970, pp. 83–121. See also his *Space and Time in Contemporary Physics*, An Introduction to the Theory of Relativity and Gravitation, trans. H. L. Brose, New York: Oxford University Press, 1920.

70. *Philosophy of Nature*, p. 56.

71. *Ibid.*, p. 57.

72. *Ibid.*

73. *Ibid.*, p. 58.

74. *Ibid.*, pp. 69–70.

75. *Ibid.*, p. 90.

76. *Ibid.*

77. *Ibid.*, p. 93.

78. See Reichenbach's most mature treatment of the causality problem, *Philosophic Foundations of Quantum Mechanics*, Berkeley: University of California Press, 1944, p. 3; for a summary of Reichenbach's thought and a bibliography, see Peter Achinstein's article in the *Encyclopedia of Philosophy*, Vol. 7, pp. 114–118.

79. In an essay entitled "The Principle of Causality and the Possibility of Its Empirical Confirmation," written in 1923 and contained in his *Modern Philosophy of Science*, Selected essays, trans. and ed. by Maria Reichenbach, Foreword by Rudolf Carnap, New York: Humanities Press, 1959, p. 109.

80. *Philosophic Foundations* . . . , p. 4

81. *Ibid.*, p. 144.

82. *Ibid.*, p. 177.

83. *Ibid.*

84. In his *Positivism*, A Study in Human Understanding, Cambridge, Mass.: Harvard University Press, 1951; a translation by J. Bernstein and R. G. Newton of his *Kleines Lehrbuch des Positivismus* (1939), p. 187.

85. *Ibid.*

86. *Ibid.*, p. 188.

87. *Ibid.*; other members of the Wiener Kreis, such as Waismann and Frank, have likewise tempered the antimetaphysical polemics of the original program, and as a consequence have been more moderate in their treatment of causal concepts. See, for example, Frank, *Philosophy of Science*, pp. 286–297, 347–348.

88. In the Introduction to his principal work, *The Logic of Modern Physics*, New York: The Macmillan Co., 1927, pp. v–vi;

see also his *The Nature of Some of Our Physical Concepts*, New York: Philosophical Library, 1952; for a good account of Bridgman's scientific accomplishments and his philosophy, see the article by Gerald Holton et al., *Dictionary of Scientific Biography*, Vol. 2, pp. 457–461; also Kockelmans, *Philosophy of Science* . . . , pp. 461–480.

89. *Logic of Modern Physics*, p. 5.

90. *Ibid.*, pp. 1–3; Kockelmans's Introduction, p. 462.

91. *Ibid.*, p. 80.

92. *Ibid.*, p. 83.

93. *Ibid.*, p. 85.

94. *Ibid.*, pp. 85–87; for a discussion of the role of causality in special relativity, see *infra*, pp. 284–287.

95. *Ibid.*, p. 88.

96. *Ibid.*, p. 89.

97. *Ibid.*, p. 102.

98. *Ibid.*

99. *Ibid.*, p. 106.

100. He is explicit on this, as can be seen from his "The Present State of Operationalism," in *The Validation of Scientific Theories*, edited, with an Introduction, by Philipp G. Frank, New York: Collier Books, 1961, pp. 76–77.

101. Notably A. C. Benjamin, *Operationism*, Springfield, Ill.: Charles C. Thomas, 1955.

102. See Vol. I, pp. 3–5, and *infra*, pp. 214, 262, 269–270.

103. In his "Discussion with Einstein on Epistemological Problems in Atomic Physics," in *Albert Einstein: Philosopher-Scientist*, ed. P. A. Schilpp, New York: Tudor Publishing Co., 1949, p. 210.

104. *Ibid.*

105. For a fuller discussion of Bohr's contribution to quantum theory and this aspect of his philosophy of science, see the article by Leon Rosenfeld in the *Dictionary of Scientific Biography*, Vol. 2, pp. 239–254, esp. pp. 248–250.

106. "Discussion with Einstein," p. 211.

107. Rosenfeld, *Dictionary of Scientific Biography*, Vol. 2, p. 250; idem, "Niels Bohr's Contribution to Epistemology," *Physics Today* 16 (Oct. 1963), 47–54.

108. Oxford: Clarendon Press, 1949; Born is particularly well known for his probability interpretation of the wave function, which is explained *infra*, p. 214.

109. *Natural Philosophy* . . . , p. 5.

110. *Ibid.*, p. 6.

111. *Ibid.*, p. 9.

112. *Ibid.*

113. *Ibid.*, pp. 3–4.

114. *Ibid.*, pp. 17–18.

115. *Ibid.*, pp. 46–47.

116. *Ibid.*, p. 92; in this connection it is significant that Born rejects Reichenbach's three-valued interpretation of such formalism, *ibid.*, p. 107.

117. *Ibid.*, pp. 120–121.

118. *Ibid.*, pp. 122–123.

119. *Ibid.*, p. 123.

120. *Ibid.*, p. 124.

121. Did space permit, the philosophical views of another physicist should also be considered at this point, those, namely, of Victor F. Lenzen, *Causality in Natural Science*, Springfield, Ill.: Charles C. Thomas, 1954. Noteworthy is Lenzen's statement that "an essential element of science is expression of the connection between events through the concept of causality" (p. 3), although he attempts to so define causality as "to eliminate the problem of its ontological status" (p. 4).

122. For a full bibliography of recent literature dealing with various aspects of scientific explanation, see Nicholas Rescher, *Scientific Explanation*, New York: The Free Press, 1970, pp. 209–240.

123. *Foundations of Science:* The Philosophy of Theory and Experiment, New York: Dover Publications, 1957; this work originally appeared in 1920 under the title *Physics: The Elements.* For fuller details on Campbell, see the article by John Nicholas in the *Dictionary of Scientific Biography*, Vol. 3, pp. 31–35.

124. *Foundations of Science*, p. 57.

125. *Ibid.*, p. 115.

126. *Ibid.*, p. 117.

127. *Ibid.*, p. 78.

128. *Ibid.*, p. 222.

129. *Ibid.*, p. 52.

130. *Ibid.*, p. 10.

131. *Ibid.*, p. 12.

132. *Ibid.*, p. 65.

133. *Ibid.*, p. 67.

134. *Ibid.*, pp. 103–104.

135. *Ibid.*, pp. 185–192.

136. *Ibid.*, pp. 129–130.

137. *Ibid.*, p. 140.

138. Some recent studies include Mary B. Hesse, *Models and Analogies in Science*, Notre Dame, Ind.: University of Notre Dame Press, 1966, and her article of the same title in the *Encyclopedia of Philosophy*, Vol. 5, pp. 354–359; the articles reprinted in B. A. Brody, ed., *Readings in the Philosophy of Science*, Englewood Cliffs, N.J.: Prentice-Hall, 1970, pp. 251–293; especially Marshall Spector, "Models and Theories," pp. 276–293; and John Losee, *A Historical Introduction to the Philosophy of Science*, New York: Oxford University Press, 1972, who discusses Carl Hempel's criticism of Campbell's position, pp. 140–142.

139. See Carnap's *Foundations of Logic and Mathematics*,

Chicago: University of Chicago Press, 1939; and particularly the excerpt and related articles reprinted in Brody, *Readings* . . . , pp. 190–222.

140. *Scientific Explanation*, A Study of the Function of Theory, Probability and Law in Science, New York & London: Cambridge University Press, 1953; on Braithwaite, see the article by Peter Achinstein in the *Encyclopedia of Philosophy*, Vol. 1, pp. 364–365; for a detailed analysis of the ways in which scientific laws can be said to provide explanations, see Achinstein's *Law and Explanation*, An Essay in the Philosophy of Science, Oxford: Clarendon Press, 1971.

141. *Scientific Explanation*, pp. 1–2.

142. *Ibid.*, p. 2.

143. *Ibid.*, p. 294; the term "nomic" is used by Braithwaite to designate the universality associated with laws, as opposed to facts, following the suggestion of W. E. Johnson in his *Logic*, Cambridge: 1924 — *ibid.*, p. 293.

144. *Ibid.*, pp. 301–303.

145. *Ibid.*, p. 303.

146. *Ibid.*, pp. 310–311.

147. *Ibid.*, pp. 319–341.

148. *Ibid.*, p. 329; this property, it may be observed, need not be associated with organisms alone, but can be applied to any system that can be modeled through the use of negative-feedback mechanisms.

149. *Ibid.*, p. 334.

150. *Ibid.*, p. 343.

151. *Ibid.*, p. 349.

152. *Ibid.*

153. *Ibid.*, pp. 99–111.

154. New York: Harcourt, Brace and World, 1961.

155. *Structure of Science*, pp. 4–5.

156. *Ibid.*, pp. 16–20.

157. *Ibid.*, pp. 20–26.

158. *Ibid.*, p. 30, fn. 2, continuation on p. 31.

159. *Ibid.*, p. 42.

160. *Ibid.*, p. 43; a summary of Aristotle's analysis of scientific explanation is given in Vol. I, pp. 11–18.

161. *Ibid.*, p. 43.

162. *Ibid.*, p. 45.

163. *Ibid.*

164. *Ibid.*, pp. 47–78.

165. *Ibid.*, p. 56; cf. also pp. 28, 68, and 70.

166. *Ibid.*, pp. 56–67; in the last condition, the "substantial part of one's knowledge" would seem to include knowledge of the potentialities and natures of the substances with which one is dealing, along the lines suggested by Harré to justify nomic universality — see *infra*, pp. 234–236.

167. *Ibid.*, p. 75.

168. *Ibid.*, p. 76.
169. *Ibid.*, pp. 77–78.
170. *Ibid.*, p. 73.
171. *Ibid.*, pp. 73–74.
172. *Ibid.*, p. 74.
173. *Ibid.*, p. 24.
174. *Ibid.*, p. 403.
175. *Ibid.*, p. 405.
176. *Ibid.*, pp. 421–422.
177. *Ibid.*, pp. 293–305.
178. *Ibid.*, p. 309.
179. *Ibid.*
180. *Ibid.;* Nagel analyzes the concept of chance on pp. 332–335, noting that while "the notion of an absolute, unqualified disorder is self-contradictory," to state that "an event 'happens by chance' is not in general incompatible with asserting the event to be determined . . ." (p. 334).
181. *Ibid.*, p. 316.
182. *Ibid.*, p. 323.
183. *Ibid.*, p. 324.
184. *Ibid.*

185. J. P. Dougherty, "Nagel's Concept of Science," *Philosophy Today* 10 (1966), 221; other noteworthy reviews are those of E. H. Madden, *Philosophy of Science* 30 (1963), 64–70; and J. J. C. Smart, *Journal of Philosophy* 59 (1962), 216–223.

186. Representative of each of these categories, respectively, would be: Henry Margenau, "Meaning and Scientific Status of Causality," *Philosophy of Science* 1 (1934), 133–148; E. E. Harris, *The Foundations of Metaphysics in Science*, New York: Humanities Press, 1965; D. J. B. Hawkins, *Causality and Implication*, London: Sheed and Ward, 1937; C. J. Ducasse, *Truth, Knowledge and Causation*, New York: Humanities Press, 1968; and A. E. Michotte, *The Perception of Causality*, trans. T. and E. Miles, London: Methuen & Co., Ltd., 1963, esp. pp. 255–266. Newer directions under phenomenological inspiration are indicated in J. J. Kockelmans, *Phenomenology and Physical Science*, Pittsburgh: Duquesne University Press, 1966, esp. pp. 163–175, and in other writings by the same author; see also the articles on causality and causation in the *Encyclopedia of Philosophy*, the *New Catholic Encyclopedia*, the *Dictionary of the History of Ideas*, and Mortimer Adler's *Syntopicon* to the Great Books of the Western World.

187. For details of Bergson's life, thought, and works, see the articles by T. A. Goudge in the *Dictionary of Scientific Biography*, Vol. 2, pp. 8–12; and in the *Encyclopedia of Philosophy*, Vol. 1, pp. 287–295.

188. See, in particular, Milič Čapek, *The Philosophical Impact of Contemporary Physics*, Princeton: D. Van Nostrand Co., Inc., 1961; and *Bergson and Modern Physics: A Re-interpretation*

and Re-evaluation, Dordrecht: Reidel, 1971; also P. A. Y. Gunter, ed., *Bergson and the Evolution of Physics*, Knoxville: University of Tennessee Press, 1969.

189. For a general summary of Whitehead's contribution, see the article by D. M. Emmet in the *Encyclopedia of Philosophy*, Vol. 8, pp. 290–296; on Whitehead's philosophy of science, in particular, see Laurence Bright, *Whitehead's Philosophy of Physics*, London: Sheed and Ward, 1958, and R. M. Palter, *Whitehead's Philosophy of Science*, Chicago: University of Chicago Press, 1960.

190. See Palter, *op. cit.*, pp. 42–146; also see Whitehead's *The Concept of Nature*, Cambridge: University Press, 1920, pp. 74–98; reprint ed., Ann Arbor: University of Michigan Press, 1957.

191. *Symbolism: Its Meaning and Effect*, New York: The Macmillan Co., 1927, p. 50.

192. *Ibid.*, p. 51.

193. *Ibid.*, pp. 51–52.

194. *Science and the Modern World*, 1925, reprint ed., New York: The Free Press, 1967, pp. 43–45; a more systematic elaboration of Whitehead's thought is to be found in his *Process and Reality*, 1929, reprint ed., New York: The Free Press, 1969.

195. On Meyerson see the article by Robert Blanché in the *Encyclopedia of Philosophy*, Vol. 5, pp. 307–308; also Kockelmans, *Philosophy of Science . . .* , pp. 328–347.

196. *Identity and Reality*, trans. Kate Loewenberg, New York: The Macmillan Co., 1930, pp. 17–18.

197. *Ibid.*, p. 43.

198. *Ibid.*, p. 45.

199. *Ibid.*, p. 43.

200. *Ibid.*

201. *Ibid.*, pp. 9–10.

202. *Ibid.*, pp. 43–47.

203. *Ibid.*, pp. 308–311.

204. *Ibid.*, pp. 439–440.

205. For biographical and bibliographical information, see the article by Vincent Tomas in the *Encyclopedia of Philosophy*, Vol. 2, pp. 421–423.

206. See *supra*, p. 42.

207. "Minds, Matter and Bodies," in *Brain and Mind*, ed. J. R. Smythies, London: Routledge and Kegan Paul, 1965, p. 84.

208. *Truth, Knowledge and Causation*, New York: Humanities Press, 1968, p. 8.

209. *Ibid.*, p. 8.

210. Edward H. Madden, "A Third View of Causality," *The Review of Metaphysics* 23 (1969), 67–84; E. H. Madden and P. H. Hare, "C. J. Ducasse on Human Agency," *The Personalist* 52 (1971), 618–629; and James Humber and E. H. Madden, "Nonlogical Necessity and C. J. Ducasse," *Ratio* 13 (1971), 119–138.

211. See, for example, the essays in Frederick C. Dommeyer, ed., *Current Philosophical Issues:* Essays in Honor of Curt John Ducasse, Springfield, Ill.: Charles C. Thomas, 1966.

212. For a good survey, see Edward A. MacKinnon, ed., *The Problem of Scientific Realism*, New York: Appleton-Century-Crofts, 1972, and particularly the introductory essay by MacKinnon, pp. 3–71.

213. *Ibid.*, esp. pp. 26–29.

214. Other types of scientific realism would be associated with the names of Grover Maxwell, J. J. C. Smart, Stephen Toulmin, and Marx W. Wartofsky.

215. Representative of this work, much of it done under the inspiration of Bernard Lonergan, would be, apart from MacKinnon, Philip McShane, *Randomness, Statistics and Emergence*, Notre Dame, Ind.: University of Notre Dame Press, 1970; and Patrick A. Heelan, *Quantum Mechanics and Objectivity:* A Study of the Physical Philosophy of Werner Heisenberg, The Hague: Martinus Nijhoff, 1965; also Heelan's "Elementary Particles, Philosophical Considerations," in *New Catholic Encyclopedia*, Vol. 5, pp. 261–263; see also Lonergan's *Insight*, A Study of Human Understanding, New York: Philosophical Library, 1957, esp. pp. 442–444, 128–139.

216. New York: D. Van Nostrand Co., Inc., 1957; Bohm's earlier views are contained in his textbook, *Quantum Theory*, Englewood Cliffs, N.J.: Prentice-Hall, Inc., 1951; his later position is also detailed in "Classical and Non-Classical Concepts in the Quantum Theory," *British Journal for Philosophy of Science* 12 (1961–62), pp. 265–280, reprinted in *Physical Reality*, ed. Stephen Toulmin, pp. 197–216.

217. *Causality and Chance . . .* , p. x.

218. *Ibid.*, p. 62.

219. *Ibid.*, p. 69.

220. *Ibid.*, p. 133.

221. *Ibid.*, pp. 133–170.

222. *Ibid.*, p. 138.

223. *Ibid.*, p. 143.

224. *Ibid.*, p. 170; for an appreciative and yet critical appraisal of this position, see P. K. Feyerabend's review of Bohm's book in the *British Journal for Philosophy of Science* 10 (1959–60), pp. 321–338, also reprinted in *Physical Reality*, ed. Stephen Toulmin, pp. 173–196.

225. Cambridge, Mass.: Harvard University Press, 1959; Bunge's other writings include *Metascientific Queries*, Springfield, Ill.: Charles C. Thomas, 1959; *Intuition and Science*, Englewood Cliffs, N.J.: Prentice-Hall, 1962; and *The Myth of Simplicity*, Englewood Cliffs, N.J.: Prentice-Hall, 1963.

226. *Causality*, pp. 46–47.

227. *Ibid.*, p. 47.

228. *Ibid.*, p. 48.

229. *Ibid.*, p. 33.
230. *Ibid.*, p. 195.
231. *Ibid.*, p. 197.
232. *Ibid.*, pp. 255–280.
233. *Ibid.*, p. 280.
234. *Ibid.*, p. 327.
235. *Ibid.*, p. 282.
236. *Ibid.*, pp. 295–298.
237. *Ibid.*, pp. 298–305.
238. *Ibid.*, p. 351.
239. *Ibid.*, p. 352.
240. *Ibid.*
241. Chicago: University of Chicago Press, 1970; a less technical statement of Harré's position is to be found in his *The Philosophies of Science:* An Introductory Survey, New York: Oxford University Press, 1972. Other writings include *An Introduction to the Logic of the Sciences,* London: Macmillan, 1960; *Theories and Things,* A Brief Study in Prescriptive Metaphysics, London: Sheed and Ward, 1961; and *The Anticipation of Nature,* London: Hutchinson, 1965.
242. *Principles of Scientific Thinking*, p. 6.
243. *Ibid.*, p. 101.
244. *Ibid.*, p. 102.
245. *Ibid.*, p. 100.
246. *Ibid.*, p. 104.
247. *Ibid.*, p. 102.
248. *Ibid.*, p. 122.
249. *Ibid.*
250. *Ibid.*, p. 123.
251. *Ibid.*, p. 125.
252. *Ibid.*, p. vii.
253. Friedrich Waismann, *The Principles of Linguistic Philosophy,* ed. R. Harré, London: Macmillan, 1965; idem, *How I See Philosophy,* ed. R. Harré, London: Macmillan, 1968. I have been informed by Harré that Waismann's literary executors (of whom he is one) have found, among his effects, a manuscript for a full-length book on causality, but that the views therein do not differ substantially from those of the 1958 essay.

CHAPTER FOUR
1. New York: Charles Scribner's Sons, 1970– ; seven volumes completed at this printing, about six more volumes projected.
2. Princeton, N.J.: Princeton University Press, 1960.
3. Chicago: University of Chicago Press, 1962; 2d enl. ed., 1970, which will be cited in what follows. Kuhn refers to Gillispie's *Edge of Objectivity,* in fact, as "a brilliant and entirely up-to-date attempt to fit scientific development into this Procrustean bed. . . ," p. 108, fn. 11.

4. *Structure of Scientific Revolutions,* pp. 168–173. This summary, based as it is on Kuhn's original text, does not pretend to do full justice to his more fully articulated views. He would admit to being a thorough-going realist, for example, and would therefore maintain that nature's refractoriness to accepted forms of puzzle-solving is what ultimately forces scientists out of one normal pattern of explanation and into another. He would also allow that a change of paradigm need not imply the rejection of all previous knowledge, and that, in fact, it may well lead to a refinement and extension of solutions already given, even while directing attention to puzzles of a quite different sort. Thus ontological and objective considerations are not ruled out by his account of scientific revolutions, though they do not figure prominently in its initial formulation.

5. *Criticism and the Growth of Knowledge,* ed. Imre Lakatos and Alan Musgrave, Cambridge: at the University Press, 1970.

6. See Popper's brief essay in *Criticism and the Growth of Knowledge,* pp. 51–58; also his *Logic of Scientific Discovery,* New York: Basic Books, 1959; idem, *Conjectures and Refutations:* The Growth of Scientific Knowledge, New York: Basic Books, 1962. In the preface to the latter work Popper presents his fundamental thesis as follows: "The way in which knowledge progresses, and especially our scientific knowledge, is by unjustified (and unjustifiable) anticipations, by guesses, by tentative solutions to our problems, by *conjectures.* These conjectures are controlled by criticism; that is, by attempted *refutations,* which include severely critical tests. . . . Those among our theories which turn out to be highly resistant to criticism, and which appear to us at a certain moment of time to be better approximations to truth than other known theories, may be described, together with the reports of their tests, as 'the science' of that time. Since none of them can be positively justified, it is essentially their critical and progressive character — the fact that we can *argue* about their claim to solve our problems better than their competitors — which constitutes the rationality of science," (p. vii).

7. See Feyerabend's "How to be a Good Empiricist — A Plea for Tolerance in Matters Epistemological," which appeared originally in *Philosophy of Science: The Delaware Seminar, II,* and has been reprinted in Brody, *Readings . . . ,* pp. 319–342.

8. For a discussion of the relativism implicit in Kuhn's analysis, see Dudley Shapere, "The Structure of Scientific Revolutions," *Philosophical Review* 73 (1964), 383–394; also Shapere's Introduction to his *Philosophical Problems of Natural Science,* New York: Macmillan, 1965, esp. pp. 17–19. Likewise of interest in this connection is Stephen Toulmin, *Human Understanding,* Oxford: Clarendon Press, 1972, Vol. 1, pp. 98–123.

9. See Vol. I, pp. 11–18.

10. See Holton's essays, "On the Thematic Analysis of Sci-

ence: The Case of Poincaré and Relativity," in *Mélanges Alexandre Koyré*, 2 vols., Paris: Hermann, 1964, Vol. 1, pp. 257–268, and those reprinted in his *Thematic Origins of Scientific Thought: Kepler to Einstein.* Cambridge, Mass.: Harvard University Press, 1973. It is noteworthy that Holton is a physicist and historian of science, with whom Kuhn was associated at Harvard, and whose views are not unlike Kuhn's own.

11. Holton argues, for example, in the first paper cited in the previous note, that such themes led Einstein to the discovery of special relativity while they prevented Poincaré (with his conventionalist view) from making the discovery, even though at the time his knowledge was superior to Einstein's. See also Stanley Goldberg, "Poincaré's Silence and Einstein's Relativity," *British Journal for the History of Science* 5 (1970), 73–84.

12. "On the Thematic Analysis . . . ," pp. 264–267.

13. *Ibid.*, p. 265.

14. *Ibid.*

15. *Ibid.*, p. 266.

16. The *z*-axis will also be the concern of the sociologist of science, for those who favor the "externalist" over the "internalist" view of the history of science. The term "theme" may be understood in a sense sufficiently broad to include all such types of influence on scientific thought. For an example, see *infra*, pp. 279 ff.

17. "There is no science of singulars" — cf. Aristotle, *Posterior Analytics*, Bk. 1, chaps. 31 and 33; also Aquinas's commentary on the same, lect. 42, nn. 5–7, and lect. 44, n. 2. The sense of this aphorism is that the singular, precisely as contingent and as falling directly under sense observation, is not itself the object of demonstration. Science is rather concerned with universals, which differ from singulars in that they cannot be otherwise. This does not prevent the scientist, however, from demonstrating conclusions about singulars under their universal aspects; it is in this way, in fact, that Aristotle treats individual lunar eclipses and the repeated waxings and wanings of the moon. The explanations he offers for these singular phenomena are "scientific" because they apply not only to earth's moon but to all other planets and satellites in solar systems generally.

18. Even nonperipatetics, such as Brody and Harré, have seen the defects in this sort of explanation; see Brody's "Towards an Aristotelean Theory of Scientific Explanation," *Philosophy of Science* 39 (1972), 20–31; and Harré, *Principles of Scientific Thinking*, p. 20. According to peripatetic teaching, an expository syllogism that concludes to Peter's mortality by subsuming him as an individual under the major premise, "all men are mortal," does not explain how or why Peter will die, but merely explicates the content of the major premise, in the sense that "all men" obviously includes "Peter."

19. Thus Bunge writes: "The over-all trend discernible in re-

cent science in connection with the general problem of determinism is not so much an increasing departure from causality as a *progressive diversification of the types of determination*, with correlative changes in the meaning and scope of the causal principle." — *Causality*, p. 346, emphasis Bunge's. Even Nagel, in the final analysis, holds that the essential characteristic of the principle of causality is that it is a principle of determinism; see *supra*, p. 215.

20. All of these cases have been discussed at length in Vol. I; consult the index of that volume.

21. *Structure of Science*, p. 403.

22. *Ibid.*, p. 405.

23. See Vol. I, pp. 75–80, 102, 104, 143.

24. This contrary to a commonly stated, but erroneous, opinion; see E. A. Burtt, *The Metaphysical Foundations of Modern Science*, 2d rev. ed., New York: Humanities Press, 1932, pp. 17–24; and G. Holton, citing F. S. Taylor, in his *Introduction to Concepts and Theories in Physical Science*, Cambridge, Mass.: Addison-Wesley, 1952, pp. 20–21.

25. *Structure of Science*, p. 405.

26. *Ibid.*, p. 30, n. 2, continued on p. 31. It is here, apparently, that science makes contact with common experience and hence with common sense.

27. For a fuller discussion, see my "The Measurement and Definition of Sensible Qualities," *The New Scholasticism* 39 (1965), 1–25.

28. See Vol. I, pp. 94–102.

29. For details, see my "Measurement and Definition . . . ," pp. 16–18, and Vol. I, pp. 43–46, 78–80, 231.

30. See Vol. I, pp. 196–205, and also the following note.

31. Thus one cannot accurately specify the color of an object without reference to the light under which it is viewed or the background against which it is seen. Similarly, if one questions whether colors exist in darkness or in the interiors of objects, answers can only be given in terms of the distinctions indicated between the formal and material cause of color. Thus, colors do not formally exist in darkness or in the interior of bodies, because they there lack the light by which they become actually visible. They are present materially, however, when the structure of matter is such that it is capable of reflecting to the eye rays in the visible portion of the spectrum, should the object be illuminated by a proper light source.

32. Kuhn concentrated precisely on these two components of classical science in his George Sarton Lecture at the History of Science Society meeting on December 28, 1972, in Washington, D.C. The lecture was appropriately entitled "Mathematical versus Experimental Tradition in the Development of Physical Science."

33. A work that brings out this point very well is R. S. West-

fall's *The Construction of Modern Science: Mechanisms and Mechanics*, New York: John Wiley & Sons, Inc., 1971; see also Harré's *The Method of Science*, A Course in Understanding Science, Based upon the *De Magnete* of William Gilbert and the *Vegetable Staticks* of Stephen Hales, London: Wykeham Publications, Ltd., 1970.

34. Isaac Newton, *Mathematical Principles of Natural Philosophy*, trans. A. Motte, rev. and ed. by F. Cajori, Berkeley: University of California Press, 1934, p. 5.

35. See Vol. I, pp. 120–149 and *passim*.

36. Our exposition is influenced by the work of Hesse and others, but it follows in the main that of Harré in his *Principles of Scientific Thinking*, pp. 33–62, with considerable abbreviation and simplification of terminology.

37. See Vol. I, pp. 98–99.

38. *Ibid.*, pp. 184–193; also Westfall, *The Construction . . .* , pp. 86–94.

39. Some idea of the sense of excitement generated by these discoveries is captured in Galileo's *Sidereus nuncius*, trans. Stillman Drake in *Discoveries and Opinions of Galileo*, New York: Doubleday Anchor, 1957, pp. 1–58; and in Robert Hooke's *Micrographia*, published by the Royal Society in 1665 and facsimile reproduced, New York: Dover Publications, 1961. Hooke's use of causal reasoning in the explanation of these and other discoveries is detailed in D. R. Oldroyd, "Robert Hooke's Methodology of Science as Exemplified in His 'Discourse of Earthquakes,' " *British Journal for the History of Science* 6 (1972), 109–130.

40. Following, but adapting, the discussion in Harré, *Principles . . .* , pp. 63–91; a related exposition is that of Richard J. Blackwell, *Discovery in the Physical Sciences*, Notre Dame, Ind.: University of Notre Dame Press, 1969.

41. For a discussion of modal transforms, and how they differ from causal transforms, see Harré, *Principles . . .* , pp. 53–56.

42. For an informative discussion of this problematic, together with the principal papers in which it is developed, see Brody, *Readings . . .* , pt. 3, esp. pp. 375–538; also Harré, *Principles . . .* , pp. 25–26, 119–122, and the bibliography on pp. 128–129.

43. See Roderick M. Chisholm, "Law Statements and Counterfactual Inference," *Analysis* 15 (1955), 97–105; reprinted in Madden, *The Structure of Scientific Thought*, pp. 229–235.

44. Cf. Harré, *Principles . . .* , pp. 139–141.

45. And, as in the case of heavy water, where the explanation of the differences between it and ordinary water is found in the molecular constitution of the two, so the explanation of the differences between birds and dribs would be sought in the genetic factors or materials that led to their speciation.

46. Cf. Harré, *Principles . . .* , pp. 185–188.

47. *Ibid.*, p. 187.

48. *Ibid.*, p. 122; text cited *supra* on p. 235.

49. For a discussion of taxa and classes, see Harré, *Principles* . . . , pp. 196–200; on the modern-day equivalents of formal and material causality as well as of the other Aristotelian types, and this in the context of scientific explanation, see N. R. Hanson, *Observation and Explanation*, A Guide to Philosophy of Science, London: George Allen & Unwin, 1972, pp. 28–45.

50. The earlier example, "All copper expands when heated," is a nontaxonomic generalization of this type, and in the face of an apparent disconfirming instance would be modified in ways similar to those discussed here as applicable to Boyle's law. Another way of dealing with the aberrant case, of course, would be to revert to taxonomic procedures again and distinguish between "true copper" or "ordinary copper" and other "nonexpanding" types.

51. Cf. Harré, *Principles* . . . , pp. 142–145.

CHAPTER FIVE

1. *Our Knowledge of the External World*, p. 223.

2. Daniel Lerner, ed., New York: The Free Press, 1965.

3. *Cause and Effect*, p. 5.

4. *Ibid.*, p. 7.

5. *Ibid.*, p. 6; some of their "disinterest," of course, could well derive from the confusing use of terminology by the very philosophers who are supposedly helping them. On this, see N. R. Hanson, "The Copenhagen Interpretation of Quantum Theory," *American Journal of Physics* 27 (1959), 1–15, reprinted in *Physical Reality*, ed. Stephen Toulmin, pp. 143–172, esp. pp. 171–172.

6. *Ibid.*, "Types of Causal Explanation in Science," p. 12; Bunge makes similar observations on the use of the term "cause" in scientific literature, *Causality*, p. 345.

7. *Ibid.*, "Noncausal Explanation," p. 147.

8. *Ibid.*, "Cause and Effect in Sociology," p. 64.

9. *Ibid.*, "Cause and Effect in the Study of Politics," p. 75.

10. See *supra*, n. 16 to chap. 4.

11. "Weimar Culture, Causality, and Quantum Theory, 1918–1927: Adaptation by German Physicists and Mathematicians to a Hostile Intellectual Environment," *Historical Studies in the Physical Sciences* 3 (1971), 1–115.

12. In Jammer's *The Conceptual Development of Quantum Mechanics*, New York: McGraw-Hill, 1966, pp. 166–167, 180.

13. "Die Revolution in der Wissenschaft," cited by Forman, p. 17.

14. Forman, "Weimar Culture . . . ," pp. 27–29.

15. *Ibid.*, p. 33.

16. *Ibid.*, p. 74.

17. *Ibid.*, p. 87.

18. *Ibid.*, pp. 76–80.
19. *Kausalgesetz und Willensfreiheit*, Berlin: 1923, cited by Forman, p. 93.
20. *Ibid.*
21. *Ibid.*, p. 101.
22. *Ibid.*, p. 100.
23. *Ibid.*, pp. 104–108; see *supra*, pp. 190–197.
24. This seems to have been the case in the Soviet Union, where dialectical materialism influenced the advocacy of causality by Russian scientists; similarly, the theistic convictions of many eighteenth- and nineteenth-century British scientists led them to a sympathetic acceptance of causal concepts.
25. Forman, "Weimar Culture . . . ," p. 36.
26. See the detailed account of the evolution of these theories by N. L. Balazs, *Dictionary of Scientific Biography*, Vol. 4, pp. 319–333.
27. A clear exposition is contained in Lenzen, *Causality in Natural Science*, pp. 70–80; our account here follows the semitechnical article by James Albertson, "Relativity," *New Catholic Encyclopedia*, Vol. 12, pp. 224–231.
28. "Relativity," p. 227.
29. *Causality and Chance . . .* , pp. 68–69.
30. *Space, Time and Gravitation*, An Outline of the General Relativity Theory, Cambridge: at the University Press, 1920; reprint ed., New York: Harper Torchbook, 1959, pp. 95–96. For Eddington's other contributions and a brief account of his own philosophy, see the article by A. Vibert Douglas, *Dictionary of Scientific Biography*, Vol. 4, pp. 277–282.
31. *Space, Time and Gravitation*, p. 95.
32. See Vol. I, pp. 205–210.
33. *Space, Time and Gravitation*, pp. 95–96.
34. As expressed in his famous letter to Richard Bentley; see *Isaac Newton's Papers and Letters on Natural Philosophy*, ed. I. Bernard Cohen, Cambridge, Mass.: Harvard University Press, 1958, pp. 302–303.
35. *Space, Time and Gravitation*, p. 96.
36. *Ibid.*
37. Balazs, *Dictionary of Scientific Biography*, Vol. 4, p. 331. On this point, however, there is no universal accord. J. D. North, for example, in his generally competent history of modern cosmology, *The Measure of the Universe*, Oxford: Clarendon Press, 1965, disapproves of using causal terminology in such a context: "There is no longer any excuse (if there was ever an excuse) for the parlance 'the curvature of space-time is the cause of gravitation'; . . ." p. 91. North admits, however, that Einstein and others regarded the gravitational field not merely as a mathematical device for describing the motion of bodies but as "the ultimate reality" (p. 42). His own preference is for conventionalism as a philosophy of sci-

ence (pp. xxvi, xxviii), and consistent with this he explicitly denies that science deals with causes or can discover causal connections (pp. 400, 404–405), or even that it can "advance by a series of steadily improving approaches to truth" (p. 407). Yet, on the other hand, North is willing to discuss such concepts as *materia prima*, while admitting that modern cosmology had shed little light on the ultimate identity of any protomatter (pp. 401–402). Apparently he would not see matter as exercising any type of casual influence, just as Mach would not associate functional dependence with causal efficacy, while for a contemporary Aristotelian both matter and form could still count as extramental explanatory factors and therefore as causes.

38. For a brief explanation, see P. R. Durbin, *Philosophy of Science: An Introduction*, New York: McGraw-Hill, 1968, pp. 134–136.

39. 2d ed., Cambridge, Mass.: Harvard University Press, 1969, p. 22. This interpretation is also endorsed by Einstein in his Foreword to Jammer's book.

40. Aquinas explains this point at great length, although the type of causality involved became a subject of dispute among medieval authors, some of whom favored an interpretation in terms of efficient causality. For details, see my "St. Thomas and the Pull of Gravity," The McAuley Lectures 1963, *Science and the Liberal Concept*, West Hartford, Conn.: St. Joseph College, 1964, pp. 143–165.

41. *Philosophical Transactions*, No. 186 (1687), in an entry preceding his review of Newton's *Principia*, pp. 291–297.

42. See *supra*, p. 116.

43. This possibility is envisaged by K. Hujer, "Galileo's Trial in the Epistemology of Einsteinian Physics," in *Atti del Symposium Internazionale di Storia, Metodologia, Logica et Filosofia della Scienza*, "Galileo nella Storia e nella Filosofia della Scienza," Florence: G. Barbèra Editore, 1967, pp. 289–295.

44. See Vol. I, pp. 28–52, 66–71, 80–88.

45. See Durbin, *Philosophy of Science*, pp. 131–157; also my *Einstein, Galileo and Aquinas*, Compact Studies, Washington: The Thomist Press, 1963, esp. pp. 21–31.

46. In his "Obituary Notice on Einstein" for the Royal Society (1955), cited by Michael Polanyi, *Personal Knowledge*, Chicago: University of Chicago Press, 1958, p. 147, fn. 1.

47. Jammer and Frank have defended the first position, but they have been challenged by Grünbaum and Spector in works cited *infra*.

48. *Philosophical Problems of Space and Time*, New York: Alfred A. Knopf, 1963, p. 419, citing Einstein's Foreword to Jammer's *Concepts of Space*.

49. *Ibid.*, p. 419.

50. *Methodological Foundations of Relativistic Mechanics,* Notre Dame, Ind.: University of Notre Dame Press, 1972, p. 82.

51. *Ibid.,* p. 112; see also Edmund Whittaker's defense of the ether concept in the preface to his two-volume *A History of the Theories of Aether and Electricity,* rev. and enl. ed., London: Thomas Nelson, 1951, Vol. 1, p. v.

52. *The Scientific Revolution, 1500–1800,* Boston: Beacon Press, 1956, p. xiii.

53. *Ibid.* Heisenberg makes a similar observation: "With respect to the finality of the results, we must remind the reader that in the realm of the exact sciences there have always been *final solutions* for certain limited domains of experience. Thus, for instance, the questions posed by Newton's concept of mechanics found an answer *valid for all time* in Newton's law and in its mathematical consequences. . . . In the exact sciences the word 'final' obviously means that there are always self-contained, mathematically representable, systems of concepts and laws applicable to certain realms of experience, in which realms *they are always valid for the entire cosmos and cannot be changed or improved.* Obviously, however, we cannot expect these concepts and laws to be suitable for the subsequent description of new realms of experience." — *The Physicist's Conception of Nature,* trans. A. J. Pomerans, London: Hutchinson, 1958, pp. 26–27 (italics mine).

54. *Structure of Scientific Revolutions,* p. 102.

55. *Methodological Foundations . . . ,* p. 151.

56. *Ibid.*

57. Apart from Jammer's *Conceptual Development . . . ,* see also Robert G. Colodny, ed., *Paradigms and Paradoxes,* The Philosophical Challenge of the Quantum Domain, Pittsburgh: University of Pittsburgh Press, 1972, for a fuller treatment of related issues.

58. See my "Elementarity and Reality in Particle Physics," in *Boston Studies in the Philosophy of Science,* Vol. 3, ed. R. S. Cohen and M. W. Wartofsky, Dordrecht: D. Reidel Publishing Co., 1968, pp. 236–263.

59. See Peter Achinstein, "The Problem of Theoretical Terms," *American Philosophical Quarterly* 2 (1965), reprinted in Brody, *Readings . . . ,* pp. 234–250; also Brody's Introduction, p. 184.

60. In the synopsis of his paper, "The Ontological Status of Theoretical Entities," in *Minnesota Studies in the Philosophy of Science,* Vol. 3, ed. Herbert Feigl and Grover Maxwell, Minneapolis: University of Minnesota Press, 1962, p. vii; this paper is also reprinted in Brody, *Readings . . . ,* pp. 224–233.

61. "The Ontological Status . . . ," pp. 7–8.

62. *Ibid.,* p. 9.

63. *Ibid.*

64. See Heisenberg, *Physics and Philosophy,* The Revolution

in Modern Science, New York: Harper Torchbook, 1958, pp. 69–70.

65. *The Concept of the Positron,* Cambridge: at the University Press, 1963, p. 43.

66. *Ibid.,* p. 42.

67. *Ibid.*

68. *Ibid.,* p. 47.

69. *Ibid.,* pp. 46–47.

70. "The Eightfold Way: A Theory of Strong Interaction Symmetry," Report CTSL-20, March 15, 1961, Synchrotron Laboratory, California Institute of Technology, Pasadena, California.

71. *The Philosophy of Science: An Introduction,* London: Hutchinson, 1953, pp. 134–139; see also his *Foresight and Understanding,* Bloomington, Ind.: Indiana University Press, 1961.

72. *Philosophy of Science,* pp. 137–138; for an interesting study of the related work of Jean Perrin, see Mary J. Nye, *Molecular Reality,* New York: American Elsevier, Inc., 1972.

73. *Ibid.,* pp. 135–136.

74. Venice: 1763, English translation of J. M. Child, 1921, reprint ed., Cambridge, Mass.: The M.I.T. Press, 1966; see Harré, *Principles of Scientific Thinking,* pp. 292–293; also p. 304, where he compares Boscovich and Kant.

75. Harré, *Principles* . . . , p. 299.

76. *Ibid.,* p. 304.

77. *Ibid.;* this somewhat cryptic statement is intelligible in the light of Harré's assertion: "The ultimate entities are causally responsible for the states of the world, without anything being causally responsible for them" (p. 297).

78. In the articles, "Measurement and Definition . . . ," and "Elementarity and Reality . . ."; see also Harré, *Theories and Things,* esp. pp. 83–106.

79. For the views of modern scientists on the relationships between quantity and quality, see *Quantity and Quality,* ed. Daniel Lerner, New York: The Free Press, 1961, particularly the essay by V. F. Weisskopf, "Quality and Quantity in Quantum Physics," pp. 53–67.

80. *Physics and Philosophy,* pp. 41, 53, 59–62, 160, 166. Aristotle presented two analyses leading to a knowledge of *hulē,* one in his *Physics* and the other in his *Metaphysics.* For a modern explanation of the first analysis, see V. E. Smith, *The General Science of Nature,* Milwaukee: Bruce Publishing Co., 1958, pp. 52–122; for a similar account of the second analysis, see Ernan McMullin, "Matter As a Principle," in *The Concept of Matter,* ed. E. McMullin, Notre Dame, Ind.: University of Notre Dame Press, 1963, pp. 169–208. The medievals investigated in some detail the relationship between this *hulē* and Aristotle's four elements; for a summary, see my "The Reality of Elementary Particles," *Proceedings of the American Catholic Philosophical Association* 38 (1964),

154–166; also "Elementarity and Reality . . . ," pp. 243–247.

81. *Physics and Philosophy*, p. 70.

82. *Ibid.*, pp. 40–41.

83. According to this terminology, the real is divided into the potential and the actual. For example, rationality in a human being is real: it is potential in the child who cannot yet actually reason, although he has the basic capability or power to do so; it is actual in the adult who does in fact reason. So, protomatter is real only in the sense of being a potentiality for assuming the various forms or determinations it can be made to assume.

84. The term "element" is relative in connotation. By way of example, syllables may be referred to as the elements out of which words are formed, and yet syllables are composed of letters as further elements. In like manner, what is regarded by the chemist as an element in his science need not be so regarded by the physicist in his; or, what is regarded by the physicist as an element in one application need not be so regarded in another.

85. The sense in which an elementary particle may be regarded as a construct is thus twofold: it may be "constructed" or contrived experimentally, by laboratory conditions, or it may be "constructed" or contrived logically, by the theoretician in an attempt to explain high-energy experiments.

86. What is involved here is not merely a question of time duration alone, but of the existence of a stable nature that seeks continued self-preservation against the ravages of extrinsic deteriorating agents. Such natures are associated with at least some objects of ordinary experience, but they are not necessarily associated with elementary particles.

87. If this is so, then the notion of "modal transform" may contribute more to their understanding than that of "causal transform." See *supra*, chap. 4, note 41. It may also be noted that material and formal causality here take on a much more nuanced and sophisticated meaning than in the statue analysis frequently used to characterize Aristotle's teaching on the four causes; recall, however, what was said on this point in Vol. I, pp. 15–16.

88. See Harré, *Principles* . . . , p. 313; and Heisenberg, *Physics and Philosophy*, p. 63; the former expresses the idea that every fundamental theory, expressed in the language of physics, must be a "field theory," whereas the latter suggests that the ultimate substrate may be identified with "energy"; for an analysis of Harré's ultimates, see E. H. Madden and Mendel Sachs, "Parmenidean Particulars and Vanishing Elements," *Studies in History and Philosophy of Science* 3 (1972), 151–166.

89. See *supra*, p. 229.

90. For an exposition and defense of this view, see Hanson, "The Copenhagen Interpretation. . . ."

91. See *supra*, pp. 192–196 and 184–186.

92. See Heisenberg's discussion of the counterproposals to the

Copenhagen interpretation by Blochinzev and Alexandrov, *Physics and Philosophy*, pp. 135–141; also my "Elementarity and Reality . . . ," p. 263, fn. 64.

93. See, in particular, his letter to Professor Edwin K. Gora of December 3, 1965, printed with my "Elementarity and Reality . . . ," p. 259, wherein he expresses a benign attitude to the interpretation we are here offering.

94. Paul A. Weiss, *Life, Order and Understanding*: A Theme in Three Variations, The Graduate Journal, Austin: The University of Texas, 1970; idem, *Within the Gates of Science and Beyond*: Science and Its Cultural Commitments, New York: Hafner Publishing Co., 1971.

95. "Footnotes on the Philosophy of Biology," *Philosophy of Science* 36 (1969), 202.

96. *Ibid.*, pp. 197–202.

97. "Cause and Effect in Biology," in *Cause and Effect*, ed. Daniel Lerner, p. 33.

98. *Ibid.*, p. 48.

99. *Ibid.*, pp. 37–38.

100. *Ibid.*, p. 37.

101. *Ibid.*, p. 38.

102. *Ibid.*, p. 39.

103. *Ibid.*, p. 49.

104. *Ibid.*, p. 39.

105. *Ibid.*

106. *Ibid.*, p. 40.

107. *Ibid.*, pp. 40–41.

108. *Ibid.*, p. 41.

109. *Ibid.*; cf. p. 40.

110. *Ibid.*, p. 42.

111. *Ibid.*

112. *Ibid.*, p. 43.

113. *Ibid.*

114. "Teleological Explanations in Evolutionary Biology," *Philosophy of Science* 37 (1970), 1–15.

115. *Ibid.*, p. 8.

116. *Ibid.*, p. 9.

117. *Ibid.*

118. *Ibid.*, p. 10.

119. *Ibid.*

120. *Ibid.*; Ayala explains in detail how his view of natural selection as teleological differs from Mayr's, pp. 10–11.

121. *Ibid.*, p. 11.

122. *Ibid.*

123. *Ibid.*; Ayala here implicitly rejects the religious concordist accounts of evolutionary process, such as that proposed by Pierre Teilhard de Chardin. His grounds for so doing seem similar to those behind Leibniz's rejection of the Newtonian argument for God's existence, on the basis that the latter implies a "special inter-

vention" in the order of nature that is neither detectable nor necessary for rational understanding. This need not imply, of course, a rejection of the cosmological argument in general; for a preliminary reconstruction of the latter, see my "The Cosmological Argument: A Reappraisal," *Proceedings of the American Catholic Philosophical Association* 46 (1972), pp. 43–57.

124. *Ibid.*, pp. 14–15; here he relies heavily on J. H. Randall, Jr., *Aristotle*, New York: Columbia University Press, 1960.

125. J. N. Deely, "The Philosophical Dimensions of the Origin of Species," *The Thomist* 33 (1969), 75–149, 251–335; for a fuller explanation of Deely's views, and their implications for developing a philosophy of science based on the concepts of biology rather than on those of mathematics and physics, see J. N. Deely and R. J. Nogar, *The Problem of Evolution*, A Study of the Philosophical Repercussions of Evolutionary Science, New York: Appleton-Century-Crofts, 1973.

126. *Ibid.*, p. 102; I would question Deely's ordering of the questions here, and suggest that perhaps the second and third questions be interchanged.

127. *Ibid.*, p. 103.

128. *Ibid.*, p. 104.

129. *Ibid.*

130. Julian Huxley, "Evolution, Cultural and Biological," in *Knowledge, Morality, and Destiny*, New York: Mentor Books, 1957, pp. 56–84; cited by Deely, p. 103.

131. Deely, "Philosophical Dimensions . . . ," p. 105.

132. C. H. Waddington, "Evolutionary Adaptation," *The Evolution of Life*, Vol. I of *Evolution After Darwin*, ed. Sol Tax, Chicago: University of Chicago Press, 1960, pp. 381–402; cited by Deely, p. 105.

133. I.e., causes are causes to each other — cf. Deely, p. 97.

134. As summarized by B. M. Ashley, "Causality and Evolution," *The Thomist* 36 (1972), p. 212.

135. Deely, "Philosophical Dimensions . . . ," pp. 290–304 and *passim*.

136. Under material causes we would, of course, include the varieties of components, elements, particles, or parts of whatever type that go to make up a whole, whereas under formal causes we would include the structures, unities, or natures with their appropriate powers that result from such composition. For the sources of such usage in Aristotle, see Vol. I, pp. 13–14 and pp. 215–216, n. 23.

137. Chapel Hill: University of North Carolina Press, 1964, pp. 3–21. See also the comprehensive work edited by the same author, *Causal Models in the Social Sciences*, Chicago: Aldine Publishing Co., 1971.

138. *The Nature and Scope of Social Science: A Critical Anthology*, New York: Appleton-Century-Crofts, 1969.

139. *Ibid.*, p. vii.

140. Englewood Cliffs, N.J.: Prentice-Hall, Inc., 1966.

141. *Action and Purpose*, p. 259.

142. *Ibid.*, p. 262.

143. *Ibid.*

144. R. Harré and P. F. Secord, *The Explanation of Social Behaviour*, Oxford: Basil Blackwell, 1972.

145. *Ibid.*, p. 5.

146. A fuller discussion of these problems would lead naturally into contemporary work by British and German philosophers on the differences between explanation and understanding, on the role of hermeneutics in the *Geisteswissenschaften*, and on the complementarity of causal and teleological explanations in accounting for human behavior; for a good survey of recent developments along these lines, see G. H. von Wright, *Explanation and Understanding*, Ithaca: Cornell University Press, 1971, which includes a fairly comprehensive bibliography. Of related interest are G. E. M. Anscombe's *Intention*, Oxford: Basil Blackwell, 1957, and *Causality and Determination*, Cambridge: at the University Press, 1971, as well as Charles Taylor's *The Explanation of Behaviour*, London: Routledge and Kegan Paul, 1964, and "Interpretation and the Sciences of Man," *The Review of Metaphysics* 25 (1971), 3–51, and Michael Scriven's "Causes, Connections and Conditions in History," in *Philosophical Analysis and History*, ed. W. H. Dray, New York: Harper & Row, 1966, pp. 238–264.

Bibliography

Aaron, Richard I., *John Locke*. 2d ed. Oxford: Clarendon Press, 1955.

Achinstein, Peter, *Law and Explanation*. An Essay in the Philosophy of Science. Oxford: Clarendon Press, 1971.

———, "The Problem of Theoretical Terms." *American Philosophical Quarterly* 2 (1965). Reprinted in *Readings in the Philosophy of Science*, edited by B. A. Brody, pp. 234–250. Englewood Cliffs, N.J.: Prentice-Hall, 1970.

Adler, Mortimer, ed., *The Great Ideas: A Syntopicon of Great Books of the Western World*. 2 vols. Chicago: Encyclopaedia Britannica, 1952.

Albertson, James, "Relativity." In *New Catholic Encyclopedia*, edited by W. J. McDonald. Vol. 12, pp. 224–231. New York: McGraw-Hill, 1967.

Anderson, Fulton H., *Francis Bacon, His Career and His Thought*. Los Angeles: University of Southern California Press, 1962.

———, *The Philosophy of Francis Bacon*. Chicago: University of Chicago Press, 1948.

Anscombe, G. E. M., *Causality and Determination*. An Inaugural Lecture. Cambridge: at the University Press, 1971.

———, *Intention*. Oxford: Basil Blackwell, 1957.

Aronson, Jerrold, "The Legacy of Hume's Analysis of Causation." *Studies in History and Philosophy of Science* 2 (1971), 135–156.

Ashley, B. M., "Causality and Evolution." *The Thomist* 36 (1972), 199–230.

Ayala, Francisco J., "Telelogical Explanations in Evolutionary Biology." *Philosophy of Science* 37 (1970), 1–15.

Bacon, Francis, *The Works of Francis Bacon*. Edited by James

Spedding, Robert L. Ellis, and Douglas D. Heath. 15 vols. New York: Hurd and Houghton, 1869.

Balazs, N. L., "Einstein: Theory of Relativity." In *Dictionary of Scientific Biography*. Vol. 4, pp. 319–333. New York: Charles Scribner's Sons, 1970–.

Benjamin, A. Cornelius, *Operationism*. Springfield, Ill.: Charles C. Thomas, 1955.

Berkeley, George, *The Works of George Berkeley, Bishop of Cloyne*. Edited by A. A. Luce and T. E. Jessop. 9 vols. Edinburgh: Thomas Nelson and Sons, Ltd., 1948–57.

——, *The Principles of Human Knowledge*. Great Books of the Western World. Vol. 35. Chicago: Encyclopaedia Britannica, 1952.

Bernard, Claude, *Cahier Rouge*. English translation by H. H. Hoff and L. and R. Guillemin. In *Claude Bernard and Experimental Medicine*, edited by F. Grande and M. B. Visscher. Cambridge, Mass.: Schenkman Publishing Co., 1967.

——, *Introduction à l'étude de la médicine expérimentale*, avec les notes critiques par le R. P. Sertillanges. Paris: Imprimerie F. Levé, 1900.

——, *An Introduction to the Study of Experimental Medicine*. Translated by H. C. Greene, with an Introduction by L. J. Henderson. New York: Henry Schuman, Inc. [1927], 1949.

Beth, E. W., "Critical Epochs in the Development of the Theory of Science." *British Journal for the Philosophy of Science* 1 (1950), 27–42.

Blackwell, Richard J., *Discovery in the Physical Sciences*. Notre Dame, Ind.: University of Notre Dame Press, 1969.

Blake, R. M., "The Role of Experience in Descartes' Theory of Method." In *Theories of Scientific Method*, edited by E. H. Madden, pp. 75–103. Seattle: University of Washington Press, 1960.

Blalock, Hubert M. Jr., *Causal Inferences in Nonexperimental Research*. Chapel Hill: University of North Carolina Press, 1964.

——, ed., *Causal Models in the Social Sciences*. Chicago: Aldine Publishing Co., 1971.

Bohm, David, *Causality and Chance in Modern Physics*. New York: D. Van Nostrand Co., Inc., 1957.

——, "Classical and Non-Classical Concepts in the Quantum Theory." In *Physical Reality*, edited by Stephen Toulmin, pp. 197–216. New York: Harper & Row, 1970.

——, *Quantum Theory*. Englewood Cliffs, N.J.: Prentice-Hall, Inc., 1951.

Bohr, Niels, "Can Quantum-Mechanical Description of Physical Reality Be Considered Complete?" In *Physical Reality*, edited by Stephen Toulmin, pp. 130–142. New York: Harper & Row, 1970.

——, "Discussion with Einstein on Epistemological Problems in Atomic Physics." In *Albert Einstein: Philosopher-Scientist*, edited by P. A. Schilpp, pp. 201–241. New York: Tudor Publishing Co., 1949.

Born, Max, *Natural Philosophy of Cause and Chance*. The Waynflete Lectures 1948. Oxford: Clarendon Press, 1949.

Boscovich, Roger, *A Theory of Natural Philosophy*. Translated by J. M. Child. 1921. Reprint. Cambridge, Mass.: The M.I.T. Press, 1966.

Bradley, J., *Mach's Philosophy of Science*. London: Athlone Press, 1971.

Braithwaite, R. B., *Scientific Explanation*. A Study of the Function of Theory, Probability and Law in Science. New York & London: Cambridge University Press, 1953.

Brandt, Frithiof, *Thomas Hobbes' Mechanical Conception of Nature*. Copenhagen: Levin & Munksgaard, 1928.

Bridgman, Percy W., *The Logic of Modern Physics*. New York: The Macmillan Co., 1927.

——, *The Nature of Some of Our Physical Concepts*. New York: Philosophical Library, 1952.

——, "The Present State of Operationalism." In *The Validation of Scientific Theories,* edited by Philipp G. Frank, pp. 75–80. New York: Collier Books, 1961.

Bright, Laurence, *Whitehead's Philosophy of Physics*. London: Sheed & Ward, 1958.

Brody, B. A., "Natural Kinds and Real Essences." *The Journal of Philosophy* 64 (1967), 431–446.

——, ed., *Readings in the Philosophy of Science*. Englewood Cliffs, N.J.: Prentice-Hall, 1970.

——, "Reid and Hamilton on Perception." *The Monist* 55 (1971), 423–441.

——, "Towards an Aristotelean Theory of Scientific Explanation." *Philosophy of Science* 39 (1972), 20–31.

Buchdahl, Gerd, "Causality, Causal Laws and Scientific Theory in the Philosophy of Kant." *British Journal for the Philosophy of Science* 16 (1965), 187–208.

——, *The Image of Newton and Locke in the Age of Reason*. London: Sheed & Ward, 1961.

——, "Inductivist *versus* Deductivist Approaches in the Philosophy of Science as Illustrated by Some Controversies Between Whewell and Mill." *The Monist* 55 (1971), 343–367.

——, *Metaphysics and the Philosophy of Science*. The Classical Origins: Descartes to Kant. Cambridge, Mass.: The M.I.T. Press, 1969.

——, "The Relevance of Descartes' Philosophy for Modern Philosophy of Science." *British Journal for the History of Science* 1 (1963), 227–249.

Bunge, Mario, *Causality*. The Place of the Causal Principle in Modern Science. Cambridge, Mass.: Harvard University Press, 1959.

——, "Causality: A Rejoinder." *Philosophy of Science* 29 (1962), 306–317.

——, *Intuition and Science*. Englewood Cliffs, N.J.: Prentice-Hall, 1962.

——, *Metascientific Queries*. Springfield, Ill.: Charles C. Thomas, 1959.

——, *The Myth of Simplicity*. Englewood Cliffs, N.J.: Prentice-Hall, 1963.

Burtt, E. A., *The Metaphysical Foundations of Modern Science*. 2d rev. ed. New York: Humanities Press, 1932.

Butts, Robert E., "Whewell on Newton's Rules of Philosophizing." In *The Methodological Heritage of Newton*, edited by R. E. Butts and J. W. Davis, pp. 132–149. Toronto: University of Toronto Press, 1970.

Campbell, N. R., *Foundations of Science*. The Philosophy of Theory and Experiment [1920]. Reprint. New York: Dover Publications, 1957.

Cannon, Walter F., "John Herschel and the Idea of Science." *Journal of the History of Ideas* 22 (1961), 215–239.

Cantor, G. N., "Henry Brougham and the Scottish Methodological Tradition." *Studies in History and Philosophy of Science* 2 (1971), 69–89.

Čapek, Milič, *Bergson and Modern Physics*. A Re-interpretation and Re-evaluation. Boston Studies in the Philosophy of Science. Vol. 7. Dordrecht: Reidel, 1971.

——, *The Philosophical Impact of Contemporary Physics*. Princeton: D. Van Nostrand Co., Inc., 1961.

Carnap, Rudolf, *Foundations of Logic and Mathematics*. Chicago: University of Chicago Press, 1939.

Chappell, Vere Claiborne, ed., *Hume*. Garden City, N.Y.: Anchor Books, 1966.

Chisholm, Roderick M., "Law Statements and Counterfactual Inference." *Analysis* 15 (1955), 97–105.

Cohen, I. Bernard, ed., *Isaac Newton's Papers and Letters on Natural Philosophy and Related Documents*. Cambridge, Mass.: Harvard University Press, 1958.

——, "Quantum in se est: Newton, Kepler, Galileo, Descartes and Lucretius." *Proceedings of the American Catholic Philosophical Association* 38 (1964), 36–46.

Colodny, R. G., ed., *Beyond the Edge of Certainty:* Essays in Contemporary Science and Philosophy. Englewood Cliffs, N.J.: Prentice-Hall, 1965.

——, ed., *Paradigms and Paradoxes*. The Philosophical Challenge of the Quantum Domain. Pittsburgh: University of Pittsburgh Press, 1972.

Bibliography 383

Comte, Auguste, *Cours de philosophie positive*. 6 vols. Paris: Bachelier, Libraire pour les mathématiques, 1830–42.

——, *A General View of Positivism*. Translated by J. H. Bridges [1865]. With an Introduction by Frederic Harrison [1908], New York: E. P. Dutton & Co., n.d.

Crombie, A. C., ed., Introduction to *Turning Points in Physics*, pp. 1–4. Amsterdam: North-Holland Publishing Co., 1959.

Dahl, Robert A., "Cause and Effect in the Study of Politics." In *Cause and Effect*, edited by Daniel Lerner, pp. 75–98. New York: The Free Press, 1965.

Deely, John N., "The Philosophical Dimensions of the Origin of Species." *The Thomist* 33 (1969), 75–149, 251–335. Reprinted Chicago: Institute for Philosophical Research, 1969.

Deely, John N. and Nogar, Raymond J., *The Problem of Evolution*. A Study of the Philosophical Repercussions of Evolutionary Science. New York: Appleton-Century-Crofts, 1973.

Denissoff, Élie, *Descartes, premier théoricien de la physique mathématique*. Trois essais sur le *Discours de la méthode*. Bibliothèques philosophiques de Louvain. Vol. 22. Louvain: Publications Universitaires, 1970.

Descartes, René, *Oeuvres*. Edited by C. Adam and P. Tannery. 12 vols. Paris: Léopold Cerf, 1897–1913.

——, *Descartes: Philosophical Writings*. Edited and translated by E. Anscombe and P. T. Geach. London: Nelson & Sons, Ltd., 1954.

——, *The Philosophical Works of Descartes*. Translated by E. S. Haldane and G. R. T. Ross. 2 vols. 1911. Corrected 1931. Reprint. Cambridge: at the University Press, 1970.

——, *Descartes: Philosophical Writings*. Edited by N. K. Smith. New York: Modern Library, 1958.

——, *Discourse on Method, Optics, Geometry, and Meteorology*. Edited and translated by Paul J. Olscamp. New York: Bobbs-Merrill, 1965.

Dolch, Heimo, *Kausalität im Verständnis des Theologen und der Begründer neuzeitlicher Physik*. Freiburg-im-Breisgau: Verlag Herder, 1954.

Dommeyer, Frederick C., ed., *Current Philosophical Issues:* Essays in Honor of Curt John Ducasse. Springfield, Ill.: Charles C. Thomas, 1966.

Dougherty, Jude P., "Nagel's Concept of Science." *Philosophy Today* 10 (1966), 212–221.

Drake, Stillman, *Discoveries and Opinions of Galileo*. New York: Doubleday Anchor, 1957.

Ducasse, Curt John, *Causation and the Types of Necessity*. Seattle: University of Washington Press, 1924. Reprinted, with an Introduction by Vincent Tomas and including other papers. New York: Dover Publications, 1969.

——, "David Hume on Causation." In *Theories of Scientific*

Method, edited by E. H. Madden, pp. 144–152. Seattle: University of Washington Press, 1960.

———, "Francis Bacon's Philosophy of Science." In *Theories of Scientific Method,* edited by E. H. Madden, pp. 50–74. Seattle: University of Washington Press, 1960.

———, "John F. W. Herschel's Methods of Experimental Inquiry." In *Theories of Scientific Method,* edited by E. H. Madden, pp. 153–182. Seattle: University of Washington Press, 1960.

———, "John Stuart Mill's System of Logic." In *Theories of Scientific Method,* edited by E. H. Madden, pp. 218–232. Seattle: University of Washington Press, 1960.

———, "Minds, Matter and Bodies." In *Brain and Mind,* edited by J. R. Smythies. London: Routledge & Kegan Paul, 1965.

———, *Nature, Mind, and Death.* La Salle, Ill.: Open Court Publishing Co., 1951.

———, *Truth, Knowledge and Causation.* New York: Humanities Press, 1968.

———, "William Whewell's Philosophy of Scientific Discovery." In *Theories of Scientific Method,* edited by E. H. Madden, pp. 183–217. Seattle: University of Washington Press, 1960.

Dugas, René, *Mechanics in the Seventeenth Century.* Translated by F. Jacquot. New York: Central Book Co., 1958.

Duhem, Pierre, *The Aim and Structure of Physical Theory.* Translated by P. P. Wiener, with a Foreword by Louis de Broglie. Princeton, N.J.: Princeton University Press, 1954.

Durbin, Paul R., *Philosophy of Science: An Introduction.* New York: McGraw-Hill, 1968.

Eames, Elizabeth R., *Bertrand Russell's Theory of Knowledge.* New York: George Braziller, 1969.

Easton, L. D., *Hegel's First American Followers, The Ohio Hegelians:* John B. Stallo, Peter Kaufmann, Moncure Conway, and August Willich, with key writings. Athens: Ohio University Press, 1966.

Eddington, Arthur Stanley, *Space, Time and Gravitation.* An Outline of the General Relativity Theory. Cambridge: at the University Press, 1920. Reprint. New York: Harper Torchbook, 1959.

Edwards, Paul, ed., *The Encyclopedia of Philosophy.* 8 vols. New York: Macmillan and Free Press, 1967.

Ellis, Brian, "The Origin and Nature of Newton's Laws of Motion." In *Beyond the Edge of Certainty,* edited by R. G. Colodny, pp. 29–68. Englewood Cliffs, N.J.: Prentice-Hall, 1965.

Ewing, A. C., *Kant's Treatment of Causality.* London: Routledge and Kegan Paul, 1924. Reprint. Hamden, Conn.: Archon Books, 1969.

Farrington, Benjamin, *The Philosophy of Francis Bacon.* An Essay on Its Development from 1603 to 1609 with New Translations of Fundamental Texts. Liverpool: Liverpool University Press, 1964.

Feyerabend, Paul K., "How to be a Good Empiricist — A Plea for Tolerance in Matters Epistemological." In *Readings in the Philosophy of Science,* edited by B. A. Brody, pp. 319–342. Englewood Cliffs, N.J.: Prentice-Hall, 1970.

——, "Professor Bohm's Philosophy of Nature." *British Journal for Philosophy of Science* 10 (1959–60), 321–338.

Forman, Paul, "Weimar Culture, Causality, and Quantum Theory, 1918–1927: Adaptation by German Physicists and Mathematicians to a Hostile Intellectual Environment." *Historical Studies in the Physical Sciences* 3 (1971), 1–115.

Frank, Philipp, *Philosophy of Science. The Link Between Science and Philosophy.* Englewood Cliffs, N.J.: Prentice-Hall, 1957.

——, ed., *The Validation of Scientific Theories.* New York: Collier Books, 1961.

Frost, Walter, *Bacon und die Naturphilosophie.* Munich: Verlag Ernst Reinhardt, 1927.

Gabbey, Alan, "Force and Inertia in Seventeenth-Century Dynamics." *Studies in History and Philosophy of Science* 2 (1971), 1–67.

Galilei, Galileo, *Sidereus nuncius.* In *Discoveries and Opinions of Galileo,* translated by Stillman Drake, pp. 1–58. New York: Doubleday Anchor, 1957.

Gell-Mann, Murray, "The Eightfold Way: A Theory of Strong Interaction Symmetry." Report CTSL-20, March 15, 1961, Synchrotron Laboratory, California Institute of Technology, Pasadena, California.

Gillispie, Charles C., ed., *Dictionary of Scientific Biography.* 7 vols. to date. New York: Charles Scribner's Sons, 1970–.

——, *The Edge of Objectivity.* An Essay in the History of Scientific Ideas. Princeton, N.J.: Princeton University Press, 1960.

Gilson, Étienne, *Études sur le rôle de la pensée médiévale dans la formation du système cartésien.* Paris: J. Vrin, 1930.

Götlind, Erik, *Bertrand Russell's Theories of Causation.* Uppsala: Almqvist & Wiksells Boktryckeri A.B., 1952.

Goldberg, Stanley, "Poincaré's Silence and Einstein's Relativity." *British Journal for the History of Science* 5 (1970), 73–84.

Grande, Francisco, and Visscher, M. B., eds., *Claude Bernard and Experimental Medicine.* Collected papers from a Symposium commemorating the centenary of the publication of *An Introduction to the Study of Experimental Medicine* and the first English translation of Claude Bernard's *Cahier Rouge.* Cambridge, Mass.: Schenkman Publishing Co., 1967.

Greenberg, Leonard, "Necessity in Hume's Causal Theory." *Review of Metaphysics* 8 (1955), 612–623.

Grünbaum, Adolf, *Philosophical Problems of Space and Time.* New York: Alfred A. Knopf, 1963.

Gunter, Peter A. Y., ed., *Bergson and the Evolution of Physics.* Knoxville: University of Tennessee Press, 1969.

Hall, A. Rupert, *The Scientific Revolution, 1500–1800.* The Formation of the Modern Scientific Attitude. Boston: Beacon Press, 1956.

Hanson, Norwood Russell, *The Concept of the Positron*. Cambridge: at the University Press, 1963.

———, "The Copenhagen Interpretation of Quantum Theory." *American Journal of Physics* 27 (1959), 1–15.

———, *Observation and Explanation*, A Guide to Philosophy of Science. London: George Allen & Unwin, 1972.

Harré, Rom, *The Anticipation of Nature*. London: Hutchinson, 1965.

———, *An Introduction to the Logic of the Sciences*. London: Macmillan, 1960.

———, *Matter and Method*. London: Macmillan, 1964.

———, *The Method of Science*. A Course in Understanding Science, based upon the *De Magnete* of William Gilbert, and the *Vegetable Staticks* of Stephen Hales. London: Wykeham Publications Ltd., 1970.

———, *The Philosophies of Science*. An Introductory Survey. New York: Oxford University Press, 1972.

———, *The Principles of Scientific Thinking*. Chicago: University of Chicago Press, 1970.

———, *Theories and Things*. A Brief Study in Prescriptive Metaphysics. London: Sheed & Ward, 1961.

Harré, Rom, and North, J. D., "William Whewell and the History and Philosophy of Science." *British Journal for the History of Science* 4 (1969), 399–402.

Harré, Rom, and Secord, P. F., *The Explanation of Social Behaviour*. Oxford: Basil Blackwell, 1972.

Harris, Errol E., *The Foundations of Metaphysics in Science*. New York: Humanities Press, 1965.

Hawkins, D. J. B., *Causality and Implication*. London: Sheed & Ward, 1937.

Heathcote, A. W., "William Whewell's Philosophy of Science." *British Journal for the Philosophy of Science* 4 (1954), 302–314.

Heelan, Patrick A., "Elementary Particles, Philosophical Considerations." In *New Catholic Encyclopedia*, edited by W. J. McDonald. Vol. 5, pp. 261–263. New York: McGraw-Hill, 1967.

———, *Quantum Mechanics and Objectivity:* A Study of the Physical Philosophy of Werner Heisenberg. The Hague: Martinus Nijhoff, 1965.

Heisenberg, Werner, *The Physicist's Conception of Nature*. Translated by A. J. Pomerans. London: Hutchinson, 1958.

———, *Physics and Philosophy*. The Revolution in Modern Science. New York: Harper Torchbook, 1958.

Hell, Bernhard, *Ernst Machs Philosophie:* eine erkenntniskritische Studie über Wirklichkeit und Wert. Stuttgart: Fr. Fommanns Verlag (E. Hauff), 1907.

Herschel, John F. W., *Essays from the Edinburgh and Quarterly Reviews*, with Addresses and Other Pieces. London: Longman et al., 1857.

——, *Outlines of Astronomy*. 11th ed. London: Longmans, Green, & Co., 1871.

——, *Preliminary Discourse on the Study of Natural Philosophy*. London: Longman, Rees, etc., 1830. The Cabinet Cyclopedia, 1832. Reprinted with an Introduction by M. F. Partridge, pp. vii–lvi. New York: Johnson Reprint Corporation, 1966.

——, *A Treatise on Astronomy*. The Cabinet Cyclopedia. London: Longmans, Rees, etc., 1833.

Hesse, Mary B., *Models and Analogies in Science*. Notre Dame, Ind.: University of Notre Dame Press, 1966.

——, "Models and Analogies in Science." In *Encyclopedia of Philosophy*, edited by Paul Edwards. Vol. 5, pp. 354–359. New York: Macmillan and Free Press, 1967.

Hobbes, Thomas, *English Works*. 11 vols. London: John Bohn, 1839.

Holton, Gerald, *Introduction to Concepts and Theories in Physical Science*. Cambridge, Mass.: Addison-Wesley, 1952.

——, "On the Thematic Analysis of Science: The Case of Poincaré and Relativity." *Mélanges Alexandre Koyré*. 2 vols. Paris: Hermann, 1964.

——, *Thematic Origins of Scientific Thought: Kepler to Einstein*. Cambridge, Mass.: Harvard University Press, 1973; reprinted from *The Graduate Journal*, Vol. 9, Supplement, 1973.

Hooke, Robert, *Micrographia*, or Some Physiological Descriptions of Minute Bodies Made by Magnifying Glasses with Observations and Inquiries thereupon [1665]. Reprint. New York: Dover Publications, 1961.

Hoppe, Hansgeorg, *Kants Theorie der Physik*. Eine Untersuchung über das Opus postumum von Kant. Frankfurt am Main: Vittorio Klostermann, 1969.

Hoskin, M. A., *William Herschel and the Construction of the Heavens*. London: Oldbourne Press, 1963.

——, *William Herschel: Pioneer of Sidereal Astronomy*. London: Sheed & Ward, 1959.

Hujer, K., "Galileo's Trial in the Epistemology of Einsteinian Physics." *Atti del Symposium Internazionale di Storia, Metodologia, Logica e Filosofia della Scienza:* "Galileo nella Storia e nella Filosofia della Scienza," pp. 289–295. Florence: G. Barbèra Editore, 1967.

Humber, J. H., and Madden, E. H., "Natural Necessity." *The New Scholasticism* 47 (1973), pp. 214–227.

——, "Nonlogical Necessity and C. J. Ducasse." *Ratio* 13 (1971), 119–138.

Hume, David, *An Enquiry Concerning Human Understanding*. Great Books of the Western World. Vol. 35. Chicago: Encyclopaedia Britannica, 1952.

——, *A Treatise of Human Nature*. Everyman's Library Edition, with an Introduction by A. D. Lindsay. 2 vols. New York: E. P. Dutton & Co., 1911.

Huxley, Julian, "Evolution, Cultural and Biological." In *Knowledge, Morality, and Destiny*, pp. 56–84. New York: Mentor Books, 1957.

Iltis, Carolyn, "Leibniz and the *Vis Viva* Controversy." *Isis* 62 (1971), 21–35.

Jammer, Max, *Concepts of Force*. A Study in the Foundations of Dynamics. Cambridge, Mass.: Harvard University Press, 1957. Rev. ed. New York: Harper Torchbook, 1962.

——, *Concepts of Space*. The History of Theories of Space in Physics. Foreword by Albert Einstein. 2d ed. Cambridge, Mass.: Harvard University Press, 1969.

——, *The Conceptual Development of Quantum Mechanics*. New York: McGraw-Hill, 1966.

Jeffreys, M. V. C., *John Locke: Prophet of Common Sense*. London: Methuen & Co., Ltd., 1967.

Jevons, William Stanley, *Elementary Lessons in Logic: Deductive and Inductive*. With copious questions and examples, and a vocabulary of technical terms, new ed. London & New York: Macmillan, 1898.

——, *The Principles of Science: A Treatise on Logic and Scientific Method*, 2d ed. London: 1877. Reprinted with a new introduction by Ernest Nagel. New York: Dover Publications, 1958.

Jones, Tom B., *The Figure of the Earth*. Lawrence, Kans.: Coronado Press, 1967.

Kant, Immanuel, *Immanuel Kant's Critique of Pure Reason*. Translated by N. K. Smith. London: Macmillan & Co., 1929. Reprint. New York: St. Martin's Press, 1965.

——, *Kant's Cosmogony*, as in His Essay on the Retardation of the Rotation of the Earth and His Natural History and Theory of the Heavens. Translated by W. Hastie. Revised and edited with Introduction and Appendix by Willy Ley. New York: Greenwood Publishing Co., 1968.

——, *Kant's Inaugural Dissertation and Early Writings on Space*. Translated by John Handyside. Chicago: Open Court, 1929.

——, *Kants Opus postumum*, Kant-Studien Nr. 50. Edited by Erich Adickes. Berlin: Reuther & Reichard, 1920.

——, *Kant's Prolegomena and Metaphysical Foundations of Natural Science*. Translated by E. B. Bax. London: George Bell & Sons, 1883.

——, *Metaphysical Foundations of Natural Science*. Translated with Introduction and essay by James Ellington. Indianapolis: Bobbs-Merrill, 1970.

——, *Universal Natural History and Theory of the Heavens*. Translated by W. Hastie, with a new Introduction by M. K.

Munitz. Ann Arbor: University of Michigan Press, 1969.

Kaplan, Abraham, "Noncausal Explanation." In *Cause and Effect*, edited by Daniel Lerner, pp. 145–155. New York: The Free Press, 1965.

Keeling, S. V., *Descartes*. 2d ed. Oxford: Oxford University Press, 1968.

Kneale, William Calvert, *Probability and Induction* [1949]. Reprinted from corrected sheets of the first edition. Oxford: Clarendon Press, 1952.

Kockelmans, Joseph J., *Phenomenology and Physical Science*. Pittsburgh: Duquesne University Press, 1966.

———, ed., *Philosophy of Science. The Historical Background*. New York: The Free Press, 1968.

Kordig, Carl R., "The Comparability of Scientific Theories." *Philosophy of Science* 38 (1971), 467–485.

———, *The Justification of Scientific Change*. Dordrecht-Holland: D. Reidel Publishing Co., 1971.

Koyré, Alexandre, *Études galiléennes*. 3 vols. Paris: Hermann, 1939.

———, *From the Closed World to the Infinite Universe*. Baltimore: Johns Hopkins Press, 1957.

———, *Newtonian Studies*. Cambridge, Mass.: Harvard University Press, 1965.

Krimerman, Leonard I., ed., *The Nature and Scope of Social Science: A Critical Anthology*. New York: Appleton-Century-Crofts, 1969.

Kuhn, Thomas S., *The Structure of Scientific Revolutions*. 1962. 2d enl. ed. Chicago: University of Chicago Press, 1970.

Lakatos, Imre, and Musgrave, Alan, eds., *Criticism and the Growth of Knowledge*. Cambridge: at the University Press, 1970.

Larsen, Robert E., "The Aristotelianism of Bacon's *Novum Organum*." *Journal of the History of Ideas* 23 (1962), 435–450.

Laudan, L. L., "The Nature and Sources of Locke's Views on Hypotheses." *Journal of the History of Ideas* 38 (1967), 211–223.

———, "Theories of Scientific Method from Plato to Mach: A Bibliographical Review." *History of Science* 7 (1968), 1–63.

———, "Thomas Reid and the Newtonian Turn of British Methodological Thought." In *The Methodological Heritage of Newton*, edited by R. E. Butts and J. W. Davis, pp. 103–131. Toronto: University of Toronto Press, 1970.

———, "Towards a Reassessment of Comte's 'Méthode Positive.'" *Philosophy of Science* 38 (1971), 35–53.

———, "The *Vis viva* Controversy, a Post-Mortem." *Isis* 59 (1968), 131–143.

———, "William Whewell on the Concilience of Inductions." *The Monist* 55 (1971), 368–391.

Leibniz, Gottfried Wilhelm, *Philosophical Papers and Letters*. A selection translated and edited with an Introduction by

Leroy E. Loemker. 2 vols. Continuous pagination. Chicago: University of Chicago Press, 1956.

——, *The Leibniz-Clarke Correspondence*, together with extracts from Newton's *Principia* and *Opticks*. Edited with Introduction and Notes by H. G. Alexander. New York: Philosophical Library, 1956.

Lenz, John W., "Hume's Defense of Causal Inference." *Journal of the History of Ideas* 19 (1958), 559–567.

Lenzen, Victor F., *Causality in Natural Science*. Springfield, Ill.: Charles C. Thomas, 1954.

Lerner, Daniel, ed., *Cause and Effect*. The Hayden Colloquium on Scientific Method and Concept. New York: The Free Press, 1965.

——, ed., *Quantity and Quality*. The Hayden Colloquium on Scientific Method and Concept. New York: The Free Press, 1961.

Locke, John, *An Essay Concerning Human Understanding*. Edited by A. C. Fraser. Great Books of the Western World. Vol. 35. Chicago: Encyclopaedia Britannica, 1952.

Lonergan, Bernard, *Insight:* A Study of Human Understanding. New York: Philosophical Library, 1957.

Losee, John, *A Historical Introduction to the Philosophy of Science*. New York: Oxford University Press, 1972.

Lowinger, Armand, *The Methodology of Pierre Duhem*. New York: Columbia University Press, 1941.

Luxembourg, Lilo K., *Francis Bacon and Denis Diderot, Philosophers of Science*. Copenhagen: Munksgaard, 1967.

McDonald, W. J., ed., *New Catholic Encyclopedia*. 15 vols. New York: McGraw-Hill, 1967.

Mach, Ernst, *The Science of Mechanics*. A Critical and Historical Account of its Development. 6th ed. Translated by T. J. McCormack, new Introduction by Karl Menger, with revisions through the 9th German ed. La Salle, Ill.: The Open Court Publishing Co., 1960.

MacKinnon, Edward A., ed., *The Problem of Scientific Realism*. New York: Appleton-Century-Crofts, 1972.

McMullin, Ernan, "Matter As a Principle." In *The Concept of Matter*, edited by E. McMullin, pp. 169–208. Notre Dame, Ind.: University of Notre Dame Press, 1963.

McShane, Philip, *Randomness, Statistics and Emergence*. Notre Dame, Ind.: University of Notre Dame Press, 1970.

Madden, E. H., "Hume and the Fiery Furnace." *Philosophy of Science* 38 (1971), 64–78.

——, Review of Ernest Nagel's The Structure of Science. *Philosophy of Science* 30 (1963), 64–70.

——. *The Structure of Scientific Thought*. An Introduction to Philosophy of Science. Boston: Houghton Mifflin Co., 1960.

———, ed., *Theories of Scientific Method:* The Renaissance Through the Nineteenth Century. Seattle: University of Washington Press, 1960.

———, "A Third View of Causality." *The Review of Metaphysics* 23 (1969), 67–84.

———, "Thomas Hobbes and the Rationalist Ideal." In *Theories of Scientific Method*, edited by E. H. Madden, pp. 104–118. Seattle: University of Washington Press, 1960.

———, "W. S. Jevons on Induction and Probability." In *Theories of Scientific Method*, edited by E. H. Madden, pp. 233–247. Seattle: University of Washington Press, 1960.

Madden, E. H., and Hare, P. H., "C. J. Ducasse on Human Agency." *The Personalist* 52 (1971), 618–629.

———, "The Powers That Be." *Dialogue* 10 (1971), 12–31.

Madden, E. H., and Sachs, Mendel, "Parmenidean Particulars and Vanishing Elements." *Studies in History and Philosophy of Science* 3 (1972), 151–166.

Mahaffy, J. P., *Descartes*. Philadelphia: J. B. Lippincott & Co., 1881.

Mandelbaum, Maurice H., *Philosophy, Science and Sense Perception*. Historical and Critical Studies. Baltimore: Johns Hopkins Press, 1964.

Marcucci, Silvestro, "William Whewell: Kantianism or Platonism." *Physis* 12 (1970), 69–72.

Margenau, Henry, "Meaning and Scientific Status of Causality." *Philosophy of Science* 1 (1934), 133–148.

Markus, R. I., "Method and Metaphysics: The Origins of Some Cartesian Presuppositions in the Philosophy of the Renaissance." *Dominican Studies* 2 (1949), 356–384.

Martin, Gottfried, *Kant's Metaphysics and Theory of Science*. Translated by P. G. Lucas. Manchester: Manchester University Press, 1955. Reprint. New York: Barnes & Noble, 1961.

———, *Leibniz: Logic and Metaphysics*. Translated by K. J. Northcott and P. G. Lucas. Manchester: University Press, 1964.

Maxwell, Grover, "The Ontological Status of Theoretical Entities." *Minnesota Studies in the Philosophy of Science*, vol. 3. Edited by Herbert Feigl and Grover Maxwell, pp. 3–27. Minneapolis: University of Minnesota Press, 1962.

Mayr, Ernst, "Cause and Effect in Biology." In *Cause and Effect*, edited by Daniel Lerner, pp. 33–50. New York: The Free Press, 1965.

———, "Footnotes on the Philosophy of Biology." *Philosophy of Science* 36 (1969), 197–202.

Medawar, Peter Brian, *Induction and Intuition in Scientific Thought*. Jayne Lectures for 1968. Philadelphia: American Philosophical Society, 1969.

Merz, J. T., *Leibniz*. London: William Blackwood & Sons, 1914.

Meyerson, Émile, *Identity and Reality*. Translated by Kate Loewenberg. New York: Macmillan Co., 1930.

Michotte, Albert Édouard, *The Perception of Causality*. Translated by T. and E. Miles. London: Methuen & Co., Ltd., 1963.

Mill, John Stuart, *Auguste Comte and Positivism*. Reprinted from the Westminster Review. London: N. Trübner & Co., 1865. Reprint. Ann Arbor: University of Michigan Press, 1961.

———, *An Examination of Sir William Hamilton's Philosophy:* and of the Principal Philosophical Questions Discussed in His Writings. 2 vols. Boston: William V. Spencer, 1865.

———, *A System of Logic,* Ratiocinative and Inductive. Being a connected view of the principles of evidence and the methods of scientific investigation. 8th ed. London: Longmans [1872]. New impression, 1959.

———, *John Stuart Mill's Philosophy of Scientific Method*. Edited with an Introduction by Ernest Nagel. New York: Hafner Publishing Co., 1950.

Mises, Richard von, *Positivism*, A Study in Human Understanding. Cambridge, Mass.: Harvard University Press, 1951.

Moked, Gabriel, "A Note on Berkeley's Corpuscularian Theories in *Siris*." *Studies in History and Philosophy of Science* 2 (1971), 257–271.

Morris, John M., "Descartes and Probable Knowledge." *Journal for the History of Philosophy* 8 (1970), 303–312.

Nagel, Ernest, *The Structure of Science*. Problems in the Logic of Scientific Explanation. New York: Harcourt, Brace and World, 1961.

———, "Types of Causal Explanation in Science." In *Cause and Effect,* edited by Daniel Lerner, pp. 11–32. New York: The Free Press, 1965.

Neurath, Otto et al., *Foundations of the Unity of Science*. 2 vols. Chicago: University of Chicago Press, 1970.

Newton, Isaac, *Mathematical Principles of Natural Philosophy*. Translated by A. Motte. Revised and edited by F. Cajori. Berkeley: University of California Press, 1934.

———, *Papers and Letters on Natural Philosophy*. Edited by I. Bernard Cohen. Cambridge, Mass.: Harvard University Press, 1958.

North, J. D., *The Measure of the Universe*. A History of Modern Cosmology. Oxford: Clarendon Press, 1965.

O'Connor, D. J., *John Locke*. London: Penguin Books, 1952. Reprint. New York: Dover Publications, 1967.

Oldroyd, D. R., "Robert Hooke's Methodology of Science as Exemplified in His 'Discourse of Earthquakes.'" *British Journal for the History of Science* 6 (1972), 109–130.

Osler, Margaret J., "John Locke and the Changing Ideal of Scientific Knowledge." *Journal of the History of Ideas* 31 (1970), 3–16.

Pacchi, Arrigo, *Convenzione e Ipotesi nella formazione della filosofia naturale di Thomas Hobbes.* Florence: La Nuova Italia Editrice, 1965.

Palter, Robert M., *Whitehead's Philosophy of Science.* Chicago: University of Chicago Press, 1960.

Parsons, Talcott, "Cause and Effect in Sociology." In *Cause and Effect,* edited by Daniel Lerner, pp. 51–73. New York: The Free Press, 1965.

Passmore, John, *A Hundred Years of Philosophy.* Rev. ed. New York: Basic Books, 1967.

Plaass, Peter, *Kants Theorie der Naturwissenschaft.* Eine Untersuchung zur Vorrede von Kants "Metaphysische Anfangsgründen der Naturwissenschaft." Göttingen: Vandenhoeck & Ruprecht, 1965.

Poincaré, Henri, *The Foundations of Science:* Science and Hypothesis, The Value of Science, Science and Method. . . . Translated by G. B. Halsted, with an Introduction by Josiah Royce. New York: The Science Press, 1921.

Polanyi, Michael, *Personal Knowledge:* Towards a Post-Critical Philosophy. Chicago: University of Chicago Press, 1958.

Popper, Karl R., *Conjectures and Refutations:* The Growth of Scientific Knowledge. New York: Basic Books, 1962.

———, *The Logic of Scientific Discovery.* New York: Basic Books, 1959.

———, "Normal Science and Its Dangers." In *Criticism and the Growth of Knowledge,* edited by Imre Lakatos and Alan Musgrave, pp. 51–58. Cambridge: at the University Press, 1970.

Priestley, F. E. L., "The Clarke-Leibniz Controversy." In *The Methodological Heritage of Newton,* edited by R. E. Butts and J. W. Davis, pp. 34–56. Toronto: University of Toronto Press, 1970.

Régis, L. M., "Analyse et synthèse dans l'oeuvre de saint Thomas." In *Studia Mediaevalia in honorem A. R. P. Martin,* pp. 303–330. Bruges: St. Catherine Press, 1948.

———, *Epistemology.* Translated by I. C. Byrne. New York: Macmillan & Co., 1959.

Reichenbach, Hans, *Modern Philosophy of Science.* Selected essays. Translated and edited by Maria Reichenbach, Foreword by Rudolf Carnap. New York: Humanities Press, 1959.

———, *Philosophic Foundations of Quantum Mechanics.* Berkeley: University of California Press, 1944.

Reid, Thomas, *The Works of Thomas Reid, D.D.,* now fully collected, with selections from his unpublished letters, by Sir William Hamilton. 6th ed. 2 vols. Edinburgh and London: Longmans, 1863.

Rescher, Nicholas, *The Philosophy of Leibniz*. Englewood Cliffs, N.J.: Prentice-Hall, Inc., 1967.

——, *Scientific Explanation*. New York: The Free Press, 1970.

Rosenfeld, Leon, "Niels Bohr's Contribution to Epistemology." *Physics Today* 16 (Oct. 1963), 47–54.

Rossi, Paolo, *Francis Bacon: From Magic to Science*. Translated by Sacha Rabinovitch. Chicago: University of Chicago Press, 1968.

Rougier, Louis, *La Philosophie géométrique de Henri Poincaré*. Paris: F. Alcan, 1920.

Ruddick, Chester T., "Hume on Scientific Law." *Philosophy of Science* 16 (1949), 89–93.

Russell, Bertrand, *Analysis of Matter*. London: 1927. Reprint. New York: Dover Publications [1954].

——, *Mysticism and Logic*, and Other Essays. London: G. Allen & Unwin, 1917.

——, *Our Knowledge of the External World*. London: 1914. Reprint. New York: W. W. Norton & Co., 1929.

——, *The Problems of Philosophy*. London: 1912. Reprint. New York: Oxford University Press, 1959.

Sabra, A. I., *Theories of Light from Descartes to Newton*. New York: American Elsevier Co., 1967.

Sarton, George, "Auguste Comte, Historian of Science. With a Short Digression on Clotilde de Vaux and Harriet Taylor." *Osiris* 10 (1952), 328–357.

Schlick, Moritz, *Gesammelte Aufsätze, 1926–1936*. Vienna: Gerold, 1938. Reprint. Hildesheim: G. Olms, 1969.

——, "Causality in Contemporary Physics." In *Physical Reality*, edited by Stephen Toulmin, pp. 83–121. New York: Harper & Row, 1970.

——, *Philosophy of Nature*. Translated by A. von Zeppelin. New York: Philosophical Library, 1949.

——, *Space and Time in Contemporary Physics*, An Introduction to the Theory of Relativity and Gravitation. Translated by Henry L. Brose. New York: Oxford University Press, 1920.

Schofield, R. E., *Mechanism and Materialism*. British Natural Philosophy in An Age of Reason. Princeton, N.J.: Princeton University Press, 1970.

Scott, J. F., *The Scientific Work of René Descartes (1596–1650)*. London: Taylor & Francis, Ltd., 1952.

Scriven, Michael, "Causes, Connections and Conditions in History," *Philosophical Analysis and History*, ed. W. H. Dray. New York: Harper & Row, 1966, pp. 238–264.

Shapere, Dudley, *Philosophical Problems of Natural Science*. New York: Macmillan, 1965.

——, "The Structure of Scientific Revolutions." *Philosophical Review* 73 (1964), 383–394.

Smart, J. J. C., *Philosophy and Scientific Realism*. New York: Humanities Press, 1963.
——, Review of Ernest Nagel, *The Structure of Science*. *Journal of Philosophy* 59 (1962), 216–223.
Smith, Norman Kemp, *The Philosophy of David Hume*. A Critical Study of Its Origins and Central Doctrines. London: Macmillan, 1941.
——, *Studies in the Cartesian Philosophy* [1902]. Reprint. New York: Russell & Russell, Inc., 1962.
Smith, Roger, "Alfred Russel Wallace: Philosophy of Nature and Man." *British Journal for the History of Science* 6 (1972), 177–199.
Smith, Vincent Edward, *The General Science of Nature*. Milwaukee: Bruce Publishing Co., 1958.
Smythies, J. R., ed., *Brain and Mind*. London: Routledge and Kegan Paul, 1965.
Spector, Marshall, *Methodological Foundations of Relativistic Mechanics*. Notre Dame, Ind.: University of Notre Dame Press, 1972.
——, "Models and Theories." In *Readings in the Philosophy of Science*, edited by B. A. Brody, pp. 276–293. Englewood Cliffs, N.J.: Prentice-Hall, 1970.
Stallo, J. B., *The Concepts and Theories of Modern Physics*. Edited by P. W. Bridgman. Cambridge, Mass.: Harvard University Press, 1960.
Strong, Edward W., *Procedures and Metaphysics:* A Study in the Philosophy of Mathematical-Physical Science in the 16th and 17th Centuries. Berkeley: University of California Press, 1936.
——, "William Whewell and John Stuart Mill: Their Controversy About Scientific Knowledge." *Journal of the History of Ideas* 16 (1955), 209–231.
Taliaferro, Robert Catesby, *The Concept of Matter in Descartes and Leibniz*. Notre Dame, Ind.: University of Notre Dame Press, 1964.
Taylor, Charles, *The Explanation of Behaviour*. London: Routledge and Kegan Paul, 1964.
——, "Interpretation and the Sciences of Man." *The Review of Metaphysics* 25 (1971), 3–51.
Taylor, Richard, *Action and Purpose*. Englewood Cliffs, N.J.: Prentice-Hall, Inc., 1966.
——, "Causation." In *Encyclopedia of Philosophy*, edited by Paul Edwards. Vol. 2, pp. 56–66. New York: Macmillan and Free Press, 1967.
Toulmin, Stephen, *Foresight and Understanding*. Bloomington, Ind.: Indiana University Press, 1961.
——, *Human Understanding*. Vol. I. Oxford: Clarendon Press, 1972.

——, *The Philosophy of Science: An Introduction.* London: Hutchinson, 1953.

——, ed., *Physical Reality.* Philosophical Essays on Twentieth-Century Physics. New York: Harper & Row, 1970.

Van Leeuwen, H. G., *The Problem of Certainty in English Thought 1630–1690.* The Hague: Martinus Nijhoff, 1963.

Vrooman, Jack R., *René Descartes, A Biography.* New York: Putnam, 1970.

Waddington, C. H., "Evolutionary Adaptation." In *The Evolution of Life,* pp. 381–402. *Evolution After Darwin,* Vol. I. Edited by Sol Tax. Chicago: University of Chicago Press, 1960.

Waismann, Friedrich, "The Decline and Fall of Causality." In *Turning Points in Physics,* edited by A. C. Crombie, pp. 84–154. Amsterdam: North-Holland Publishing Co., 1959. Reprinted in Waismann's *How I See Philosophy,* pp. 208–256. London: Macmillan, 1968.

——, *How I See Philosophy.* Edited by R. Harré. London: Macmillan, 1968.

——, *The Principles of Linguistic Philosophy.* Edited by R. Harré, London: Macmillan, 1965.

Wallace, William A., "The Cosmological Argument: A Reappraisal." *Proceedings of the American Catholic Philosophical Association* 46 (1972), 43–57.

——, *Einstein, Galileo and Aquinas:* Three Views of Scientific Method. Compact Studies. Washington: The Thomist Press, 1963.

——, "Elementarity and Reality in Particle Physics." *Boston Studies in the Philosophy of Science.* Vol. 3. Edited by R. S. Cohen and M. W. Wartofsky, pp. 236–263. Dordrecht: D. Reidel Publishing Co., 1968.

——, "The Measurement and Definition of Sensible Qualities." *The New Scholasticism* 39 (1965), 1–25.

——, "The Reality of Elementary Particles." *Proceedings of the American Catholic Philosophical Association* 38 (1964), 154–166.

——, "St. Thomas and the Pull of Gravity." The McAuley Lectures 1963. *Science and the Liberal Concept,* pp. 143–165. West Hartford, Conn.: St. Joseph College, 1964.

——, "Toward a Definition of the Philosophy of Science." *Mélanges à la mémoire de Charles De Koninck,* pp. 465–485. Quebec: Les Presses de l'Université Laval, 1968.

Walsh, Harold T., "Whewell and Mill on Induction." *Philosophy of Science* 29 (1962), 279–284.

——, "Whewell on Necessity." *Philosophy of Science* 29 (1962), 139–145.

Wartofsky, Marx W., *Conceptual Foundations of Scientific Thought:* An Introduction to the Philosophy of Science. New York: Macmillan, 1968.

Weiss, Paul A., *Life, Order and Understanding:* A Theme in Three Variations. The Graduate Journal. Austin: University of Texas Press, 1970.
———, *Within the Gates of Science and Beyond:* Science and Its Cultural Commitments. New York: Hafner Publishing Co., 1971.
Weisskopf, V. F., "Quality and Quantity in Quantum Physics." In *Quantity and Quality,* edited by Daniel Lerner, pp. 53–67. New York: The Free Press, 1961.
Westfall, Richard S., *The Construction of Modern Science: Mechanisms and Mechanics.* New York: John Wiley & Sons, 1971.
———, *Force in Newton's Physics.* The Science of Dynamics in the Seventeenth Century. New York: American Elsevier Co., 1971.
Whewell, William, "Comte and Positivism." *Macmillan's Magazine* 13 (1866), 353–362.
———, *History of the Inductive Sciences,* From the Earliest to the Present Time. 2d ed. 3 vols. London: John W. Parker, 1847.
———, *History of Scientific Ideas.* 3d ed. 2 vols. London: John W. Parker, 1858.
———, *Novum Organum Renovatum.* Being the Second Part of the Philosophy of the Inductive Sciences. The Third Edition, with large additions. London: John W. Parker, 1858.
———, *On the Philosophy of Discovery.* Chapters Historical and Critical. Including the completion of the third edition of the Philosophy of the Inductive Sciences. London: John W. Parker, 1860.
———, *The Philosophy of the Inductive Sciences,* Founded Upon Their History. 2d ed. 2 vols. London: John W. Parker, 1847. Reprinted, with an Introduction by John Herivel. New York: Johnson Reprint Corporation, 1967.
———, *William Whewell's Theory of Scientific Method.* Edited with an Introduction by R. E. Butts. Pittsburgh: University of Pittsburgh Press, 1968.
White, P. J., "Materialism and the Concept of Motion in Locke's Theory of Sense-Idea Causation." *Studies in History and Philosophy of Science* 2 (1971), 97–134.
Whitehead, Alfred North, *The Concept of Nature.* Cambridge: at the University Press, 1920. Reprint. Ann Arbor: University of Michigan Press, 1957.
———, *Process and Reality.* 1929. Reprint. New York: The Free Press, 1969.
———, *Science and the Modern World.* 1925. Reprint. New York: The Free Press, 1967.
———, *Symbolism: Its Meaning and Effect.* Barbour-Page Lecture, University of Virginia, 1927. New York: The Macmillan Co., 1927.
Whittaker, Edmund T., A *History of the Theories of Aether and*

Electricity. Rev. and enl. ed. 2 vols. London: Thomas Nelson, 1951.

Wiener, Philip P., ed., *Dictionary of the History of Ideas.* Studies of Selected Pivotal Ideas. 4 vols. New York: Charles Scribner's Sons, 1973.

Wilkie, J. S., "The Problem of the Temporal Relation of Cause and Effect." *British Journal for the Philosophy of Science* 1 (1950), 211–229.

Woolf, Harry, ed., *Science As a Cultural Force.* Baltimore: Johns Hopkins Press, 1964.

Wright, G. H. von, *Explanation and Understanding.* Ithaca: Cornell University Press, 1971.

Yost, R. M., Jr., "Locke's Rejection of Hypotheses About Sub-Microscopic Events." *Journal of the History of Ideas* 12 (1951), 111–130.

Index

399

analysis, 10; causal, 154–160; factorial vs. reductive, 317, 318, 326; infinite, 52; linguistic, 228

analysis and synthesis, 8, 9, 18, 53; *see also* resolution and composition

Anderson, F. H., 339, 379

Anscombe, G. E. M., 330, 378, 379, 383

antecedence, 196; principle of, 193, 194

antecedent: invariable, 107, 167; necessary, 167; ontological, 326

appearance(s), 52, 67, 68; saving the, 112; *see also* phenomena

Aquinas, Thomas (1225?–1274), 97, 115, 246, 247, 251, 293, 367, 372

Aristotelianism, 233, 340, 354

Aristotelian(s), 17–19, 25, 51, 62, 77, 127, 151, 153, 155, 159, 206, 209, 249, 257, 294, 308, 315, 342

Aristotle (384–322 B.C.), v, 154, 155, 167, 240, 248, 325, 330, 361, 375; and classical philosophers, 5, 17, 20, 33, 46; and contemporary science, 274, 279, 292, 305, 311, 315, 316; and methodologists of classical science, 76–78, 82, 127; and "why" questions, 209, 210, 213, 216; *Posterior Analytics*, v, 46, 158, 243, 244, 271, 325, 367

Aronson, J., 334, 379

Ashley, B. M., 377, 379

astronomy, 96, 114, 115, 118, 125, 143, 264; physical, 256; sidereal, 96, 113, 117

atheism, 98, 142

atom, 125, 219, 228, 252, 270, 302, 304, 323, 324, 342, 354; Bohr, 262, 275; reality of the, 168, 169

attraction, 255; Berkeley on, 32, 35, 36; Comte on, 89, 94, 95, 122; force of, 151; gravitational, 59, 289–290

attribute, 269; conventional, 304; phenomenal, 253; qualitative, 253; *see also* property

Avenarius, R., 355

axiom, 78, 123, 131, 174

Ayala, F., 312–315, 317, 376, 379

Babbage, Charles (1792–1871), 96

Bacon, Francis (1561–1626), 19, 77–86, 158, 246, 335, 339, 347, 379; and classical science, 251, 254, 256; and methodologists of classical science, 88, 89, 92, 96, 97, 107, 114, 118, 122, 129, 145; *Novum organum*, 80, 81, 84, 85, 254

Balazs, N. L., 371, 380

Bax, E. B., 338, 388

Becker, C., 280

becoming, 218; *see also* process

behavior, human, 318–322

belief, 173, 180, 196

Bellarmine, Robert (1542–1621), 293

Benjamin, A. C., 359, 380

Bentley, Richard (1662–1742), 371

Bergson, Henri (1859–1941), 218, 222, 362

Berkeley, George (1685–1753), 30–38, 157, 255, 290, 332, 333, 336, 380; and classical philosophers, 4, 22, 29, 41, 44, 46, 49, 51, 59, 60; *De motu*, 30–34, 37; *Principles of Human Knowledge*, 30, 37; *Siris*, 30, 34

Bernard, Claude (1813–1878), 77, 141–154, 158, 159, 245, 246, 308, 312, 352–354, 380; *Introduction to the Study of*

Experimental Medicine, 142,
150; *Le Cahier rouge,* 142,
150, 151
Bernstein, J., 358
Beth, E. W., 380
biology, 141, 261, 264, 266, 279,
314; evolutionary, 310, 316;
mathematical, 317; molecular, 317; philosophy of, 309
bird(s), 272, 273, 369; causes
of migration of, 310
Blackwell, R. J., 369, 380
Blake, R. M., 329, 380
Blalock, H., 318–319, 380;
*Causal Inferences in Nonex-
perimental Research,* 318
Blanché, R., 363
blood, 246; circulation of, 155,
261, 263, 323–325
body, 18, 23, 24, 26, 42, 49, 62,
128, 251
Bohm, D., 229–230, 269, 287,
307, 308, 364, 380; *Cau-
sality and Chance in Modern
Physics,* 229
Bohr, Niels (1885–1962), 190–
192, 213, 281, 305, 307, 359,
380
Boltzmann, Ludwig (1844–
1906), 169, 182
Born, Max (1882–1970), 190,
192–196, 213, 214, 281, 308,
359, 360, 381; *Natural Philosophy of Cause and Chance,*
193
Boscovich, Roger (1711–1787),
303, 374, 381; *A Theory of
Natural Philosophy,* 303
Boutroux, Émile (1845–1921),
173, 222
Bowman, P. A., vii
Boyle, Robert (1627–1691), 55;
law of, 201, 275, 370
Bradley, J., 355, 381
Braithwaite, R. B., 203–206,
213, 246, 272, 361, 381;
Scientific Explanation, 203
Brandt, F., 330, 331, 381

Bridges, J. H., 342, 383
Bridgewater Treatises, 98
Bridgman, Percy W. (1882–
1961), 169, 187–190, 191,
359, 381, 395; *The Logic of
Modern Physics,* 190
Bright, L., 363, 381
British Association for the Ad-
vancement of Science, 97, 118
Brodie, Benjamin C., Jr. (1817–
1880), 355
Brody, B. A., 360, 361, 367,
369, 379, 381, 385
Broglie, Louis de (1875–1960),
225, 229, 357, 384
Brose, H. L., 358, 394
Brougham, Henry (1778–
1868), 335
Brouwer, L. E. J. (1881–1966),
281
Brown, Thomas (1778–1820),
344
Brown, T. M., 327
Buchdahl, G., 327–329, 331–
334, 336, 337, 339, 351, 381
Bunge, M., 230–233, 245, 337,
364, 367, 368, 370, 382;
Causality, 230
Buridan, Jean (1295?–1358?),
247
Burtt, E. A., 368, 382
Butts, R. E., 334, 347–349, 382,
389, 397
Byrne, I. C., 338, 393

Cajori, F., 392
Cambridge, 118
Campbell, Norman Robert
(1880–1949), 198–202, 262,
360, 382
Cannon, W. F., 343, 344, 346,
382
Cantor, G. N., 335, 382
capacity, 235, 236; *see also*
power
Čapek, M., 362, 382
Carnap, Rudolf (1891–1970),
185, 202, 358, 360, 382, 393

Carnot, Sadi (1796–1832), 224
Cassini, Jean-Dominique (1625–
1712), 325, 346
category: Kantian, 67, 69, 71,
74; ultimate, 193, 197
Catholic(s), 87, 180, 207, 319
causa, 245, 316
causal: anomaly, 185–186;
chain, 204; efficacy, 28, 29,
37, 60, 164, 173, 197, 219–
221, 230, 233; explanation,
varieties of, 238–276; future,
285; nexus, 38, 42; past, 286
causality, 4, 14, 29, 34, 35, 44,
45, 47, 62, 70, 164, 199, 200,
213, 225, 309; concept of, 3,
21, 22, 277, 278; decline and
fall of, vi, 163, 165–197;
defense of, 282; deterministic, 16, 195; empirical, 74;
law of, 181, 215; levels of,
74; mechanical, 20; meta-
physical, 74; perception of,
47, 110, 221, 226; principle
of, 24, 61, 67, 68, 157, 168,
182, 183, 215, 216, 223, 224;
strong or maximal meaning
of, 159, 164; trancendental,
74; weak or minimal meaning
of, 159, 164, 287, 326
causation, 4, 38, 40–44, 47, 51,
101, 102, 130, 159, 164, 181,
197, 217, 226, 231, 287, 308,
319, 326; axioms of, 123;
dynamic, 218; historical, 125;
law of, 131, 135, 139; problem of, 233, 234
cause, 244, 245, 247, 277, 278;
in classical philosophy, 5, 11,
12, 16, 18, 21, 23, 40, 41,
46–48, 60; in methodologists
of classical science, 78, 82,
84, 89, 100, 103, 104, 107,
120, 122, 134, 139, 155; in
recent philosophy, 181, 212,
222, 223, 225, 227; active,
14, 34, 37; assumed, 136;

common, 103, 104; concealed,
43; concurrent, 109; con-
trary, 43; corporeal, 34;
counteracting, 108, 109; determinate, 147; determining,
149; ecological, 310; effective, 149; entire, 20, 157; external, 63, 73, 74, 90, 107;
extraneous disturbing, 104;
extrinsic physiological, 310;
false, 19, 117; first, 8, 10, 15,
21, 46, 88, 93, 94, 125, 126,
150, 157, 168; general, 15,
16, 43, 55; genetic, 310; historical, 203; hypothetical, 10,
112, 124; idea of, 123;
imagined, 136; immediate,
143, 146, 148, 150, 159;
improper sense of, 48; incorporeal, 37; internal, 167, 279;
intrinsic physiological, 310;
known, 17, 109, 123, 136;
mechanical, 54, 56, 115, 122,
157, 254, 255; metaphysical,
46, 48, 158; modifying, 109;
natural, 138; necessary, 149;
"new," 123, 137; occult, 178;
ontological, 131, 132; opposing, 111; partial, 20, 133;
particular, 15, 42, 201; phenomenal, 131, 156, 158, 249,
250; physical, 46, 48, 49,
116, 131, 132, 138, 158, 255,
335; possible, 10, 19, 104,
109; producing, 99; primary,
15, 142, 143, 150, 156; proper, 10; proximate, 8, 10, 56,
96, 99, 104, 105, 111, 143,
155, 156, 310; real, 32, 34,
36, 43, 49, 102, 104, 105,
109, 111, 136, 149, 157, 184;
remote, 83; secondary, 15,
16, 156; special, 16; supernatural, 138; supreme, 126;
theoretical, 124; total, 14;
ultimate, 43, 49, 56, 93, 101,
104, 131, 132, 137, 138, 142,

discovery, 130, 146, 259, 297; logic of, 85, 113, 140; order of, 125; *see also* causes, discovery of
Dobzhansky, T., 313, 315
Dolch, H., 329, 330, 383
Dommeyer, F. C., 363, 383
Donahue, J. M., vii
Dougherty, J. P., 362, 383
Douglas, A. V., 371
Drake, S., 369, 383, 385
Dray, W. H., 378, 394
drib, 272, 369; *see also* bird(s)
Driesch, Hans (1867–1941), 281
Dublin, 30
Ducasse, C. J., 126, 141, 225–228, 334, 340, 341, 343–345, 347, 348, 351, 362–364, 383–384
Dugas, R., 337, 384
Duhem, Pierre (1861–1916), 177–180, 182, 200, 222, 281, 357, 384
duration, 14, 213, 375; intuition of, 218; transient, 306
Durbin, P. R., 372, 384
dynamics, 51, 71, 262, 296; classical, 296; relativistic, 296

Eames, E. R., 357, 384
earth, 115; diurnal rotation of, 19, 114–117, 139, 174–177, 180, 255, 293–295, 323–325; movement around sun, 177, 293–295; size and shape of, 115, 175, 295, 346; spheroidal figure of, 115–117, 125, 175, 295, 323–325
Easton, L. D., 355, 384
economy of thought, 169, 170, 199
Eddington, Arthur Stanley (1882–1944), 289–291, 371, 384
Edinburgh, 129
Edwards, P., 334, 384

effect, 8, 12, 247; formal, 250; possible, 10; *see also* cause and effect
efficacy, 16, 37, 38, 56, 59, 158, 159, 165, 231; *see also* causal efficacy
efficient cause, 14–16, 19–21, 33, 37, 46–49, 56–58, 72, 83, 84, 131, 132, 134, 138, 155–157, 159, 231, 249, 250, 264, 287, 291, 292, 297, 303, 308, 317–321, 355, 356, 372; *see also* causality; causation; cause
effort, 102, 344; *see also* action
Einstein, Albert (1879–1955), 165, 169, 188, 194, 281, 367, 371, 372, 388; relativity theories of, 283–297
elasticity, 43, 72, 157
electron, 215, 252, 298, 300, 302
element, 13, 103, 125, 215, 248, 263, 275, 306, 374, 375
Ellington, J., 388
Ellis, B., 356, 384
Ellis, R. L., 340, 341, 380
Emmet, D. M., 363
empiricism, 4, 16, 22, 23, 27, 30, 60, 61, 66, 97, 129, 187, 188, 227, 325; logical, 216; radical, 40, 181
empiricist(s), 4, 45, 60, 78, 92, 127, 129, 141, 158, 206, 219, 239, 247, 249, 252, 253, 271, 276
Encke, Johann Franz (1791–1865), 113
end, 16, 21, 309; proximate, 314; ultimate, 314; *see also* final cause, goal, teleology
energy, 168, 214, 262, 296, 307, 375; conservation of, 169; immanent, 315; mass, 296; rest, 296
Engelhardt, W. von, 336
entelechy, 55, 151

methodologists of classical
science, 97, 119, 126, 129,
146; *Critique of Pure Reason*,
61, 64, 66, 70, 74, 119, 126;
*Metaphysical Foundations of
Natural Science*, 61, 70,
256; *Opus postumum*, 61;
*Thoughts on the True Esti-
mation of Living Forces*, 62,
67; *Universal Natural History*, 64
Kantian(s), 217, 349
Kaplan, A., 279, 389
Kaufmann, P., 355
Keeling, S. V., 327, 389
Kepler, Johannes (1571–1630),
vi, 77, 86, 120, 139, 140,
155, 246, 255
Kneale, W. C., 351, 389
knowledge, 8, 17, 21, 22, 28,
29, 41, 45, 65, 69, 154, 181,
323, 324; causal, 11, 70, 75,
81, 143, 155; certain, 78,
82, 167, 173; cumulative
growth of, v, vi, 109, 113,
115, 128, 237–240, 243,
249, 255, 257, 264–266,
271, 274, 275, 293, 295, 297,
302, 323, 366; demonstrative,
5; empirical, 68; experi-
mental, 26; general, 27; inductive, 80; metaphysical,
119; nonintuitive, 130; provisional, 179, 180; real, 128;
schematic, 180; sense, 27;
theory of, 41, 42, 120, 217,
220, 249; universal, 26
Kockelmans, J. J., 339, 354, 355,
357, 359, 362, 363, 389
Kordig, C. R., 389
Koyré, A., 59, 328, 337, 341,
389
Kramers, Hendrik A. (1894–
1952), 305
Krimerman, L., 319, 389
Kuhn, T. S., 238–240, 263,
274, 296, 323, 365–368, 389;

*The Structure of Scientific
Revolutions*, 239

Lagrange, Joseph Louis (1736–
1813), 96
Lakatos, I., 239, 366, 389
Laplace, Pierre Simon de
(1749–1827), 64, 96, 163,
164, 215; *Philosophical Essay on Probabilities*, 163
Lardner, Dionysius (1793–
1859), 97; *Cabinet Cyclopaedia*, 97, 112
Larmor, Joseph (1857–1942),
290
Larsen, R. E., 340, 389
latent: configuration, 84, 159;
process, 83, 84
lattice, 267, 268, 270
Laudan, L. L., 332, 334, 339,
341–343, 347, 348, 351, 389
Lavoisier, Antoine (1743–
1794), 296
law, 34, 84, 88, 89, 91, 96, 101,
103, 110, 120, 159, 178,
197, 198, 202, 209, 210, 223;
abstract, 109; causal, 203,
205, 210, 211, 230, 235, 248,
271–276, 285; developmental,
212, 213; empirical, 137;
eternal, 56; experimental,
179, 201, 208; general, 87,
106, 116, 131, 203, 221;
higher-level, 205; historical,
212; kinematical, 232; mathematical, 30, 270; morphological, 232; natural, 183,
203; noncausal, 232; probability, 195; scientific, 150,
151, 179, 222; social, 319;
socio-historical, 232; statistical, 196, 208, 232; taxonomical, 232; ultimate, 139;
universal, 208
law: of thought, 47, 48; of the
three stages, Comte's, 87,
121–122, 142, 315

Whitehead, Alfred North (1861–
1947), 219–222, 363, 397;
Principia Mathematica, 219
Whittaker, Edmund Taylor
(1873–1956), 294, 373, 397
whole, 18, 152, 213, 268
Wien, Wilhelm (1864–1928),
281, 282
Wiener, P. P., 357, 384, 398
Wiener Kreis, 169, 181, 182,
184, 202, 225, 236, 358
Wilkie, J. S., 398
will, 21, 24, 37, 46, 47, 74, 102
Willich, A., 355

Wippel, J. F., vii
Wittgenstein, Ludwig (1889–
1951), 181, 236; *Tractatus
Logico-Philosophicus*, 181
Wolff, Christian (1679–1754),
60
Woolf, H., 398
Wright, G. H. von, 378, 398

Yost, R. M., 331, 398

Zabarella, Jacopo (1533–1589),
97, 256
Zeppelin, A. von, 358, 394